The Air F

Volun

Air Law and **Meteorology**

'Recommended reading'
Civil Aviation Authority

POOLEY'S
Air Pilot Publishing

Copyright © 2018 Pooleys-Air Pilot Publishing Limited

ISBN 978-1-84336-240-1

First edition published 1987
Second revised edition 1987
Third revised edition published 1993
Fourth revised edition published 1997
Fifth revised edition 1999
Sixth edition 2001
Seventh edition 2004
Eighth revised edition 2008
Ninth revised edition 2010
Tenth revised edition 2011
Eleventh revised edition 2013
Twelfth edition May 2014
Thirteenth edition Nov. 2015
Thirteenth revised edition Feb. 2017
Fourteenth edition Sept. 2017
Fifteen edition Nov. 2018

Origination by Pooleys-Air Pilot Publishing Limited

Published by Pooleys-Air Pilot Publishing Ltd
Elstree Aerodrome, Elstree, Hertfordshire, WD6 3AW. UK.
Tel: +44 (0)208 207 3749
Web: www.pooleys.com
Email: sales@pooleys.com

The Air Pilot's **Manual**

Volume 2

Contents

Editorial Team

Dorothy Saul-Pooley LLB (Hons) FRAeS

Dorothy held a UK ATPL, now EASA Part-FCL CPL (A) and a CPL (H) and is both an instructor and examiner on aeroplanes and an instructor on helicopters. She is Head of Training for a school dedicated to running Flight Instructor courses at Shoreham. She is also a CAA Flight Instructor Examiner. In addition, having qualified as a solicitor in 1982, Dorothy acted for many years as a consultant specialising in aviation and insurance liability issues, and has lectured widely on air law and aviation insurance. This highly unusual combination of qualifications led to her appointment as Honorary Solicitor to the Guild of Air Pilots and Navigators (GAPAN).

Dorothy is a Fellow of the Royal Aeronautical Society, Past Chairman of the GAPAN Instructor Committee of which she was a founding member and the prime instigator of the Guild's Joint Forum with Central Flying School at RAF Cranwell for Senior Flying Instructors. She is a Past Chairman of the Education & Training Committee. After serving as a Warden on the Court of GAPAN for three years, she was appointed Master for the year 2014-2015 of the newly renamed Honourable Company of Air Pilots. She is also Chairman of the Professional Flying Instructors Association.

In 2003 Dorothy was awarded the Jean Lennox Bird Trophy for her contribution to aviation and support of Women in Aviation and the BWPA (British Women Pilots Association). In 2013, Dorothy received the prestigious award of a Master Air Pilots Certificate from GAPAN. In 2015 she was awarded the Brabazon Cup by the BWPA for her outstanding achievement in aviation. A regular contributor to seminars and conferences, Dorothy is the author and editor of a large number of flying training books and has published articles in legal and insurance journals and many in aviation magazines.

Helena Hughes

On leaving university in 1989 Helena obtained a PPL in America, converting to UK licence on her return. Shortly afterwards she started work in Air Traffic Control at London Luton Airport, earning her controller's licence in 1990. During her time at Luton she was involved in controller training as both an instructor and assessor. Helena continues to be an operational Air Traffic Control Officer and is currently posted to Thames Radar. She holds a CPL/IR and has been a flying instructor since 1998, teaching PPL and associated ratings. She is a Ground and R/T examiner and has written both PPL and ATPL Radiotelephony Training Manuals.

Philip Baxter BA (Hons) LLB (Hons)

Philip held a UK ATPL (A), is an Instructor and has been a PPL Examiner. He began his working life in the Civil Service, having joined from school, and stayed for more years than he now cares to remember! He worked in a wide variety of (mostly) very interesting jobs, within several Departments, which included one period as Private Secretary to a government Minister, another (reflecting his long-standing interest in aviation matters) dealing with aircraft noise and ICAO 'Annex 16' issues as well as pollution from aircraft engines; and another as a technical author. Much of the remainder of his Civil Service career was related to telecommunications, ranging from international Treaties to technical standardisation. This included representing his departmental interests on Standards Committees in particular, both internationally and domestically. Both his Degrees, the first in Science and Technology, the second in Law (providing an unusual combination) were awarded following part-time study with the Open University. Since 'retiring' early from a senior middle-management grade, Philip worked for six years as a full-time Flight Instructor and Flight Examiner, accruing some three and a half thousand instructional hours. Phil teaches ground school subjects for the Flying Instructor course and has also been Vice Chairman of the Professional Flight Instructors' Association (PFIA).

Robert Seaman BSc MRI FRMetS

Rob Seaman is a professional pilot on the Airbus family, a flight instructor and meteorologist who is committed to connecting these professions together for the benefit of flight safety. With a life-long passion for aviation he was awarded a Royal Air Force flying scholarship (1998), the Norman Motley Flight Instructor Scholarship (2007), elected Liveryman of the Honourable Company of Air Pilots (2016) and was expert advisor on the United Kingdom Flight Safety Committee. Rob's key interest is in the practical application of human factors to meteorological threats so as to enhance their management on the flight deck. His previous career in the Met Office culminated as Head of Policy Advice relating climate change and the environment to foreign and defence policy. This drew on experience gained from previous roles supporting civil and military aviation operations; as a Senior Applied Scientist developing weather related decision aids to increase efficiency and effectiveness, and as an Operational Meteorologist supporting the military at HQ Air Command, the Falklands and the Middle East. Rob studied Physics at Imperial College, is an Associate of the Royal College of Science and Fellow of the Royal Meteorological Society.

Acknowledgements

The Civil Aviation Authority, Captain R. W. K. Snell, Shaun McConnell, David Hockings, Helena Hughes, Geoffrey Farmiloe AFRIN, LLB (Hons), LLM, Daljeet Gill, Philip Odell, Esther Law and the many other instructors and students whose comments have helped to improve this manual.

A Condensed History of the Air Pilot Manuals

For over 30 years the Air Pilot Manuals have led the academic training of pilots in the United Kingdom and in many countries around the world.

I first met Trevor Thom, a professional pilot and natural teacher, in Melbourne during a visit to Australia in January 1985. He already had his series of PPL Manuals for the Australian market and I asked him to produce a series for the New Zealand market where we had a small aviation business. Having completed this task, Trevor immediately began writing the first of the Air Pilot Manuals for the United Kingdom market and this project began in earnest on 5th December 1985.

Both Trevor Thom and Robert Johnson commenced the task in my office at Feldon. By the end of the following year, all four volumes were complete and were published in February 1987. By the end of that year, we estimated that 95% of all the UK Flying Schools were using our manuals. Volumes 5, 6 and 7 followed, so completing the full series.

Unfortunately, Trevor Thom had a serious accident at home which prevented him from continuing with the editing of the manuals. His rights were eventually sold to David Robson, another experienced pilot and natural teacher, who progressively improved the drawings and brought colour into the manuals for the first time.

Over the years there have been many assistant editors, in particular Peter Godwin, whose help I first asked for in the very early days with Trevor Thom and which continued until quite recently. The rights in the Air Pilot Manuals are now vested with the Pooley family and they continue to be edited and published from our offices and the school at Shoreham Airport.

The Air Pilot Manuals have an outstanding reputation for accuracy and are continuously updated. They are recommended CAA reading material and are referred to extensively in the CAA examination answer booklet.

Robert Pooley
CStJ FRIN FRAeS

Preface to the Fifteenth Edition

K eeping up to date with legal changes is challenging, because the law is changing all the time. In this edition, we have expanded on the European regulations which are still in a transitional period of implementation. We have included the European rules of the air. Please be aware that there are almost daily changes to some aspects of aviation law, so you must check the CAA and EASA websites frequently.

To highlight the difference between UK CAA material and ICAO or EASA material, we use a lighter typeface for the ICAO material.

NOTE Please check our websites for updates and links to references mentioned in the text. Please refer to **www.pooleysapp.com** and to the Pooleys websites: **www.pooleys.com** and **www.pooleysfis.com**.

Section **One**

Air Law

Aviation Law and Legislation

Introduction

It is a fact of life that most activities we undertake, whether for leisure or work, are regulated to some degree, very often with safety being a prime purpose. As you learn to fly and gain wider experience you will encounter many types of rules and procedures, governing such things as the operation of aircraft, types of airspace, licence privileges and Rules of the Air.

In order to set your study of aviation law in context it is useful to understand where the rules and regulations are to be found and how they relate to each other.

Almost since aviation began, the rules and regulations have developed on an international basis.

International Civil Aviation Organization (ICAO)

To highlight the difference between UK CAA material and ICAO, EASA or JAR material, we use a lighter typeface for the ICAO material (as opposite).

After the First World War ended, civil flying resumed in 1919 and, with four years of accelerated development during the war, aircraft performance had improved immeasurably. The benefits of air travel to facilitate the rapid crossing of international boundaries and to communicate with distant nations for transportation and trade were realised. However, many problems had to be overcome, such as overflying sovereign territories of different nations and landing safely at prepared airfields.

The Paris Convention of 1919 was the first major international meeting of aviation-oriented nations, though it was more a European than a worldwide gathering. Nonetheless, general principles of air law and aviation procedures were agreed and adopted.

Further conferences followed until the historic Chicago Convention in 1944 placed a moral obligation on contracting States (nations) to provide safe and efficient ground and flight organisations in their territories for the development of international aviation. Following the entry into force of the Chicago Convention, a permanent International Civil Aviation Organization was formed in 1947. It was based in Montreal, Canada, where it remains to this day. The purpose of ICAO is to promote aviation standards and recommended practices internationally.

The United Kingdom, like most nations of the world, is an active member of ICAO.

Standardisation has occurred to a remarkable degree since the signing of the *Chicago Convention* in 1944, although, as is always the case in international affairs, some differences remain.

For example:

- Cruising levels in Western nations are based on feet, whereas in some Eastern European countries they are based on metres.

- Many countries including the UK now use the hectopascal (hPa) as the unit for pressure (on ICAO recommendation), after many years using the millibar. The units represent the same amount of pressure, i.e. 1 hPa = 1 mb). The United States uses inches of mercury.

- The airspace classification system introduced in the UK is also being adopted by most countries; however, there are small differences in how the system is being implemented in each country. The UK currently has no Class B airspace but in the USA, Class B is being allocated to Terminal Control Areas (and the descriptive term for the airspace is being dropped). The specifications of ATC service, VMC minima, clearance requirements, radio equipment, etc. for each airspace class are much the same.

However, these differences do not detract from the fact that basic flight rules and procedures are similar throughout the world.

Chicago Convention

The broad principles of the ICAO as laid down by the Chicago Convention are known as **Articles**. The text of these Articles is set out in the ICAO document known as DOC 7300 and is amended when necessary. Implementation is the responsibility of the contracting State.

DOC 7300 contains the text of the Convention on International Civil Aviation as signed at Chicago in 1944. A summary of some of its 96 Articles applicable to student and private pilots follows. You need to become familiar with these articles because they form part of the PPL syllabus and are included in some examinations. The term *State* denotes a contracting nation to the Chicago Convention.

Article 1 – Sovereignty

Each State (nation) that has signed the Convention is recognised to have complete and exclusive sovereignty over the airspace above its territory.

Article 2 – Territory

A State's territory is the land and territorial waters over which the State has sovereignty.

Article 4 – Misuse of civil aviation

Each State agrees not to use civil aviation for any purpose contrary to the aims of the Convention (i.e. for illegal purposes or for war).

*The words **shall** and **should** have precise meanings in ICAO documents. For instance, where it says a pilot **shall** do something, it means he/she must, the pilot is required to.*
*Where it says a pilot **should** do something, it means he/she doesn't have to, but in the interests of good airmanship and flight safety it is recommended that the pilot does.*

Article 5 – Right of non-scheduled flight

Each State will allow aircraft from all other States (except for scheduled international flights) to fly into or through its airspace, and to land without prior permission. States also have the right to require overflying aircraft to land. Where terrain is remote and navigation facilities are inadequate, States may require overflying aircraft to follow prescribed routes, or to obtain prior permission for the flight.

Article 10 – Landing at customs airport

Each State may require aircraft entering its territory to land at a customs airport for a customs examination, unless the flight has permission to cross the territory without landing. Similarly, aircraft departing a State may be required to depart from a customs airport.

Article 11 – Applicability of air regulations

Any aircraft, regardless of its nationality, shall obey the regulations and operational procedures of the State in which it is flying.

Article 12 – Rules of the Air

Each State shall ensure that aircraft operating within its territory, or aircraft carrying its nationality mark, wherever they may be, follow the rules of the air. Over the high seas, the rules of the Convention apply. Each State shall endeavour to prosecute violators of the regulations.

Article 13 – Entry and clearance regulations

Regulations of a State relating to entry, clearance, immigration, passports, customs and quarantine must be complied with by or on behalf of passengers, crew or cargo on entry into, departure from or while within the territory of that State.

Article 16 – Search of aircraft

Each State has the right to search aircraft from other States on landing or prior to departure, and to inspect documents.

Article 17 – Nationality of aircraft

Aircraft have the nationality of the State in which they are registered.

Article 18 – Dual registration

An aircraft may not be registered in more than one State, though its registration may be changed from one State to another.

Article 19 – National laws governing registration

Registration or transfer of registration in any State shall comply with that State's laws and regulations.

Article 20 – Display of marks

All aircraft operating internationally shall display their appropriate nationality and registration marks.

Article 22 – Facilitation of formalities
Each State shall facilitate flights between territories of contracting States, and prevent unnecessary delays to those flights, especially in relation to customs, immigration and quarantine procedures.

Article 23 – Customs and immigration procedures
Each State shall establish customs and immigration procedures in accordance with international practice.

Article 24 – Customs duty
Aircraft entering another State's territory shall be admitted temporarily free of duty, subject to the State's customs regulations. Fuel, oil, spare parts and regular equipment that are on board an aircraft on arrival in another State, and retained on board on departure, shall be exempt from duty. This does not apply to anything that is unloaded from the aircraft.

Spare parts imported into a State for use by an aircraft from another State on international operations shall be free of duty.

Article 25 – Aircraft in distress
Each State shall assist aircraft in distress in its territory, and allow the owners of the aircraft and that State in which the aircraft is registered to assist as appropriate.

Article 26 – Investigation of accidents
Should an aircraft registered in one State be involved in an accident in another State, and the accident results in death or serious injury or indicates a serious technical defect in the aircraft or navigation facilities, the State in which the accident occurs shall carry out an inquiry in accordance with ICAO procedures. The State in which the aircraft is registered shall be allowed to observe the inquiry.

Article 28 – Air navigation facilities and standard systems
Each State shall facilitate international aviation by:
• providing radio services, meteorological services and air navigation facilities to ICAO standards;
• operating standard systems for communications, markings, signals and lighting;
• cooperating internationally in the publication of aeronautical maps and charts.

Article 29 – Documents carried in aircraft
All aircraft flying internationally shall carry the following documents:
• Certificate of Registration;
• Certificate of Airworthiness;
• appropriate licences for each crew member;
• journey logbook;

- appropriate radio licences;
- if carrying passengers, a list of their names and places of embarkation (boarding) and destination;
- if carrying cargo, a manifest and detailed declarations of cargo.

Article 30 – Aircraft radio equipment
Aircraft operating in other States may carry radio transmitting equipment only if it is licensed by the State in which the aircraft is registered. The use of that equipment shall comply with the regulations of the State that is being flown over.

Radio transmitting equipment may be used only by crew members who are licensed to do so by the State in which the aircraft is registered.

Article 31 – Certificates of airworthiness
All aircraft operating internationally must have a valid Certificate of Airworthiness issued by the State in which it is registered.

Article 32 – Licences of personnel
Pilots and flightcrew members engaged in international operations shall hold licences issued by the State in which the aircraft is registered.

For flight over its own territory, each State reserves the right to refuse to recognise flight crew licences and certificates of competency granted to its nationals by another State.

Article 33 – Recognition of certificates and licences
Certificates of airworthiness and flightcrew licences issued by the State in which the aircraft is registered shall be recognised by other contracting States, provided the requirements for the issue of such certificates and licences meet ICAO standards.

Article 34 – Journey logbooks
All aircraft on international operations shall keep a journey logbook, containing details of the aircraft, its crew and each journey, in accordance with ICAO standards.

Article 35 – Cargo restrictions
Weapons or munitions of war may not be carried in or above a State's territory except by permission of that State.

States may prohibit the carriage of any other items within their territory for reasons of public order or safety.

Article 36 – Photographic apparatus
States may prohibit or regulate the use of photographic apparatus in aircraft over their territories.

Article 37 – Adoption of international standards and procedures
Each State undertakes, as far as possible, to implement uniformity in aviation regulations, standards and procedures. To help this process

ICAO shall adopt and amend international standards and recommended practices dealing with such matters as:
- communications systems and air navigation aids, including ground markings;
- airports and landing areas;
- rules of the air and air traffic control procedures;
- licensing of flightcrew and maintenance staff;
- airworthiness of aircraft;
- recognition and identification of aircraft:
- meteorological services;
- logbooks;
- aeronautical maps and charts;
- customs and immigration procedures;
- aircraft in distress and accident investigation.

Article 39 – Endorsement of certificates and licences
Aircraft that have failed to meet any international standard of airworthiness or performance at certification shall show on its airworthiness certificate full details of such failure(s).

Flightcrew licence holders who fail to satisfy any condition laid down in the international standard relating to that licence shall have full details of such failure(s) shown on their licence.

Article 40 – Validity of endorsed certificates and licences
Aircraft and flightcrew may operate internationally only if their certificates or licences permit it. The use of any aircraft or certificated aircraft part in a State other than the one in which it was originally registered shall be at the discretion of the State into which the aircraft or part is imported.

Article 43 – ICAO name and composition
An organisation named The International Civil Aviation Organization is formed by the Convention. It is made up of an Assembly, a Council, and other necessary bodies.

Article 44 – ICAO objectives
The Organization aims to develop international air navigation and international air transport so as to:
- ensure the safe and orderly growth of civil aviation throughout the world;
- encourage aircraft design and operation for peaceful purposes;
- encourage development of airways, airports and navigation facilities for international civil aviation;
- provide the world with safe, regular, efficient and economical air transport;
- promote fair competition and avoid discrimination between States;

Article 47 – Legal capacity

Each State shall grant to ICAO such legal capacity as may be necessary to perform its functions.

ICAO Annexes

The terms used in ICAO Annexes are summarised on page 201. You should become familiar with these terms.

The ICAO Articles are augmented by numerous international conferences and committees to discuss and agree various aviation issues such as: Rules of the Air, Operation of Aircraft, Aerodromes, Air Traffic Services etc. This information is disseminated in the form of 19 Annexes. These are supplementary documents detailing information on specific subjects and completely define aviation terms, standards and recommended practices ("SARPs"). These Annexes are regularly reviewed and amended and may themselves be further supplemented by regional procedures where necessary.

Extracts from some of these Annexes applicable to student and private pilots are set out in later chapters, with the UK differences where applicable. The paragraph numbers refer to the paragraph numbers in the Annex concerned, should you wish to do further research.

NOTE National differences from the ICAO system that prevail in the UK are shown in AIP GEN 1-7. You need to be familiar with these national differences as well as with the international system, since these form part of the PPL examinations.

The European Aviation Safety Agency (EASA)

The United Kingdom is an active member of ICAO, as are most large nations. While standardisation has occurred to a large extent, national differences remain. European nations, though close to each other geographically, ended up with many variations in their aviation systems and regulations.

Since the foundation of the European Union (EU), successive British governments have sought to standardise aviation practices with their European partners. This led to the harmonisation of flight crew licensing and a code of practice was adopted by EU member States.

The European Aviation Safety Agency (EASA) has taken over the regulation of licensing for pilots and aircraft. EASA has far-reaching regulatory powers which have a significant effect on all levels of aviation (except for Very Light Flying Machines for recreational use). EASA has assumed full responsibility for both flight operations and flight crew licensing (and therefore training) and the EU rules became effective in the UK as of 17 September 2012. We are still in a transitional period, through to 2019, in some cases, and what the effects of Brexit may be remain unclear.

The main regulatory setting up of the system was adopted in September 2003, and it has had a huge impact on the aviation industry. The main regulations passed by the EC which are pertinent to us as private pilots are:

- EC Regulation (216/2008), the 'Basic Regulation'
- EC Regulation (1178/2011), the 'Aircrew Regulation'
- EU Regulation (445/2015), amending the Aircrew Regulation.

The basic regulation contains various annexes dealing with topics such as airworthiness, licensing, medical and air traffic management. Subdivisions of annexes are called Parts and list the rules relating to a particular topic, such as Part ORA, dealing with the regulation of organisations (ie. training schools). These rules are required to be implemented by Acceptable Means of Compliance (AMCs) and Guidance Material (GMs).

A table of the regulations is appended on page 213

Aviation Law in the United Kingdom

Aviation law in the United Kingdom is enacted by Parliament and published in statutory documents. The principal source of regulations for the private pilot is the **Air Navigation Order** (see page 14). Another is the **Air Navigation (General) Regulations.**

The authority responsible for civil aviation in the United Kingdom is the **Civil Aviation Authority** (CAA). Schedule 1 defines the 'competent authority' as meaning in relation to the UK, the CAA. (In relation to any other country, it means the authority responsible under the law of that country for promoting the safety of civil aviation.) One of its main functions is to provide an **Aeronautical Information Service** (AIS) to collect and disseminate the information necessary for safe and efficient air navigation. It does this through four documentation channels:

1. The United Kingdom **Aeronautical Information Publication** (UK AIP) is published in three parts, with a regular amendments service, and contains information under the following headings:

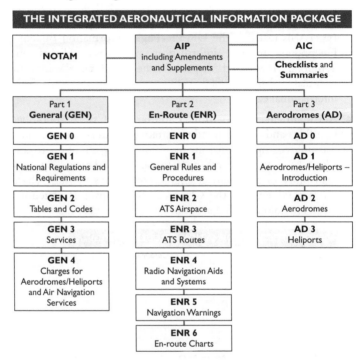

■ *Figure 1-1* **The UK AIP and related documents**

Be aware that many schools now rely on the internet service to view updates to the UK AIP and may not hold a paper copy at all.

The NATS website is found at: **www.nats.aero/do-it-online/ais/**

NOTE ICAO Annex 15 (Aeronautical Information Services) deals with international requirements.

2. **NOTAMs** (Notices to Airmen), distributed via the NATS AIS website, contain information on any aeronautical facility, service, procedure or hazard – timely knowledge of which is required by people concerned with flight operations and which may be given one of three categories:

NOTAM CATEGORIES	
NOTAMN	*new information*
NOTAMR	*replacing previous information*
NOTAMC	*cancelling a previous NOTAM*

3. **Pre-Flight Route and Aerodrome Information Bulletins** (GENs) should be readily available to you. They are a vital part of your pre-flight planning. Daily updated information and answers to queries may be obtained from the NATS Aeronautical Information Service (AIS), tel: 01489 887462, or on the internet at the address on page 11, together with the NOTAMs issued as the UK Pre-Flight Information Bulletins. Freephone updated information on Royal Flights and Temporary Restricted Airspace for the *Red Arrows* display team is available daily on 0500 354802 or +44(0)1489 887515 for international calls.

4. **Aeronautical Information Circulars** (AICs) are published monthly and concern administrative matters and advance warnings of operational changes, and draw attention to and advise on matters of operational importance, e.g. the availability of aeronautical charts, corrections to these charts and amendments to the Chart of UK Airspace Restrictions. AICs are colour-coded according to their subject matter:

AERONAUTICAL INFORMATION CIRCULARS (AICs)	
Subject	*Colour of paper*
Air Safety	pink
Administrative	white
Operational and Air Traffic Services	yellow
UK Restrictions Charts	mauve
Maps/Charts	green

NOTE that the *Air Law* examination may refer to the contents of a specific AIC. You should read all relevant AICs, particularly the more important pink ones, which will be available in a folder at your flying training organisation or on the Internet at the address on page 11. These include:

IMPORTANT AIR SAFETY AICs	
Frost, Ice and Snow on Aircraft	AIC P088/2014
Icing (Induction System) on Piston Engines	AIC P077/2009
Take-Off, Climb and Landing Performance	AIC 127/2006 (Pink 110)
Effect of Thunderstorms and Associated Turbulence	AIC P056/2010
Wake Turbulence	AIC P092/2017
Duty to Report Aircraft Accidents and Serious Incidents	AIC P061/2015
Helicopter Flight in Degraded Visual Conditions	AIC 067/2013

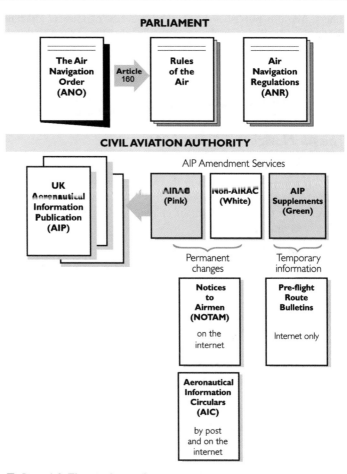

■ Figure 1-2 **The regulatory documents**

Explanatory Publications

Since all the documents detailed must cover the full range of aviation activity, their contents in total are quite daunting for a private pilot. To present vital matters in a simpler form, the CAA produces subsidiary Civil Aviation Publications (CAP), including:

- **CAP 804, which contains the requirements of Flight Crew Licences and took effect from 17 September 2012, replacing LASORS.** (Now available for reference only)
- **CAP 413** on Radiotelephony (R/T or RTF) procedures;
- **CAP 637**, an excellent guide to visual aids and signals for pilots and ground personnel.

The CAA also publishes an invaluable series of *General Aviation Safety Sense* leaflets, which are generally available at flying schools and aero clubs, or the CAA website: www.caa.co.uk/safetysense.

There are also some non-CAA documents that are useful in clarifying operational practices, such as *Pooley's Flight Guide*, published annually and available throughout the UK.

The Air Navigation Order 2016

The Air Navigation Order (also referred to as the 'Order' or as the 'ANO') is a *statutory instrument* that was enacted by Parliament to form the basis of civil aviation in the UK. It has been amended several times to take account of changes arising from the EASA Aircrew Regulation.

Parts and Articles in the ANO

The Air Navigation Order is arranged in **Parts**, each relating to an item of major importance, e.g. Part 4 – *Airworthiness of Aircraft*.

The Parts of the ANO each contain a number of **Articles** and these are numbered consecutively from the start of the ANO, dealing with particular subjects within the broader scope of the Part.

Appendices in the ANO

Further detail in the ANO is given in a series of Appendices to the Order, known as **Schedules**, e.g. *Schedule 1, Interpretation*. This schedule contains definitions.

People concerned with planning and developing flight operations will refer to the ANO, e.g. to determine requirements in such matters as equipment, licensing of crew members, documents and records, registration of aircraft and their operation as well as to Part NCO of the EC Regulation. The private pilot, however, will probably find that only occasional reference to specific Articles in the ANO is sufficient, although some knowledge of the contents is required.

Penalties (General ANO Schedule 13)

Pilots who contravene the Air Navigation Order (ANO) or Regulations made under the Order are held liable, and this Article defines the extent of liability and the maximum penalties which may be imposed if convicted of such contraventions.

Interpretation (Schedule 1 ANO)

Schedule 1 gives the legal definitions for the terms used in the ANO, many of which concern the private pilot and some of which are commonly misconstrued. It also acts as a glossary to the ANO.

Now complete: **Practice Questions - Aviation Law & Legislation**

1. Under the terms of the Chicago Convention each contracting State has:

   (a) Shared sovereignty over the airspace above its land and territorial waters.

   (b) Exclusive sovereignty over the airspace above its land borders.

   (c) Exclusive sovereignty over the airspace above its land and territorial waters.

   (d) Exclusive sovereignty over the airspace above its land borders and shared sovereignty over the airspace above its territorial waters.

2. With regard to the Chicago Convention, an aircraft entering the territory of a contracting state:

   (a) May be required to land at a customs airport.

   (b) Is always required to land at a customs airport.

   (c) May be required to land at a port of entry.

   (d) May be required to land at an immigration airport.

3. ICAO requires that an aircraft on an international flight must carry:

   (a) The Certificate of Airworthiness, Certificate of Registration and the latest Certificate of Maintenance Review.

   (b) The Certificate of Airworthiness, Certificate of Registration, Crew Licences and a journey log book.

   (c) The Certificate of Airworthiness, a current weight and balance and aircraft radio licences.

   (d) The Certificate of Airworthiness, Certificate of Registration, Crew Licences, a journey log book, appropriate radio licences and, if applicable, passenger and cargo manifests.

4. To operate radio transmitting equipment over the territory of a contracting state:

  (a) *The operator must be licensed by the state of registry of the aircraft.*
  (b) *The radio station must be licensed by the state of registry of the aircraft.*
  (c) *Both the radio station and the operator must be licensed by the state of registry of the aircraft.*
  (d) *Either the radio station or the operator must be licensed by the state of registry of the aircraft.*

5. Each contracting ICAO State:

  (a) *Must gain the permission of the operator in advance before an aircraft is searched.*
  (b) *Has the right to search aircraft from other States on landing and prior to departure and to inspect documents.*
  (c) *Has no right to search an aircraft from another State.*
  (d) *Has the right to search aircraft from other States if it is suspected that they are carrying illegal substances.*

6. Pink coloured AICs contain information relating to:

  (a) *Administrative matters.*
  (b) *Air Traffic Services.*
  (c) *UK restrictions charts.*
  (d) *Air safety.*

7. A NOTAMC:

  (a) *Contains information relating to a Class C hazard to air navigation.*
  (b) *Contains new information, and is the third NOTAM issued on a particular day.*
  (c) *Cancels a previous NOTAM.*
  (d) *Continues a previous NOTAM.*

Rules of the Air

SERA and the UK Rules of the Air

European Union Regulations (EU) No (923/2012) of 26th September 2012 laid down Rules of the Air and Operational Provisions relating to services and procedures in air navigation common to all European Union Member States. Whilst the UK appears set to leave the European Union in the not too distant future, negotiations on that are under way at the time of writing and it is expected that the United Kingdom will keep them in place for the time being at least.

Regulation (EU) No (923/2012) also amended a number of other regulations. The objective was to apply Rules of the Air based upon Standards and Recommended Practices of the International Civil Aviation Organisation (ICAO) and to harmonise application of the ICAO airspace classification, with the aim of ensuring seamless provision of safe and efficient air traffic services within a single European sky.

The single European sky initiative was developed to assist EU Member States to fulfil their obligations under the 1944 Chicago convention on International Civil Aviation (adopted by ICAO) and commonly known as "The Chicago convention") by providing for interpretation and implementation common to all EU Member States. The objective was to support the concept of more integrated operating airspace within the context of the EU's common transport policy, to establish common procedures for design planning and management while ensuring the efficient and safe performance of air traffic management; and adherence to a common set of Rules.

A transparent regulatory system, providing legal certainty and predictability, was seen as a key enabler of safe cross-border operations. Standardised Rules of the Air and related Operational Provisions relating to services and procedures in air navigation are established and supplemented, where appropriate, with Guidance Material and/or Acceptable Means of Compliance.

To achieve these objectives, only differences commonly agreed by European Member States would be notified to ICAO by the Member States on areas which are covered by Union law. Those differences are to be monitored continuously.

The Rules of the Air have been established to allow aircraft to operate as safely as is reasonably possible. Air safety depends to a large extent on all pilots understanding the basic rules and operating within them.

ICAO Annex 2 sets out the international standards of the Rules of the Air. The UK and its European partners in the EU fully endorse these international standards.

Standardised European Rules of the Air ('SERA') have been enacted under European Laws and replace most, but not all, of the UK Rules of the Air Regulations. A significant number of changes have been made to the rules previously prevailing in the UK.

SERA applies to every aircraft operating in EU airspace irrespective of type or state of registration. Since SERA does not cover all aspects of the rules of the air, member states are permitted to retain supplementary rules that complement SERA. The UK has retained some regulations under Article 249 of the ANO and they are found in a separate document (Statutory Instrument) often bound together with the ANO in a CAA publication referenced as CAP 393. These rules are supported by permissions and exemptions and the relevant ones will be described in the following text.

Many of the permissions and exemptions granted are for defined (short) periods, therefore it is essential that you check the validity of such rules before relying on them. (CAA website: ORS4 (Official Record Series 4)).

In this chapter we will be dealing with those topics covered in the rules which are applicable to aerial operations by a Private Pilot's Licence holder.

The Rules of the Air apply to:
- all aircraft in the UK (including the neighbourhood of offshore installations, where the low-flying rule is concerned); and
- to all UK-registered aircraft wherever they may be.

The rules or SERA may be departed from to the extent necessary for avoiding immediate danger or for complying with the law of any other country in which the aircraft might be. When a rule is departed from for safety reasons, the circumstances must be reported in writing within ten days afterwards, to the competent authority.

Collision Avoidance in the Air (SERA.3201)
With many aircraft sharing the same airspace, it is often necessary to take collision avoidance action. A collision risk exists when one aircraft is at the same level or approaching another, its range is decreasing and its relative bearing remains constant (Figure 2-1).

Some basic rules understood by all pilots, and applied when necessary, are essential to avoid aerial collisions.

General

- Regardless of any ATC clearance, it is the duty of the *commander* (pilot-in-command) of an aircraft to take all possible measures to see that the pilot does not collide with any other aircraft.
- An aircraft must not fly so close to other aircraft as to create a danger of collision.
- Aircraft must not fly in formation unless the commanders have agreed to do so.
- An aircraft which is obliged to give way to another aircraft must avoid passing over, or under, or crossing ahead of, the other aircraft (unless passing well clear of it).
- An aircraft with right of way should maintain its course (heading) and speed.
- For the purposes of this rule, a sailplane (glider) and a machine towing it are considered to be a single aircraft under the command of the commander of the towing machine. Aeroplanes and helicopters must give way to aircraft towing sailplanes.

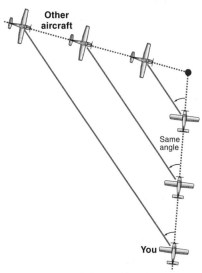

■ Figure 2-1 **A constant relative bearing**

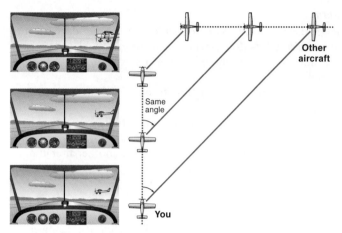

■ Figure 2-2 **Fixed position of another aircraft in the windscreen indicates a constant relative bearing and therefore a collision risk**

Approaching Head-On (SERA.3210)

When two aircraft are approaching head-on or nearly so, and there is danger of collision, each must turn right (Figure 2-3).

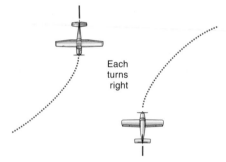

■ Figure 2-3 **Approaching head-on – each turns right to avoid a collision**

Overtaking

An aircraft which is being overtaken in the air has right of way and the overtaking aircraft, whether climbing, descending or level, must keep out of the way by turning right (Figure 2-4). An overtaking situation could be considered to be that where the overtaking aircraft is within 70° of the overtaken aircraft's centreline.

A glider overtaking another glider may, however, turn either right or left.

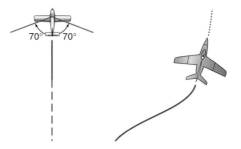

■ *Figure 2-4* **Overtaking – keep right**

Converging Aircraft (SERA 3210(C)(2)(i-iv))

- An aircraft in the air must give way to other converging aircraft as follows:
  - power-driven heavier than air aircraft must give way to airships, sailplanes and balloons;
  - airships must give way to sailplanes and balloons;
  - sailplanes must give way to balloons.
- Subject to the above paragraph, when two aircraft are converging at about the same altitude, the aircraft which has the other on its right must give way. Power-driven aircraft must give way, however, to those towing other aircraft or objects such as banners.

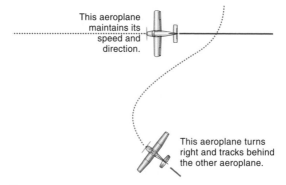

This aeroplane maintains its speed and direction.

This aeroplane turns right and tracks behind the other aeroplane.

■ *Figure 2-5* **Give way to the right**

Flight in the Vicinity of an Aerodrome

A heavier-than-air aircraft, sailplane or airship flying in the vicinity of an aerodrome or moving on an aerodrome shall, unless the aerodrome's ATC unit otherwise authorises:

- conform to the pattern of traffic formed by other aircraft intending to land at that aerodrome, or keep clear of the airspace in which the pattern is formed;

- make all turns to the left unless ground signals direct otherwise.

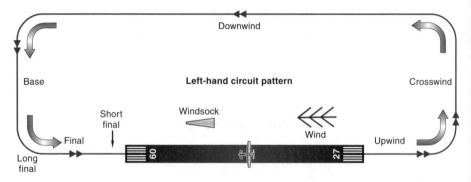

■ *Figure 2-6* **Make left-hand circuits, unless right-hand circuits are indicated**

NOTE Sometimes ATC approves a straight-in approach to an arriving aircraft, which will then normally report "long final" at 8 nm, and "final" at 4 nm from the runway.

Order of Landing (Rule 9, Rule of the Air Regs. 2015)

An aircraft landing or on final approach has right of way over others in flight or on the surface.

- In the case of two or more heavier–than–air aircraft approaching any place for landing, the lower aircraft has right of way (although it must not cut in front of, or overtake, another which is on final approach); provided that:
  - when ATC has given any aircraft an order of priority for landing they must approach to land in that order; and
  - when the commander of an aircraft is aware that another is making an emergency landing the pilot must give way, and at night (even if the pilot already has permission to land) must not attempt to land until given further permission.
- In all cases, power-driven heavier–than–air aircraft shall give way to sailplanes.

Landing and Take-Off (Rule 10, Rules of the Air Regs. 2015)

- An aircraft must take off and land in the direction indicated by ground signals or, in their absence, into wind unless good aviation practice demands otherwise.
- An aircraft must not land on a runway which is not clear of other aircraft, unless an aerodrome ATC unit otherwise authorises. If an aircraft is on the runway, Air Traffic Control may give you an instruction "land after", which is **not** a clearance to land. The decision is yours, based on whether you

judge that sufficient separation exists. Such an instruction is never issued at night.

- Where take-offs and landings are not confined to a runway:
  - a flying machine or glider when landing must leave clear on its left any aircraft which has landed, or is already landing, or is about to take off (i.e. keep to the right of other aircraft). If such a flying machine or glider is obliged to turn when taxiing on the landing area, it shall turn to the left after the commander has satisfied himself that such action will not interfere with other traffic movements; and
  - a flying machine about to take off must manoeuvre so as to leave clear on its left any aircraft which has taken off, or is about to take off.

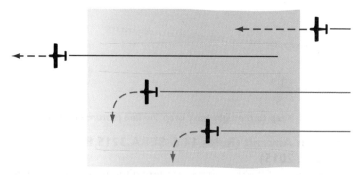

■ *Figure 2-7* **Turn left after landing when operations are not confined to a runway**

- A flying machine after landing must move clear of the landing area as soon as possible unless the aerodrome ATC unit otherwise authorises.

Use of Radio in an Aerodrome Traffic Zone

When flying in an Aerodrome Traffic Zone, a pilot must maintain appropriate radio (or other) communication with the aerodrome authority (Air Traffic Control, Aerodrome Flight Information Service or Air/Ground radio).

NOTE Aerodrome Traffic Zones (ATZs) are covered in detail in Chapter 5, *Airspace*.

Right-Hand Traffic Rule

An aircraft flying in sight of the ground and following a road, railway, canal, coast or other line feature was required prior to SERA to keep the line feature on its left, except when flying in controlled airspace, and where it was instructed to do otherwise by the appropriate Air Traffic Control authority. This is no longer a legal requirement, but common sense would suggest that this practice is useful to ensure separation from aircraft flying in the opposite direction and following the same line feature and the UK CAA strongly recommends such practice.

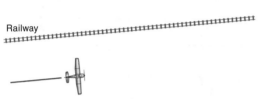

■ *Figure 2-8* ***Keep to the right (and keep the line feature on your left)***

Lights on Aircraft (Rules 14 & SERA.3215 Rules of the Air Regs. 2015)

The direction of flight of aircraft is more difficult to determine by night than by day. To assist in the identification of aircraft position and heading by night, aircraft must display such lights as are specified for the particular category of aircraft. These lighting requirements generally apply when the aircraft is moving on the ground also. No other lights may be displayed that would impair the effectiveness of the required lights.

If any required light fails in flight and cannot be repaired or replaced at once the aircraft must **land** as soon as it can safely do so unless ATC authorises continuation of the flight. (Rule 15, Rules of the Air Regulations 2015).

Knowing the arcs of the basic aircraft navigation lights helps in assessing collision risk. On flying machines and airships the **green** main navigation light on the **right** (or starboard) wing and **red** main navigation light on the **left** (or port) wing show through 110 degrees from dead ahead out to their respective sides. The white tail-light shows through 70 degrees either side of dead astern. An anti-collision light, where carried on an aircraft, is a flashing red light showing in all directions.

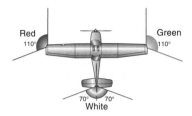

■ Figure 2-9 **Aeroplane lights**

If at night you see the red navigation light of an approaching aircraft out to the left, then your paths will not cross (i.e. red to red is safe). A red light out to the right, however, could mean that the risk of a collision exists.

The situation is reversed for the green light of an approaching aircraft – out to the right it is safe, out to the left there is a risk of collision. Green to green is safe.

If both the red and green lights are visible, then the other aeroplane is flying directly towards you. If the white light is visible, it is flying away from you.

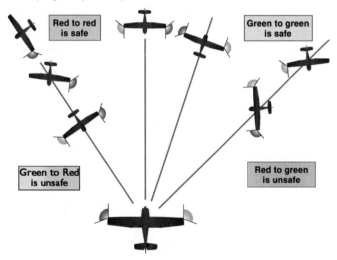

■ Figure 2-10 **Using navigation lights to avoid collision**

In the case of airships there is also a white nose-light showing through 110 degrees either side of dead ahead. A glider may show either the basic lights for a flying machine, as just described, or a steady red light visible in all directions. Free balloons are required to show a steady red light visible in all directions.

In the United Kingdom, **night** is defined for the Rules of the Air as being:
• from 30 minutes after sunset;
• until 30 minutes before sunrise.

Low Flying Prohibitions (SERA.3105 &.5005(f))

The UK rules differ slightly from those adopted by SERA and specific permissions have been granted allowing the continuance of the 'low flying rules' prevailing in the UK prior to the adoption of the European regulations, as follows:

(1) Subject to paragraph (2), an aircraft shall comply with the low flying prohibitions in paragraph (3) except with the permission of the CAA.

(2) If an aircraft is flying in circumstances such that more than one of the low flying prohibitions apply, it shall fly at the greatest height required by any of the applicable prohibitions.

(3) The low flying prohibitions are as follows:

Failure of power unit
An aircraft shall not be flown below such height as would enable it to make an emergency landing without causing danger to persons or property on the surface in the event of a power unit failure.

The 500 feet rule
Except with the written permission of the CAA, an aircraft shall not be flown closer than 500 feet to any person, vessel, vehicle or structure.

500 ft

500 ft

■ *Figure 2-11 **Maintain 500 ft clearance***

The 1000 feet rule
Except with the written permission of the CAA, an aircraft flying over a **congested area** of a city, town or settlement shall not fly below a height of 1,000 feet above the highest fixed obstacle within a horizontal radius of 600 metres of the aircraft.

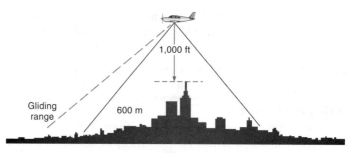

■ *Figure 2-12* **'Land clear' and 1000 ft rules over congested areas**

The land clear rule

An aircraft flying over a congested area of a city, town or settlement shall not fly below such height as would permit the aircraft to land clear of the congested area in the event of a power unit failure. Landing must be made without undue hazard to persons or property on the surface.

Flying over open air assemblies

Except with the written permission of the CAA, an aircraft shall not fly over an organised open-air assembly of more than 1,000 persons below the higher of the following heights:-

(i)   1,000 feet; or

(ii) such height as would permit the aircraft to land clear of the assembly in the event of a power unit failure.

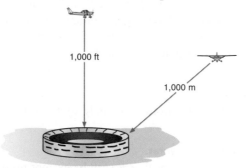

■ *Figure 2-13* **Maintain 1000 ft clearance from large open-air gatherings and beyond 1000 metres when taking off or landing**

Landing and taking off near open air assemblies

An aircraft shall not land or take-off within 1,000 metres of an organised, open-air assembly of more than 1,000 persons except:

(i)   at an aerodrome, in accordance with procedures notified by the CAA; or

(ii)   at a landing site which is not an aerodrome, in accordance
        with procedures notified by the CAA and with the written
        permission of the organiser of the assembly.

Exemptions from the Low Flying Prohibitions

The exemptions from the low flying prohibitions are as follows:

Landing and taking off

(i)   Any aircraft shall be exempt from the low flying
        prohibitions in so far as it is flying in accordance with
        normal aviation practice for the purpose of:
        (a) taking off from, landing at or practising approaches to
             landing at; or
        (b) checking navigational aids or procedures at, a
             Government or licensed aerodrome.

(ii)   Any aircraft shall be exempt from the 500 feet rule when
        landing and taking-off in accordance with normal aviation
        practice or air-taxiing.

Landing and taking off at a training aerodrome

Any aeroplane of which the maximum total weight authorised
does not exceed 2730 kg (or 3175 kg in the case of a helicopter
or gyroplane) shall be exempt from the low flying prohibitions in
so far as it is taking off from, landing at or practising approaches
to a training aerodrome and is engaged in flight instruction or a
flying test for the purpose of qualifying for a pilot's licence, aircraft
rating or night qualification. A "training aerodrome" means an
aerodrome which the commander of the aircraft is satisfied on
reasonable grounds has adequate facilities for the safe conduct of
such flights.

Captive balloons and kites

None of the low flying prohibitions shall apply to any captive
balloon or kite.

Special VFR flight and notified routes

(i)   Subject to paragraph (ii), any aircraft shall be exempt from
        the 1,000 feet rule if:
        (a) it is flying on a Special VFR flight; or
        (b) it is operating in accordance with the procedures
             notified for the route being flown.

(ii)   Unless the written permission of the CAA has been
        obtained, landings may only be made by an aircraft flying
        under this exemption at a licensed or Government
        aerodrome.

Balloons and helicopters over congested areas

(i) A balloon shall be exempt from the 1,000 feet rule if it is landing because it is becalmed.

(ii) Any helicopter flying over a congested area shall be exempt from the land clear rule.

Police air operator's certificate

Any aircraft flying in accordance with the terms of a police air operator's certificate shall be exempt from the 500 feet rule, the 1,000 feet rule and the prohibitions on flying over open air assemblies and on landing and taking off near open air assemblies.

Flying displays etc

An aircraft taking part in a flying display, air race or contest shall be exempt from the 500 feet rule if it is within a horizontal distance of 1,000 metres of the gathering of persons assembled to witness the event.

Glider hill-soaring

A glider shall be exempt from the 500 feet rule if it is hill-soaring.

Picking up and dropping at an aerodrome

Any aircraft picking up or dropping tow ropes, banners or similar articles at an aerodrome shall be exempt from the 500 feet rule.

Manoeuvring helicopters

(i) Subject to paragraph (ii), a helicopter shall be exempt from the 500 feet rule if it is conducting manoeuvres, in accordance with normal aviation practice, within the boundaries of a licensed or Government aerodrome or, with the written permission of the CAA, at other sites.

(ii) When flying in accordance with this exemption the helicopter must not be operated closer than 60 metres to any persons, vessels, vehicles or structures located outside the aerodrome or site.

Dropping articles with CAA permission

Any aircraft shall be exempt from the 500 feet rule if it is flying in accordance with the regulations permitting dropping of articles for the purposes of public health or as a measure against weather conditions, with the permission of the CAA; or in accordance with an aerial application certificate granted by the CAA.

WARNING Be aware that the CAA will prosecute in cases of alleged low flying. Not only is it illegal to carry out low-level flypasts, it does nothing for the image of light aviation in the eyes of those people who campaign regularly for the closure of airfields. Even if the prosecution is not proved, you will have the expense of defending the case. If you lose the case, you will have the stigma of a criminal record, and, possibly, incur a heavy fine and the CAA's legal costs. In addition, low-level flying is simply dangerous. High-tension cables, aerials and masts may not be marked on charts and are often difficult to see. Leave low flying to the military and crop sprayers, who have been trained properly for this role.

Reporting Hazardous Conditions

The commander of an aircraft must report as soon as possible (to ATC) any hazardous flight conditions encountered, giving details pertinent to the safety of other aircraft. Typical situations worthy of reporting are severe windshear or turbulence, rapidly deteriorating visibility or an unserviceable runway.

Aerobatics (Rule 4, Rules of the Air Regs. 2015)

Aerobatics are not permitted over a congested area. (A 'congested area' is one which is substantially used for residential, industrial, commercial or recreational purposes within a city, town or settlement.) Within controlled airspace aerobatics may be permitted with the specific approval of the controlling authority.

Simulated Instrument Flight (SERA.3220)

When simulated instrument flying is taking place (i.e. a pilot is flying the aircraft with his/her external field of view artificially restricted), the aircraft must have dual flying controls, and a second pilot (known as a *safety pilot*) must be present who can assist the other (note that a student pilot does not qualify for this assistant role). If necessary, a third person is to be carried as an observer to ensure an adequate lookout.

Practice Instrument Approaches

A pilot practising instrument approaches in Visual Meteorological Conditions (VMC) should inform ATC and must carry a 'competent observer'.

Misuse of Signals and Markings (Rule 18, Rules of the Air Regs. 2015)

Signals and markings specified in the rules for a particular meaning or purpose must not be used except with that meaning or for that purpose. Signals which may be confused with a specified signal must not be made, and military signals must not be used except with lawful authority.

Rules of the Air (ICAO Annex 2)

In addition to the Rules of the Air, pilots making international flights need to be familiar with interception procedures.

Interception of Civil Aircraft

In order to comply with ICAO standards, pilots leaving UK airspace to make international air navigation flights are required to carry a copy of the procedures to be followed in the event of interception of their aircraft for reasons of military necessity, public safety or to prohibit flight over restricted or danger areas of another State's territory. You will find these procedures in the CAA's *General Aviation Safety Sense Leaflet no. 11, Interception Procedures*. A summary of this leaflet follows.

Interception is rare, but if you are intercepted the most important things to do are to keep calm, and to follow precisely any instructions you are given.

Procedures

If you are intercepted by another aircraft you must immediately:
* follow the instructions given by the intercepting aircraft, interpreting and responding to visual signals as described below;
* notify, if possible, the appropriate Air Traffic Services Unit;
* attempt to establish radio communication with the intercepting aircraft or control unit on 121.50 MHz, giving your callsign and the nature of your flight;
* squawk code 7700 on your transponder, unless otherwise instructed by the ATSU.

Signals from intercepting aircraft

The standard signals used by intercepting aircraft and the responses you (the intercepted aircraft) should give are summarised below.

INTERCEPTING AIRCRAFT	INTERCEPTED AIRCRAFT
"You have been intercepted. Follow me."	**"Understood, will comply."**
The intercepting aircraft rocks its wings from a position slightly above and ahead of your aircraft. After your acknowledge-ment, it makes a slow level turn, normally to the left, onto the desired heading.	*Rock your wings and follow the intercepting aircraft* **immediately***.*

NOTE At night, flash your navigation lights at irregular intervals in addition to the above response. If your aircraft cannot fly fast enough to keep up with the intercepting aircraft, it will fly a series of racetrack patterns and rock its wings each time it passes you.

The signal to indicate that you may proceed with your flight is:

INTERCEPTING AIRCRAFT	INTERCEPTED AIRCRAFT
"You may proceed." *The intercepting aircraft makes an abrupt break-away manoeuvre from your aircraft, consisting of a climbing turn of 90° or more without crossing the line of flight of your aircraft.*	**"Understood, will comply."** *Rock your wings.*

If the intercepting aircraft wants you to land, it will signal as below:

INTERCEPTING AIRCRAFT	INTERCEPTED AIRCRAFT
"Land at this aerodrome." *The intercepting aircraft circles the aerodrome, lowering its landing gear and overflying the runway in the direction of landing. At night the intercepting aircraft will also show steady landing lights.*	**"Understood, will comply."** *Lower landing gear (if possible), follow intercepting aircraft and, if after overflying the runway you consider landing is safe, do so.*

Signals from intercepted aircraft
Should you need to signal to the intercepting aircraft, you may make the following standard signals:

INTERCEPTED AIRCRAFT	INTERCEPTING AIRCRAFT
"Aerodrome designated is inadequate." *Raise your landing gear (if possible) while overflying landing runway at a height above 1,000 ft and below 2,000 ft above the aerodrome level, and continue circling the aerodrome.*	**"Follow me to an alternate aerodrome."** *Intercepting aircraft will raise its landing gear and rock wings to indicate "Follow me."* OR **"You may proceed."** *Intercepting aircraft makes an abrupt break-away climbing turn.*
"I cannot comply." *Switch all available lights on and off at regular intervals, but in a manner that is distinct from flashing lights.*	**"Understood."** *Intercepting aircraft makes an abrupt break-away climbing turn.*
"I am in distress." *Switch all available lights on and off at irregular intervals.*	**"Understood."** *Intercepting aircraft makes an abrupt break-away climbing turn.*

NOTE Avoid using hand signals because they could be misinterpreted.

Radio communication

If you establish radio contact with the intercepting aircraft but do not share a common language, use the following phrases to acknowledge instructions and convey essential information.

INTERCEPTED AIRCRAFT		
Phrase	**Pronunciation**	**Meaning**
Callsign	**Kol** sa-in	My callsign is (callsign)
Wilco	**Vill**-co	Understood, will comply
Can not	**Kann** nott	Unable to comply
Repeat	Ree-**peet**	Repeat your instruction
Am lost	**Am losst**	Position unknown
Mayday	**Mayday**	I am in distress
Hijack	**Hijack**	I have been hijacked
Land (place-name)	**Laand** (place name)	I request to land at (place-name)
Descend	Dee-**send**	I require descent

The following phrases should be used by the intercepting aircraft:

INTERCEPTING AIRCRAFT		
Phrase	**Pronunciation**	**Meaning**
Callsign	**Kol** sa-in	My callsign is (callsign)
Follow	**Fol**-lo	Follow me
Descend	Dee-**send**	I require descent
You land	**You laand**	Land at this aerodrome
Proceed	Pro-**seed**	You may proceed

If you receive instructions from another source that conflict with those given by the intercepting aircraft's visual signals or radio instructions, you shall request immediate clarification while continuing to obey the visual instructions. Again, it is not a good idea to try and make hand signals, they can be easily misunderstood – not a good situation if you are head-to-head with a jet fighter!

Finally, if you are ever intercepted in foreign airspace, tell the CAA's Data and Analysis Department about it. As interceptions are rare, your experience may provide useful information to others.

Signals from the ground

Visual signals may be used to warn unauthorised aircraft flying in, or about to enter a restricted, prohibited or danger area. These are, by day or night, a series of projectiles discharged from the ground at intervals of 10 seconds, each showing, on bursting, red and green stars or lights. This will indicate to an unauthorised aircraft that it is flying in, or about to enter a restricted, prohibited or danger area, and that the aircraft is to take such remedial actions as may be necessary (normally to leave the area as quickly as possible without descending).

Now complete: **Practice Questions - Rules of the Air**

---

1. The ultimate responsibility for taking all possible measures to avoid a collision between aircraft lies with:

    (a) Air Traffic Control.
    (b) The Pilot-in-Command.
    (c) The most highly qualified pilot on board.
    (d) The Air/Ground Communications Operator.

2. In the air, when two aircraft are approaching head on, or approximately so:

    (a) Each aircraft will alter course to the right in order to pass well clear.
    (b) Each aircraft will alter course to the left in order to pass well clear.
    (c) The aircraft with the greater speed has the right of way.
    (d) The aircraft may turn left or right according to the particular circumstances in order to pass well clear.

3. The minimum height to fly over the congested areas of cities, towns or settlements or over an open–air assembly of persons is:

    (a) 600 m (2,000 feet) above the highest obstacle within a radius of 600 m from the aircraft;
    (b) 300 m (1,000 feet) above the highest obstacle within a radius of 600 m from the aircraft;
    (c) 600 m (2,000 feet) above the highest obstacle within a radius of 300 m from the aircraft;
    (d) 300 m (1,000 feet) above the highest obstacle within a radius of 300 m from the aircraft.

4. In relation to converging aircraft in the air, the correct order is:

    (a) Balloons must give way to airships and sailplanes.
    (b) Sailplanes must give way to powered aircraft, airships and balloons.
    (c) Powered aircraft must give way to airships, sailplanes and balloons.
    (d) Airships must give way to powered aircraft, sailplanes and balloons.

5. When two or more aircraft are approaching to land at the same place, assuming that neither has an emergency and no ATC order has been specified:

(a) *The lower aircraft has the right of way.*
(b) *The fastest aircraft has the right of way, but must not cut in front of or overtake another aircraft on final.*
(c) *The closest aircraft to the runway threshold has the right of way.*
(d) *The lower aircraft has the right of way, but must not cut in front of or overtake another aircraft on final.*

6. When two aircraft are converging, the one which has the right of way, must:

(a) *Maintain its speed and height.*
(b) *Maintain its heading and height.*
(c) *Maintain its speed and heading.*
(d) *Maintain its speed, heading and height.*

7. Whilst flying at night you see the green navigation light of another flying machine on a steady relative bearing of 330° at a similar level.

(a) *There is a risk of collision, you should maintain heading and speed.*
(b) *There is no risk of collision.*
(c) *There is a risk of collision, you should climb or descend.*
(d) *There is a risk of collision, you should turn right.*

Aerodromes

Aerodromes (UK ANO)

General Characteristics

An aerodrome is an area of land or water used for the taking off and landing of aircraft. Aerodromes are divided into various categories depending on their use. The *Aerodromes* (AD) section of the UK Aeronautical Information Publication (AIP) contains an aerodrome directory giving specific information on physical characteristics, local hazards and flying restrictions.

Limitations on the Use of Aerodromes

Certain restrictions apply at some aerodromes and not at others.

At military aerodromes, and at civil aerodromes with an ordinary licence, **prior permission to land** is needed from the aerodrome authority, and at unlicensed aerodromes the **prior permission of the owner or person in charge.** This may be designated in documents as 'PPR', which stands for *prior permission required.*

PPR usually means that you should telephone the airfield operator or owner before departure, particularly if there is no radio frequency published for the airfield. Remember that if you simply turn up and land without seeking permission you are trespassing on private property. Further, there may be safety implications as a particular airstrip may be usable only in a certain direction or in certain wind conditions. It may be prone to waterlogging or there could be specific noise abatement procedures to be followed.

Failure to seek permission and the requisite information could lead to an accident, and subsequent refusal by the insurance company to pay for the claim because you would have breached the Air Navigation Order.

Permission to use a military aerodrome must always be obtained before taking off for the aerodrome concerned. It is likely that you will have to demonstrate a higher level of insurance cover to land at a military aerodrome.

The civil use of military aerodromes is restricted to the normal hours of watch, and to aircraft on inland flights. At some military aerodromes, civil use is further restricted to certain classes of traffic (e.g. scheduled services, charter flights or private aircraft).

The above restrictions on aerodrome use would not apply in the case of an in-flight emergency. Aerodromes not listed in AIP AD (*Aerodromes* section of the Aeronautical Information Publication) may be used in an **emergency** or if **prior permission** from the owner or operator is obtained.

Rules of the Air relating to Aerodromes

Use of Aerodromes for Instruction in Flying (ANO Article 209)

If a flight is for the purpose of instruction in flying to enable a person to become qualified for the grant of a pilot's licence or for the inclusion of a rating or carrying out flying tests for any of these purposes, then before an unlicensed aerodrome or non-EASA certified aerodrome may be used:

- the operator of such an aerodrome must be satisfied that the aerodrome has adequate facilities for the safe conduct of such flight; and

- the commander of the aircraft must not take off unless the pilot is similarly satisfied.

Aviation Fuel at Aerodromes (ANO Article 220)

No person shall cause or permit any fuel to be used in an aircraft if the pilot knows or has reason to believe that it is not fit for such use. Fuel must not be used in aircraft unless it has been dealt with in accordance with certain stipulations for the storage and sampling of aviation fuel stocks at aerodromes.

NOTE As a guide to pilots and others, and in an attempt to avoid refuelling with the wrong type of fuel, **Avgas** equipment at aerodromes is usually marked in **red.**

Notification of Arrival and Departure

If an aircraft is expected at an aerodrome the commander must inform the authorities at the aerodrome as soon as possible if the destination is changed or arrival will be delayed by 45 minutes or more. This is to avoid any unnecessary *overdue action.*

Wherever possible an aircraft's commander must report upon arrival, and prior to departure, to the appropriate authority at an aerodrome.

Customs Facilities

Designated Customs and Excise Airports for the purposes of international travel are listed in the GEN (General) section of the UK AIP, together with hours of attendance and special requirements.

Aeronautical Light Beacons

Aeronautical light beacons are installed at various civil and military aerodromes in the UK. Their hours of operation vary, but broadly speaking they can be expected to be on at night and by day in bad visibility, whenever the aerodrome is operating.

Aeronautical light beacons include:
- **Identification beacons**, which flash a two-letter Morse group every 12 seconds (**green** at civil aerodromes and **red** at military aerodromes); and
- **Aerodrome beacons** which give an alternating-colour flash signal instead (usually **white/white** or (less commonly) **white/ green**). They are not normally provided in addition to an identification beacon.

AERONAUTICAL LIGHT BEACONS

Civil aerodrome beacon

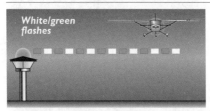

Civil aerodrome beacon

Civil identification beacon
(two-letter Morse code group, flashed every 12 seconds)

Military identification beacon
(two-letter Morse code group, flashed every 12 seconds)

Movement of Aircraft on Aerodromes (Rule 12, Rules of the Air Regs. 2015)

An aircraft must not taxi on the apron or the manoeuvring area of an aerodrome without the permission of the aerodrome authorities.

The **manoeuvring area** of an aerodrome is that part of the aerodrome provided for the take-off and landing of aircraft and for the movement of aircraft on the surface (i.e. taxiing), excluding aprons and maintenance areas. An **apron** is a paved area of an aerodrome used for purposes such as loading and unloading of aircraft, aircraft turn-around operations, maintenance and repair, and any other approved purpose other than flight operations.

Access on Aerodromes (Rule 13)

A person shall not, without permission, go onto a part of an aerodrome provided for the use of aircraft. This applies to any part that is not a public right of way.

Right of Way on the Ground (SERA.3210)

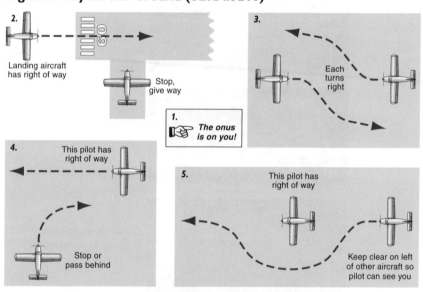

■ *Figure 3-1* **Five rules for taxiing on the manoeuvring area of an aerodrome**

1. Regardless of any ATC clearance it is the duty of an aircraft commander to do all possible to avoid collision on the ground with other aircraft or vehicles or with any obstacle (where an aircraft is being towed and the commander of the aircraft is not on board, then that duty lies with the person in charge of the vehicle towing the aircraft).

2. Aircraft on the ground must give way to those taking off or landing, and to any vehicle towing an aircraft.

3. When two aircraft are approaching head-on, or nearly so, each must turn right.

4. When two aircraft are converging, the one which has the other on its right must give way, avoiding crossing ahead of the other unless passing well clear.

5. An aircraft which is being overtaken by another has right of way, and the overtaking aircraft must keep out of the way by turning left until past and well clear.

Aerodrome Traffic Zones (ATZs)

A certain amount of airspace surrounding most aerodromes in the UK has been designated as Aerodrome Traffic Zones, usually because of the intensity of aerial activity. See Chapter 5 for details of the dimensions of an ATZ and the airspace surrounding it.

Runway Characteristics

Declared distances at aerodromes are agreed by the relevant authority – in the UK this is the CAA, and the distances are published in the Aerodrome section of the AIP.

- **Take-off run available (TORA).** The length of runway declared available and suitable for the ground run of an aeroplane taking off.
- **Take-off distance available (TODA).** The length of the take-off run available plus the length of the clearway, if provided.
- **Accelerate-stop distance available (ASDA).** The length of the take-off run available plus the length of the stopway, if provided.

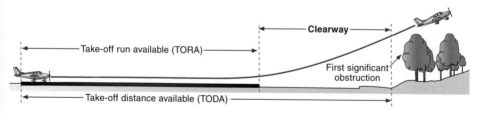

■ Figure 3-2 **TODA, TORA and clearway**

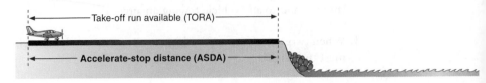

■ *Figure 3-3a* **Accelerate-stop distance (ASDA) equals TORA in this case**

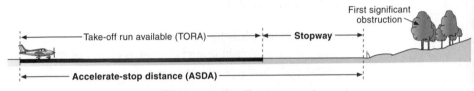

■ *Figure 3-3b* **Accelerate-stop distance (ASDA) including stopway**

- **Landing distance available (LDA).** The length of runway declared available and suitable for the ground run of an aeroplane landing.

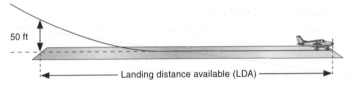

■ *Figure 3-4* **Landing distance available (LDA)**

Aerodromes (ICAO Annex 14)

Annex 14 describes ICAO standards and recommended practices for aerodromes. This Annex contains the basic specifications for the physical characteristics, configuration, performance, personnel and procedures for aerodromes that are considered desirable for safe and efficient international air navigation. Contracting States will endeavour to conform to these standards in accordance with the Chicago Convention.

Summaries of extracts relevant to PPL candidates follow. Remember that the small paragraph numbers refer to those in the ICAO Annex in case you want to study further. It is also well worth reading the CAA's *Visual Aids Handbook* (CAP 637), which is an excellent pictorial guide for pilots and personnel engaged in the handling of aircraft.

Finally, don't forget to review the terminology used in ICAO Annexes, which is summarised on page 201.

Water on a Runway

2.9.4 When water is present on a runway, a description of the runway surface conditions on the centre half of the width of the runway should be made available to pilots using the following terms:

* **Damp** – the surface shows a change in colour due to moisture.
* **Wet** – the surface is soaked but there is no standing water.
* **Water patches** – significant patches of standing water are visible.
* **Flooded** – extensive standing water is visible.

Note also the definitions of slush and snow on page 213.

Wind Direction Indicator

5.1.1 Aerodromes shall have at least one wind direction indicator. Wind direction indicators shall be located so as to be visible from aircraft in flight or on the movement area, and to be free from air disturbances by nearby objects.

Landing Direction Indicator

5.1.2 Where provided, a landing direction indicator should be located in a conspicuous place on an aerodrome.

Markings

5.2.1.4 Runway markings shall be white.

5.2.1.5 Taxiway markings and aircraft stand markings shall be yellow.

Runway Threshold and Wingbar Lights

5.3.10.9 Runway threshold and wingbar lights shall be fixed unidirectional lights showing green in the direction of approach to the runway.

5.3.11 A runway equipped with runway edge lights shall also be equipped with runway end lights (ideally at least six lights).

Runway end lights shall be placed at right angles to the runway axis as near as possible to the end of the runway (not more than 3 metres outside the end).

Runway end lights shall be fixed, showing red in the direction of the runway.

Aerodrome Signs

5.4.3 Mandatory instruction signs should be white on a red background.

Obstacle Lights

6.3.25 On vehicles other than emergency or security vehicles, the low intensity obstacle lights should be flashing yellow.

6.3.33 High intensity obstacle lights are required to be flashing white.

Aerodrome Signals and Markings (SERA.3301 & Rules of the Air Regs. 2015 - Section 5)

A **signals area** is positioned near the control tower at some aerodromes to allow messages to be passed to a pilot without the use of radio:
* **in flight**, by signals laid out on the ground; and
* **on the ground**, by signals hoisted up a mast located in the signals area.

Signals and Markings in the Signals Area

Direction of Take-Off and Landing

A **white 'T'** signifies that aeroplanes and gliders taking off or landing shall do so parallel with the shaft of the 'T' and towards the cross arm, unless otherwise authorised by the appropriate ATC unit.

A **white disc** at the head of the 'T' means that the direction of landing and the direction of take-off do not necessarily coincide. This latter situation may also be indicated by a **black ball** suspended from a mast. A rectangular **green flag** flown from a mast indicates that a right-hand circuit is in force.

■ *Figure 3-5* **Direction of take-off and landing**

Use Hard Surfaces Only

A **white dumb-bell** signifies that movements of aeroplanes and gliders on the ground shall be confined to paved, metalled or similar hard surfaces. The addition of black strips in each circular portion of the dumb-bell, at right angles to the shaft, signifies that aeroplanes and gliders taking off or landing must do so on a runway, but that movement on the ground is not confined to hard surfaces.

■ *Figure 3-6* **Use of hard surfaces signals**

Right-Hand Circuit

A red-and-yellow striped arrow bent through 90 degrees around the edge of the signals area and pointing in a clockwise direction means that turns are to be made to the right before landing and after take off.

■ *Figure 3-7* **Right-hand circuit indicator**

Where the circuit direction at an aerodrome is variable (left-hand or right-hand) a rectangular **red flag** on the signals mast indicates that a **left-hand** circuit is in operation. A rectangular **green flag** signifies that the circuit is **right-hand**.

Special precautions

A horizontal red square panel with a single yellow diagonal means that the state of the manoeuvring area is poor and precautions must be observed in approaching to land and on landing.

■ *Figure 3-8* **Special precautions signal**

Landing Prohibited

A red square panel with a diagonal yellow cross signifies that landing is prohibited, and that the prohibition is likely to be prolonged.

■ *Figure 3-9* **Landing prohibited signal**

Helicopter Operations

A **white 'H'** in the signals area means that helicopters must take off and land only within a designated area (that area itself being marked by a much larger white 'H').

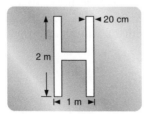

(a) A white letter H is displayed in the signals area

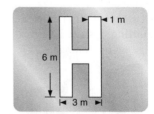

(b) A white letter H indicates the area to be used only by helicopters for take-off and landing

■ *Figure 3-10* **Helicopter operations markers**

Gliding (Sailplanes)

A double white cross and/or two red balls suspended from a mast, one above the other, signify that glider-flying (sailplane flying) is taking place at the aerodrome. (A similar but much larger signal is used to mark an area on the aerodrome which is to be used only by gliders).

A **yellow cross** indicates the tow-rope dropping area.

Tow-ropes, banners, etc. can only be picked up or dropped at an aerodrome, and then only as directed by the aerodrome authority, or in the designated area (yellow cross) with the aircraft flying in the direction appropriate for landing.

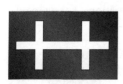

■ Figure 3-11 **Gliding (Sailplane flying) in progress**

Signals on Paved Runways and Taxiways

Unserviceable Portion of Runway or Taxiway

Two or more white crosses along a section of runway or taxiway, with the arms of the crosses at an angle of 45 degrees to the centreline of the runway or taxiway at intervals of not more than 300 metres, signify that the section of the runway or taxiway marked by them is unfit for the movement of aircraft.

■ Figure 3-12 **Unfit section of runway (white) or taxiway (yellow)**

Orange and white markers as illustrated in Figure 3-13, spaced not more than 15 metres apart, signify the boundary of that part of a paved runway, taxiway or apron which is unfit for the movement of aircraft. Each marker comprises a base board supporting a slatted vertical board, both of which are striped orange–white–orange.

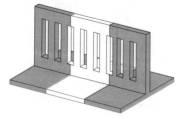

■ Figure 3-13 **Boundary of unserviceable area marker**

Holding Point on Paved Taxiway

Parallel yellow lines – usually marked as a set of double continuous and double broken lines – across a taxiway signify a holding point, beyond which no part of an aircraft or vehicle may proceed in the direction of the runway, without ATC permission.

Of the two sets of lines, the **broken yellow lines** are located on the runway side, enabling the pilot to determine if the holding point affects him. Moving in the reverse direction towards a holding point, with the broken yellow lines encountered first (for example, having turned off the runway after landing), the holding point does not require a clearance to cross it.

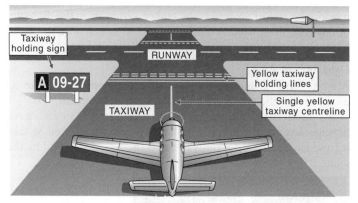

■ Figure 3-14 **Typical taxiway markings and holding position sign**

NOTE Older holding points may be marked with white lines, but most are now yellow. Also, older holding points may still be marked with a single continuous line and a single broken line.

Markers on Unpaved Manoeuvring Areas

Aerodrome Boundary Markers

Orange/white striped wedge-shaped markers (like elongated wheel-chocks in shape), placed not more than 45 metres apart, indicate the boundary of an aerodrome. These are supplemented by flat orange/white markers, also placed 45 metres apart, on any structures which lie on the boundary.

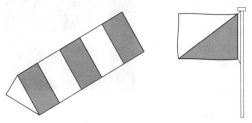

■ Figure 3-15 **Boundary marker**

Unserviceable Portion

The orange/white striped wedge-shaped markers shown in Figure 3-15 are also used to mark the boundary of an unpaved area which is unserviceable for aircraft movement. These alternate with square flags showing equal orange and white triangular areas. Within this marked area the bad ground is itself marked with one or more white crosses (as described above).

Runway/Stopway Boundary Markers

White, flat rectangular markers, flush with the surface and placed not more than 90 metres apart, indicate the boundary of an unpaved runway or of a stopway. (A stopway is a prepared rectangular area of ground at the end of a runway, in the direction of take-off, designated as a suitable area in which an aircraft can be stopped in the case of an interrupted take-off.)

Light Aircraft Area

A white letter 'L' indicates a part of the manoeuvring area to be used only for the taking off and landing of light aircraft.

If a dumb-bell displayed in the aerodrome signals area has a red 'L' superimposed, it means that light aircraft are allowed to take off and land either on a runway or on the area designated by the white 'L'.

■ Figure 3-16 **Light aircraft areas**

Runway to be Used

A white 'T' (placed on the left side of a runway when viewed from the landing direction) indicates that *it* is the runway to be used. Where there is no runway it indicates the direction for take-off and landing.

■ Figure 3-17 **Runway to be used**

Landing Dangerous

A white cross displayed at each end of a runway indicates that landing is dangerous and that the aerodrome is used for storage purposes only.

■ *Figure 3-18* **Landing dangerous**

Emergency Use Only

A white cross and a single white bar displayed at each end of the runway at a disused aerodrome indicates that the runway is fit for emergency use only. Runways so marked are not safe-guarded and may be temporarily obstructed.

■ *Figure 3-19* **Emergency use only**

Displaced Threshold Markings

The threshold marking on a runway delineates the beginning of the usable portion of that runway (at the downwind end). Sometimes the threshold marking is moved, or displaced, some distance up the runway from the end of the paved area. Such a **displaced threshold** may be either temporary, to allow for maintenance, for instance, or permanent.

There are various displaced threshold markings, depending on the type (if any) of aircraft movement permitted in the first portion of the runway, and whether the displacement is temporary or permanent. Some pre-threshold areas may be usable for take-off, but not for landing; some may be unfit for any kind of aircraft movement. See overleaf.

Normal 'piano key' threshold marking for a paved runway. '09' is the runway designator – the runway direction rounded off to the nearest 10°, 090° in this case

Permanently displaced threshold White arrows indicate that the pre-threshold area is available for taxi and take-off, but not for landing

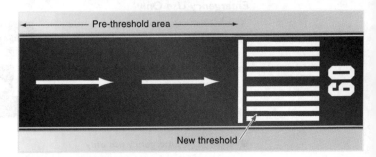

Pre-threshold area

New threshold

Permanently displaced threshold White crosses indicate that the pre-threshold area is unfit for movement of aircraft and unsuitable as a stopway

White crosses, not more than 300 metres apart, arms at 45° to runway centreline

Temporarily displaced threshold Pre-threshold area is available for taxi and take-off, but not for landing

Temporarily displaced threshold Pre-threshold area is unfit for movement of aircraft.

■ *Figure 3-20* **Normal threshold marking (top) and displaced threshold markings**

Summary of Aerodrome Signals Visible only when on the Ground

In the Signals Area

1. A black ball on a mast signifies that the directions of take-off and landing are not necessarily the same.

2. Two red balls on a mast signify that gliding is taking place.

3. A rectangular red/yellow chequered flag or board means that aircraft may move on the manoeuvring area and apron only with the permission of ATC.

■ *Figure 3-21* **ATC in operation**

4. If the circuit direction at the aerodrome is variable, and a **left-hand circuit** is in operation, a **red flag** will be flown from the mast. A **green flag** on the mast signifies that a **right-hand circuit** is in force at the aerodrome. (Note that the colours of the flags for left and right circuits are the same as for aircraft navigation lights.)

■ *Figure 3-22* **Signals area at Wycombe (WP); clockwise from bottom left corner – special precautions; gliding in progress; (white dash symbol is part of dumb-bell not in use); right-hand circuits; and in centre: take-off and landing direction (towards the cross-arm)**

Away from the Signals Area

5. A square yellow board bearing a black 'C' indicates the location where a pilot should report to ATC or other aerodrome authority.

■ *Figure 3-23* **Location of aerodrome authority**

Light Signals

You should be aware of standard light signals and pyrotechnics that ATSU personnel may beam to aircraft. The signals differ in meaning according to whether you are in flight or on the ground. Green flashes, for instance, when beamed at an aircraft in flight mean "Return for a landing", whereas when beamed to an aircraft on the ground they mean "Authorised to taxi".

FROM ATSU TO AIRCRAFT

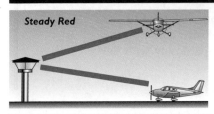

Steady Red

Do not land. Give way to other aircraft and continue circling.

Stop.

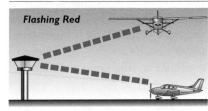

Flashing Red

Do not land. Aerodrome closed (go to another aerodrome).

Move clear of landing area.

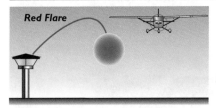

Red Flare

Do not land; wait for permission.

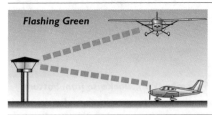

Flashing Green

Return to this aerodrome and wait for permission to land.

Cleared to taxi on the manoeuvring area if pilot satisfied no collision risk exists.

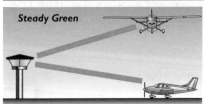

Steady Green

Cleared to land if pilot satisfied no collision risk exists.

Cleared to take-off if pilot satisfied no collision risk exists.

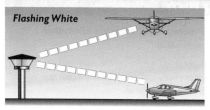

FROM ATSU TO AIRCRAFT

Flashing White

Land at this aerodrome after receiving a steady green light and await further instructions.

Return to starting point on aerodrome.

Light signals can also be sent *from* an aircraft, but the equipment (such as flares) is rarely available for a pilot to use. The one signal that can be used in almost any aircraft, however, is flashing the landing lights or position navigation lights on and off (usually visible from the ground only at night) to indicate "I am compelled to land".

FROM AIRCRAFT TO ATSU

Flashing landing and/or navigation lights

I am compelled to land.

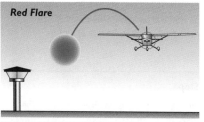

Red Flare

Immediate assistance required.

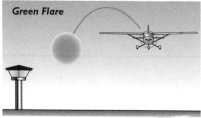

Green Flare

By night
May I land?

By day
May I land in a different direction from that indicated by the landing T?

Marshalling Signals

FROM MARSHALLER TO PILOT

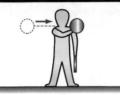

Proceed under guidance of another marshaller

Right or left arm down, the other arm moved across body and extended to indicate position of the other marshaller.

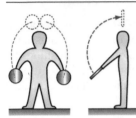

Move ahead

Arms repeatedly moved upward and backward, beckoning onward.

Open up starboard engine(s) or turn to port

Right arm down, left arm repeatedly moved upward and backward. The speed of arm movement indicates the rate of turn.

Open up port engine(s) or turn to starboard

Left arm down, the right arm repeatedly moved upward and backward. The speed of arm movement indicates the rate of turn.

Stop

Arms repeatedly crossed above the head. The speed of arm movement indicates the urgency of the stop.

FROM MARSHALLER TO PILOT

Start engine

A circular motion of the right hand at head level, with the left arm pointing to the appropriate engine.

Chocks inserted

Arms extended, the palms facing inwards, then swung from the extended position inwards.

Chocks away

Arms down, the palms facing outwards, then swung outwards.

Cut engines

Either arm and hand placed level with the chest, then moved laterally with the palm facing downwards.

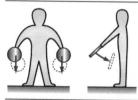

Slow down

Arms placed down, with the palms towards the ground, then moved up and down several times.

Slow down engine(s) on indicated side

Arms placed down, with the palms towards the ground, then either the right or left arm moved up and down indicating that the motors on the left or right side, as the case may be, should be slowed down.

FROM MARSHALLER TO PILOT

This bay

Arms placed above the head in a vertical position.

Release brakes

Raise arm, with fist clenched, horizontally in front of the body, then extend fingers.

Engage brakes

Raise arm and hand, with fingers extended, horizontally in front of body, then clench fist.

All clear – marshalling finished

The right arm raised at the elbow with the palm facing forwards.

Start engine(s)

Left hand overhead with the number of fingers extended, to indicate the number of the engine to be started, and circular motion of right hand at head level.

Back aircraft tail to starboard

Point left arm down, move right arm down from overhead, vertical position to horizontal forward position, repeating right arm movement.

FROM MARSHALLER TO PILOT

Back aircraft tail to port

Point right arm down, move left arm down from overhead, vertical position to horizontal forward position, repeating left arm movement.

 indicates that the signal is applicable only to helicopter operations.

 Hover

Arms placed horizontally sideways.

 Land

Arms placed down and crossed in front of the body.

ARMS PLACED HORIZONTALLY SIDEWAYS, WITH THE PALMS UP, BECKONING UPWARDS. THE SPEED OF ARM MOVEMENT INDICATES THE RATE OF ASCENT.

MEANING: **MOVE UPWARDS.**

ARMS PLACED HORIZONTALLY SIDEWAYS, WITH THE PALMS TOWARDS THE GROUND, BECKONING DOWNWARDS. THE SPEED OF ARM MOVEMENT INDICATES THE RATE OF DESCENT.

MEANING: **MOVE DOWNWARDS.**

FROM MARSHALLER TO PILOT

EITHER ARM PLACED HORIZONTALLY SIDEWAYS, THEN THE OTHER ARM MOVED IN FRONT OF THE BODY TO THAT SIDE, IN THE DIRECTION OF THE REQUIRED MOVEMENT; REPEATED SEVERAL TIMES.

MEANING: **MOVE HORIZONTALLY IN THE DIRECTION INDICATED.**

ARMS PLACED DOWN, THE PALMS FACING FORWARD, THEN REPEATEDLY SWEPT UP TO SHOULDER LEVEL AND BACK DOWN.

MEANING: **MOVE BACK.**

 **Release load**

Left arm extended horizontally forward, then right arm making a horizontal slicing movement below left arm.

FROM PILOT TO MARSHALLER

Brakes engaged

Raise arm and hand with fingers extended horizontally in front of face, then clench fist:

Brakes released

Raise arm with fist clenched horizontally in front of face, then extend fingers:

Insert chocks

Arms extended palms facing outwards, move hands inwards to cross in front of face:

Remove chocks

Hands crossed in front of face, palms facing outwards, move arms outwards:

Ready to start engines

Raise the number of fingers on one hand indicating the number of the engine to be started. For this purpose the aircraft engines shall be numbered in relation to the marshaller facing the aircraft, from his right to his left.

For example, No. 1 engine shall be the port outer engine, No. 2 shall be the port inner, No. 3 shall be the starboard inner, and No. 4 shall be the starboard outer.

FROM MARSHALLER TO AIRCRAFT
STANDARD EMERGENCY HAND SIGNALS

1. Recommend Evacuation

Evacuation recommended based on aircraft rescue and fire-fighting and incident commander's assessment of external situation.

Arm extended from body and held horizontal with hand upraised at eye level. Execute beckoning arm motion angled backward. Non-beckoning arm held against body. Night -same with wands.

2. Recommend STOP

Recommend evacuation in progress be halted. Stop aircraft movement or other activity in progress.

Arms in front of head-crossed at wrists

Night - same with wands.

3. Emergency Contained

No outside evidence of dangerous conditions or 'All Clear'.

Arms extended outward and down at 45 degree angle, arms moved inward below waistline simultaneously until wrists crossed, then extended outward to starting position. Night - same with wands.

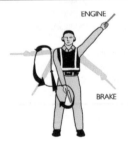

ENGINE

BRAKE

4. FIRE

Move right hand in a 'Fanning' motion from shoulder to knee, while at the same time pointing with left hand to area of fire.

Night - same with wands.

Now complete: **Practice Questions - Aerodromes**

1. If you have given notice of your intended arrival at an aerodrome, you must ensure that the appropriate authority at that aerodrome is advised of:

   (a) *Any change in destination or estimated delay of 45 minutes or more.*

   (b) *Any estimated delay of 30 minutes or more.*

   (c) *Any estimated delay of 60 minutes or more.*

   (d) *Any change in destination or estimated delay of 30 minutes or more.*

2. The Take-off run available (TORA) may be defined as the:

   (a) *Length of the clearway and stopway.*

   (b) *Runway length.*

   (c) *Part of the runway declared as suitable for the ground run of an aeroplane taking off plus any associated clearway.*

   (d) *Part of the runway declared as suitable for the ground run of an aeroplane taking off.*

3. Runway threshold lights are:

   (a) *Fixed green lights showing in the direction of the runway.*

   (b) *Fixed white lights showing in the direction of the approach to the runway.*

   (c) *Flashing lights showing in all directions alternating red and white.*

   (d) *Fixed green lights showing in the direction of the approach to the runway.*

4. On the ground, when two aircraft are approaching head on, or approximately so:

   (a) *Each aircraft will stop, or where practicable, alter course to the right in order to pass well clear.*

   (b) *Each aircraft will stop, or where practicable, alter course to the left in order to pass well clear.*

   (c) *The aircraft with the greater speed has the right of way.*

   (d) *The aircraft may turn left or right according to the particular circumstances in order to pass well clear.*

5. ICAO recommends that the colours used for marking are:

   (a) Orange on taxiways, blue on runways.
   (b) White on runways, yellow on taxiways.
   (c) Yellow on runways, white on taxiways.
   (d) Yellow.

6. A white "T" with a white disc alongside the cross–arm in line with the stem of the "T" displayed in the signal area means:

   (a) Parachuting is taking place at the aerodrome.
   (b) Take-offs and landings must be in the same direction.
   (c) The direction of landing and take-off do not necessarily coincide.
   (d) The state of the manoeuvring area is poor and care must be taken.

7. The meaning of a steady red light directed from an aerodrome to (i) an aircraft in flight and (ii) an aircraft on the ground is:

   (a) (i) Airfield unavailable for landing (ii) go back to your starting point on the aerodrome.
   (b) (i) Give way to other aircraft and continue circling (ii) stop.
   (c) (i) Wait for permission to land (ii) cleared for take off.
   (d) (i) Position downwind (ii) stop.

Answers: 1a, 2d, 3d, 4a, 5b, 6c, 7b.

Altimeter-Setting Procedures

Terminology

Atmospheric pressure decreases as altitude. The altimeter, the flight instrument that is used to determine the vertical position of an aircraft with reference to sea level or ground level, is a barometer. A barometer measures atmospheric pressure, but the altimeter has a scale calibrated in feet rather than in units of pressure.

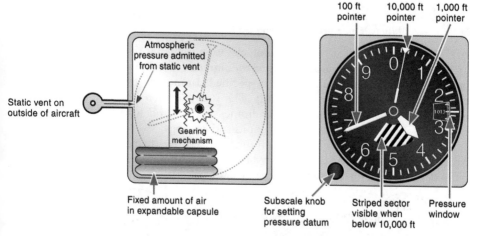

■ *Figure 4-1* ***The altimeter is a pressure-sensitive instrument***

The pressure at the earth's surface changes from time to time and from place to place, so it is necessary to have some means of selecting the base level pressure from which height (or altitude) will be measured. To achieve this, altimeters have a **subscale** which can be altered with a knob – the 'subscale-setting knob'.

The pressure set on the altimeter subscale determines the pressure level from which the altimeter will indicate height or altitude. The usual pressure references are:

QNH. The *mean sea level* pressure at that time causing the altimeter to indicate **altitude** – the vertical distance above mean sea level (amsl). This is necessary when separation from terrain and separation from other aircraft is of concern, since the ground and obstacles are shown as heights amsl (i.e. elevations) on aeronautical charts.

QNH varies from time to time and from place to place as pressure systems move across the face of the earth, so the pilot needs to update the QNH on the altimeter subscale, both periodically and as the pilot flies from region to region.

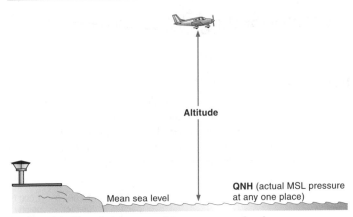

■ Figure 4-2 **Altitude is measured from mean sea level**

QFE. The pressure level at the aerodrome elevation (which is the highest point on the landing area) causing the altimeter to indicate **height** – the vertical distance above a specified datum, usually chosen to be above aerodrome level (aal). This is useful when the only concern is height above the aerodrome, and so QFE is a common setting to use for take-offs, circuits and landings.

QFE at an aerodrome will vary with time, any changes being passed to the pilot by ATC. QFEs at different aerodromes will differ depending upon elevation and the pressure pattern.

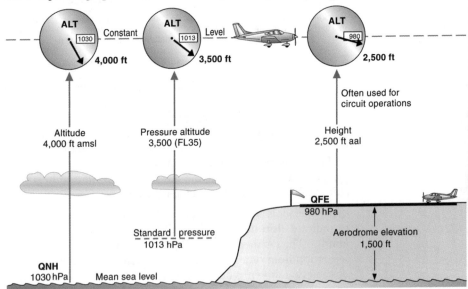

■ Figure 4-3 **Typical altimeter settings on a day of high pressure**

STANDARD PRESSURE. Setting the subscale to 1013.2 hectopascals or millibars – (see *Note* which follows) causes the altimeter to read **pressure altitude (PA)**. This is useful for vertical separation from other aircraft that are using the same altimeter setting. It is standard procedure to set 1013 at the higher cruising levels where terrain clearance is no longer a concern.

Using standard pressure avoids the need to update QNH with changes in time and/or location. To avoid confusing *pressure altitude* with *altitude,* pressure altitude generally has the last two zeros removed and is then referred to as a **flight level**, e.g. PA 3,500 is FL35.

NOTE You will recall that the term **hectopascal (hPa)** has been adopted as the international standard for the unit of atmospheric pressure; in the UK, the hectopascal replaced the millibar with effect from 17 November 2011. Hectopascals are also used in most other countries. The unit size is identical, i.e. **1 mb = 1 hPa.** Below 5,000 ft, 1 hPa equals approximately 30 feet.

Altimeter Setting Regions

The UK is divided into twenty **Altimeter Setting Regions (ASRs)** so that, when en route, all aircraft flying on QNH in the same region will have the appropriate Regional Pressure Setting (RPS) set, allowing the pilots to ensure vertical separation between their aircraft. *You must know which Altimeter Setting Region you are in, and when you are moving from one region to another.* The Regional Pressure Setting is often colloquially known as the **Regional QNH.**

The actual QNH will vary throughout the region, depending upon the pressure pattern. *The RPS is the lowest forecast QNH value for each hour,* thereby ensuring that the pilot will be at, or slightly higher than, the altitude indicated.

The RPS is updated each hour by the Air Traffic Service (ATS) and as the aircraft passes from one Altimeter Setting Region to another. No Aerodrome QNH in that region should be lower than the value of the RPS.

A chart showing all the UK Altimeter Setting regions appears in the UK Aeronautical Information Publication (AIP), ENR (En-Route) section, page 6-1-7-1. Figure 4-4 shows an excerpt from the chart.

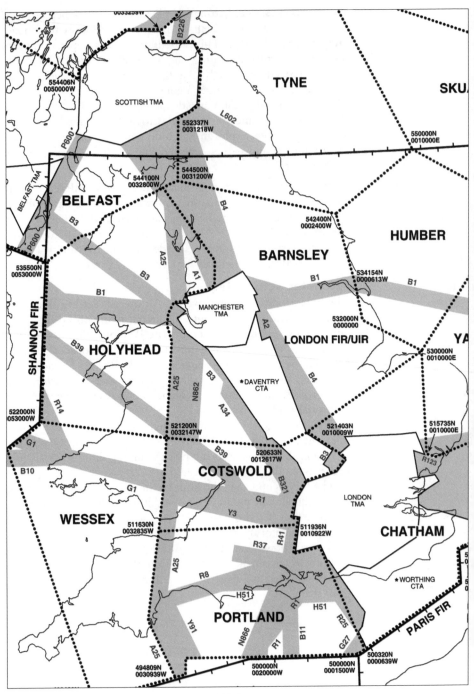

■ Figure 4-4 **UK Altimeter Setting Regions (ASRs)**

Vertical Separation from Terrain and Air Traffic

Altitude information is useful both for separation from terrain (since height on charts is given *above mean sea level)* and from other aircraft, so when flying below transition level, QNH (sea level pressure) is set on the altimeter subscale as the reference datum.

The **transition altitude** is the altitude below which the vertical position of aircraft is controlled by reference to altitude – with pilots having QNH set on their altimeter subscales. Transition altitude is 3,000 ft amsl over most of the UK. Exceptions beneath certain airspace are listed in the UK Aeronautical Information Publication (AIP), ENR 1-7-1. UK AIP AD 2.17 lists the UK transition altitudes.

When flying at a level well above the terrain, where separation between air traffic is the primary consideration, the standard pressure setting of 1013 hPa is used as the reference datum.

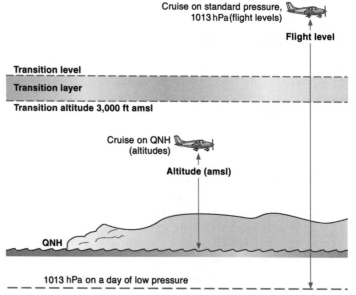

■ *Figure 4-5* **Transition from altitudes to flight levels**

Above the transition altitude, the term *flight level* is used, so standard pressure (1013) should be set on the altimeter subscale. This ensures safe vertical separation between Instrument Flight Rules (IFR) traffic. 1013 is used (subject to some exceptions, as specified in the UK AIP, ENR 1-7) by all aircraft in *controlled airspace,* or above 3,000 ft in *uncontrolled airspace.*

The **transition level** is the lowest flight level available for cruising above the transition altitude, the airspace between them being known as the *transition layer.*

Since the altimeter subscale setting will normally be changed when entering the transition layer, it is usual to express vertical displacement in terms of *flight level after climbing through* the transition altitude, and in terms of altitude *after descending through* the transition level.

In a flight plan:
* **altitudes** should be specified for that part of the flight below the transition altitude; and
* **flight levels** for that part of the flight above the transition level.

Cruising levels should be chosen:
* so that adequate terrain clearance is assured;
* so that any Air Traffic Service requirements are met; and
* to comply with the *semicircular* rules for cruise level, as specified for Visual or Instrument Flight Rules, if appropriate. See page 72.

A Typical Cross-Country Flight

Altimetry procedures are much easier in practice than they seem when you read the regulations. A typical cross-country flight between two aerodromes, remaining in uncontrolled airspace and probably not above 3,000 ft amsl, is illustrated below.

The main points are that:
* **Regional pressure setting is set en route** so that the altimeter indicates height above mean sea level.
* **In the circuit area** at each aerodrome, the altimeter subscale is set, according to the pilot's preference, to either:
  - **Aerodrome QFE,** so that the altimeter indicates height above aerodrome level (aal); or
  - **Aerodrome QNH,** so that the altimeter indicates height above mean sea level (amsl) or *altitude.*

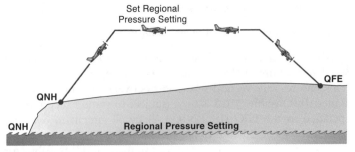

■ *Figure 4-6* **A typical cross-country flight**

Take-Off and Climb

There are two altimeter readings that can be of value to a pilot for take-off and climb:

- **height above aerodrome level** (with QFE set) – useful for flying in the circuit, e.g. when a 1,000 ft circuit is flown 1,000 ft is indicated on the altimeter; and
- **altitude** (i.e. height above mean sea level, with QNH set) – useful for terrain and obstacle clearance.

WITHIN CONTROLLED AIRSPACE, where Air Traffic Control has a responsibility to separate air traffic, a pilot may use:

- either Aerodrome QNH or Aerodrome QFE for **take-off.** If the aircraft is fitted with two altimeters, one should be set to Aerodrome QNH to assist with vertical separation from other aircraft and terrain. (In other words, first altimeter set to Aerodrome QNH, and the second altimeter either to the same setting or on Aerodrome QFE); and
- Aerodrome QNH during **climb** to, and while at or below, the transition altitude. Vertical position will be expressed as *altitude* on Aerodrome QNH.

After clearance to climb above the transition altitude has been given and the climb commenced, it is recommended that vertical position be expressed as a flight level, *provided* that the aircraft is not more than 2,000 ft below the transition altitude (unless specifically requested otherwise by ATC). Flight levels are based on *standard pressure* 1013 hPa at all times and used to maintain vertical separation from other traffic using the same subscale setting. This occurs above the **transition level.**

OUTSIDE CONTROLLED AIRSPACE, a pilot may use either Aerodrome QNH or QFE for take off and climb. Vertical position should be reported as *altitude.* When under Instrument Flight Rules, however, vertical position *must be expressed as a flight level (based on 1013) after climbing through the transition altitude.*

Pilots taking off at aerodromes beneath Terminal Control Areas (TMAs) or Control Areas (CTAs) should use Aerodrome QNH when flying below the transition altitude and beneath these areas (to assist in vertical separation). However, Aerodrome QFE may be used within the circuit.

En Route

It is important to update the Regional Pressure Setting periodically, and whenever you enter a new altimeter setting region. If you are flying into an area of lower pressure, the aeroplane will gradually descend if the original RPS is not altered and this will be potentially dangerous!

Another effect results from a decreasing temperature because it increases the air density, the result being that a given pressure level is *lower in cold air than in warm air*. Thus, flying from a warm area to a cold area, the aeroplane will gradually descend.

In a very cold air mass, the aeroplane could be as much as 10% lower than the height indicated on the altimeter. The aeroplane should still be flown at a level according to the altimeter but, as the pilot-in-command, you should consider 'when flying from high to low, **beware below**'.

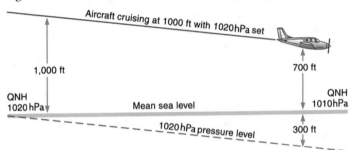

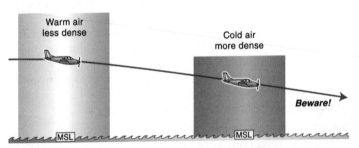

■ *Figure 4-7* **When flying from high to low, beware below (valid for both low temperatures and low pressures)**

In areas of low pressure, the 1013 hPa pressure level is *below* mean sea level and so FLs will be lower than at first thought. For example, if the QNH is 996 hPa, the 1013 hPa pressure level is almost 500 ft below mean sea level. FL40 will therefore be only 3,500 ft amsl.

If the intention is to be separated by 1,000 ft vertically from traffic or terrain at 3,000 ft amsl, then FL45 is the minimum suitable flight level, since it will (in this pressure situation) equate to an altitude of 4,000 ft.

A chart to convert altitudes to flight levels and vice versa is included at the end of the chapter.

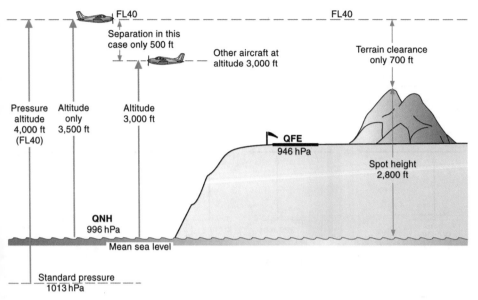

■ *Figure 4-8* **Select the minimum suitable flight level carefully, especially when the QNH is low**

Operations Within Controlled Airspace

Above 3,000 ft amsl, or above the appropriate transition altitude, whichever is the higher, en route aircraft are flown at *flight levels* (i.e. with standard pressure 1013 hPa set), to assist in separation from other traffic.

Regional pressure setting is to be used en route, usually on the second altimeter, for checking terrain clearance. Aircraft flying in a Control Zone (CTR) or Terminal Control Area (TMA), at or below the transition altitude, will be given the appropriate QNH in their ATC clearance to enter the zone or area.

Operations Outside Controlled Airspace

AT OR BELOW 3,000 ft amsl, pilots may use the RPS or QNH of an aerodrome in the vicinity to set their altimeter subscale.

Pilots flying beneath a Terminal Control Area (TMA) or a Control Area (CTA), however, should use the QNH of an aerodrome situated beneath that area when flying below the *transition altitude*. This will not differ greatly from the RPS and will be the same setting that aeroplanes above in the TMA or CTA are using. This will prevent inadvertent penetration of any controlled airspace above (because of any differences between local QNH and RPS).

When penetrating a Military Air Traffic Zone (MATZ), the pilot will normally be given the Aerodrome QFE to enable vertical separation between aircraft. If there is more than one aerodrome in a combined MATZ (CMATZ), the lowest-value Aerodrome QFE will be given. This is known as the **clutch QFE**. However, in some circumstances when crossing a MATZ the QNH will be given.

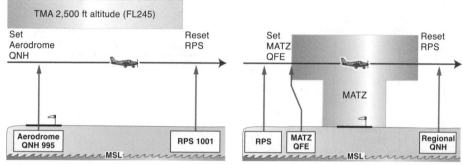

■ *Figure 4-9* **Aerodrome QNH (rather than RPS) may be required en route**

CAA CAP 413 details procedures for penetration of a MATZ by civil aircraft.

Outside controlled airspace, vertical position in flight plans and communications with the Air Traffic Service Unit is to be expressed as altitude. At or below 3,000 ft amsl on an Advisory Route, the RPS should be set.

In level flight above 3,000 ft amsl (or above the appropriate transition altitude, whichever is the higher), pilots flying under the Instrument Flight Rules (IFR) must have 1013 hPa set on an altimeter and conform to the **semi-circular rule** when selecting cruising levels. Vertical position will then be expressed as a *flight level*. RPS should be used for checking terrain clearance.

VFR TRAFFIC ABOVE 3,000 ft amsl (or above the transition altitude), may operate on RPS (for example, when the flight involves various headings and/or cruise heights); however, en route flights choosing to fly semi-circular levels *must* use the standard altimeter setting, 1013 hPa.

The semicircular rule is a means of vertically separating traffic flying in different directions. Whilst it is required for all IFR traffic, it is strongly recommended for VFR flights as well. The rule is based on magnetic track (rather than heading) since, in strong crosswind conditions, fast and slow aircraft maintaining identical tracks will have significantly different headings.

As shown in the table 4-10, IFR traffic must fly at whole 1000s of feet and VFR flights should fly at even or odd 1000s of feet plus 500 feet.

TABLE OF CRUISING LEVELS											
TRACK*											
From 000 degrees to 179 degrees						From 180 degrees to 359 degrees					
IFR Flights - Level			VFR Flights - Level			IFR Flights - Level			VFR Flights - Level		
FL	Feet	Metres	FL	Feet	Metres	FL	Feet	Metres	FL	Feet	Metres
010	1000	300	-	-	-	020	2000	600	-	-	-
030	3000	900	035	3500	1050	040	4000	1200	045	4500	1350
050	5000	1500	055	5500	1700	060	6000	1850	065	6500	2000
070	7000	2150	075	7500	2300	080	8000	2450	085	8500	2600
090	9000	2750	095	9500	2900	100	10000	3050	105	10500	3200
110	11000	3350	115	11500	3500	120	12000	3650	125	12500	3800
130	13000	3950	135	13500	4100	140	14000	4250	145	14500	4400
150	15000	4550	155	15500	4700	160	16000	4900	165	16500	5050
170	17000	5200	175	17500	5350	180	18000	5500	185	18500	5650
190	19000	5800	195	19500	5950	200	20000	6100	205	20500	6250
210	21000	6400	215	21500	6550	220	22000	6700	225	22500	6850
230	23000	7000	235	23500	7150	240	24000	7300	245	24500	7450
250	25000	7600	255	25500	7750	260	26000	7900	265	26500	8100
270	27000	8250	275	27500	8400	280	28000	8550	285	28500	8700
290	29000	8850	-	-	-	300	30000	9150	-	-	-
310	31000	9450	-	-	-	320	32000	9750	-	-	-
330	33000	10050	-	-	-	340	34000	10350	-	-	-
350	35000	10650	-	-	-	360	36000	10950	-	-	-
370	37000	11300	-	-	-	380	38000	11600	-	-	-
390	39000	11900	-	-	-	400	40000	12200	-	-	-
410	41000	12500	-	-	-	430	43000	13100	-	-	-
450	45000	13700	-	-	-	470	47000	14350	-	-	-
490	49000	14950	-	-	-	510	51000	1550	-	-	-
etc.	etc.	etc.				etc.	etc.	etc.			

*Magnetic track, or in polar areas at latitudes higher than 70 degrees and within such extensions to those areas as may be prescribed by the competent authorities, grid tracks as determined by a network of lines parallel to the Green Meridian superimposed on a polar stereo graphic chart in which the direction towards the North Pole is employed as the Grid North.

■ Figure 4-10 **Table of cruising levels**

Approach and Landing

When an aircraft is descending from a *flight level* to an *altitude* preparatory to commencing approach for landing, ATC will pass the **Aerodrome QNH** (which may differ slightly from the RPS, but should never be less than it).

On vacating the cruising flight level, the pilot will change to QNH unless further flight level reports have been requested, in which case the QNH will be set after the final flight level report is made. Thereafter the pilot will continue on the Aerodrome

QNH until approaching the circuit area or established on final approach, when QFE or any other appropriate altimeter setting may be used. The only logical settings, of course, are either Aerodrome QNH or Aerodrome QFE.

On a **radar final approach** where the radar controller issues tracking and descent guidance, the pilot will assume that an aircraft is using QNH and altitudes passed by the controller will be related to QNH. A reminder of the assumed setting will be included in the radio phraseology.

To ensure safety it is recommended that all pilots use QNH, but if a pilot advises that the pilot is using QFE, altitudes will be amended by the radar controller as necessary and *height* (AGL) will be substituted for *altitude* in the radio calls.

Vertical positioning of aircraft during approach will, below transition level, be controlled by reference to altitudes (QNH) and then to heights (QFE) if so requested. Pilots landing beneath Terminal Control Areas (TMAs) and Control Areas (CTAs) should use Aerodrome QNH when below the transition altitude and beneath these areas, except that the Aerodrome QFE may be used within the circuit area.

Missed Approach

On a missed approach (a go-around) pilots may continue with the altimeter setting selected for final approach, but reference to vertical position should be in terms of altitude on Aerodrome QNH, unless otherwise instructed by ATC.

Now complete: **Practice Questions - Altimeter Setting Procedures**

1. With QNH set on the altimeter subscale, vertical position is reported as:

(a) *Flight level*
(b) *Height*
(c) *Elevation*
(d) *Altitude*

2. A "Regional Pressure Setting" is:

(a) *The lowest QNH within an Altimeter Setting Region for each hour.*
(b) *The highest QNH within an Altimeter Setting Region for each hour.*
(c) *The lowest forecast QNH within an Altimeter Setting Region for each hour.*
(d) *The highest forecast QNH within an Altimeter Setting Region for each hour.*

3. What is the purpose of using (i) QFE (ii) QNH?

(a) *(i) For knowing the height above aerodrome level (ii) for separation from other air traffic.*
(b) *(i) For separation from other air traffic (ii) for terrain and obstacle clearance.*
(c) *(i) For terrain and obstacle clearance (ii) for knowing the height above aerodrome level.*
(d) *(i) For knowing the height above aerodrome level (ii) for terrain and obstacle clearance.*

4. When flying, the QNH should be updated periodically. If this is not done the most hazardous situations are found when:

(a) *Flying from high pressure to low pressure or from warmer to colder air.*
(b) *Flying from low pressure to high pressure or from colder to warmer air.*
(c) *Flying from high pressure to low pressure or from colder to warmer air.*
(d) *Flying from low pressure to high pressure or from warmer to colder air.*

5. VFR aircraft cruising above 3,000 feet:

(a) *Must adopt a level according to the semi-circular system; the lowest westbound level is 4,500 feet.*

(b) *Should adopt a level according to the semi-circular system; the lowest westbound level is 3,500 feet.*

(c) *The lowest westbound level is 4,500 feet; the semi-circular system is not mandatory for VFR aircraft but should be considered as best practice.*

(d) *The lowest westbound level is 3,500 feet; the semi-circular system is not mandatory for VFR aircraft but should be considered as best practice.*

6. When flying beneath a Terminal Control Area or Terminal Manoeuvring Area, the altimeter sub-scale setting to be used is:

(a) *The appropriate Regional Pressure Setting.*

(b) *The QFE of an aerodrome situated beneath the TMA.*

(c) *The QNH of an aerodrome situated beneath the TMA.*

(d) *The lowest between either the Regional Pressure Setting or the QNH of an aerodrome beneath the TMA.*

7. The Transition Altitude is:

(a) *Altitude at and below which vertical position is controlled by reference to QNH.*

(b) *3000 feet AMSL.*

(c) *Altitude above which vertical position is controlled by reference to SPS.*

(d) *A level below which QNH must be used and is published in the UK AIP (AD).*

8. What is the correct semi-circular cruising level to adopt for a VFR aircraft maintaining a heading of 055°M?

(a) *FL 40*

(b) *FL 45*

(c) *FL 50*

(d) *FL 55*

Airspace

Flight Information Regions

United Kingdom airspace has two Flight Information Regions –
the London and Scottish Flight Information Regions (abbreviated
FIR).

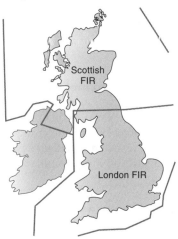

■ *Figure 5-1* **London and Scottish Flight Information Regions (FIRs)**

The London and Scottish FIRs extend upwards from the surface
to 19,500 feet (FL195). Above this the airspace is known as *upper
airspace,* and abbreviated as UIR for *Upper Information Region,* i.e.
the London and Scottish UIRs (from FL195 to FL660).

■ *Figure 5-2* **Boundary between London and Scottish FIRs, as shown on
the CAA 1:500,000 aeronautical chart**

Within the confines of the FIR structure, airspace is subdivided according to the amount and type of aeronautical activity which takes place in it. For example, the airspace around London is very busy, with a lot of commercial airline operations, business traffic, light aircraft on training and private flights, some military flights, plus gliders, balloons and microlights, etc. All this occurs in quite a small geographic area therefore the airspace needs to be regulated closely to ensure safe use by the high volume of aircraft.

In contrast, the airspace over the Outer Hebrides needs little regulation because of the larger area and low density of traffic.

More comprehensive Air Traffic Services are provided in the busier airspace.

The Subdivision of Airspace

There are two distinct categories of airspace: **controlled airspace** and **uncontrolled airspace**. Within these two categories, various 'Classes' have been allocated to different parts, in line with a *classification system for civil airspaces* specified by the International Civil Aviation Organisation (ICAO). This system is designed both to simplify airspace structure and to establish more commonality between countries.

The ICAO system grades airspace from A to G in order of importance. It begins with Class A, the highest status, which is allocated to the busiest controlled airspace. Classes B, C, D and E are allocated to other controlled airspace. Classes F and G cover all *uncontrolled airspace*. Specific VFR weather criteria and levels of Air Traffic Service apply to each airspace class.

Controlled Airspace

In controlled airspace, Air Traffic Control is provided to all flights. **UK controlled airspace** is made up of various aerodrome Control Zones (CTR), Terminal Control Areas (TMA), Control Areas (CTA) and Airways.

- **A Control Zone (CTR)** is airspace around certain aerodromes in which Air Traffic Control (ATC) is provided to all flights. A Control Zone extends from ground level to a specified altitude or a specified flight level (FL), depending on height and has a minimum lateral dimension of 5 nm either side of the centre of the aerodrome in the direction of the approach path. Most UK CTRs (such as Edinburgh, Newcastle, East Midlands, London/Gatwick, Belfast and Cardiff) even the exceptionally busy London/Heathrow airport are Class D Control Zones.
- **A Terminal Control Area** is a Control Area established at the confluence of controlled airspace routes in the vicinity of one or more major aerodromes. *Terminal Control Area* is sometimes

abbreviated as *TCA,* but more commonly as **TMA** (from the earlier designation *Terminal Manoeuvring Area).* There are currently four TMAs in the United Kingdom, with the busy London and Manchester TMAs allocated Class A, the Belfast TMA Class E, and the Scottish TMA Class D mostly above 6,000 ft amsl and Class E at and below 6,000 ft amsl.

- **A Control Area (CTA)** is a portion of airspace in which Air Traffic Control is provided, and which extends upwards from a specified base altitude or flight level to an upper limit expressed as a flight level. The busy Control Areas in the UK (e.g. Cotswold, Daventry and Worthing CTAs) are Class A and the less busy ones (e.g. Birmingham, Luton and Stansted CTAs) are Class D airspace.

- **An Airway** is a Control Area in the form of a corridor and is delineated by radio navigation aids. Each Airway has an identification code (e.g. A25 or *Alpha Two Five,* R8 or *Romeo Eight),* and extends 5 nm each side of a straight line joining certain places, with specified vertical limits.

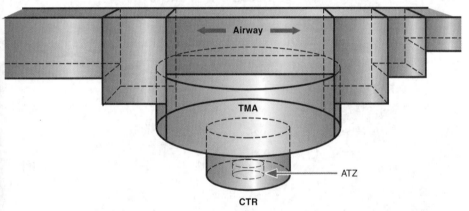

■ *Figure 5-3* **A Control Zone (CTR), Terminal Control Area (TMA) and an Airway**

All Airways are Class A except where they pass through a TMA, CTA or CTR of lower status. They are used by airliners (and other Instrument Flight Rules traffic) travelling between the principal aerodromes. As it approaches an aerodrome, the lower level of an Airway is usually stepped down to provide controlled airspace protection for air traffic on climb and descent.

As Class A airspace is unavailable to VFR flights, Class B is not allocated in the UK and Class C is at FL195 and above, VFR operations in controlled airspace in the UK will usually be confined to Classes D and E.

Depiction of Controlled Airspace on Charts

Controlled airspace up to FL195 (19,500 ft), and its classification, is depicted on the ICAO 1:500,000 (half-million) aeronautical chart series published by the CAA. The CAA 1:250,000 (quarter-million) series shows all controlled airspace with a base at or below 3,000 ft amsl.

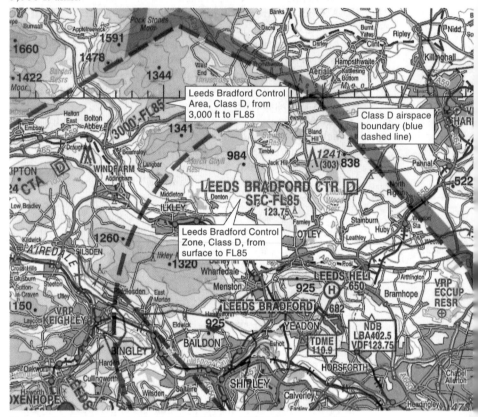

■ Figure 5-4 *Part of the Leeds Bradford CTA and CTR shown on a CAA 1:250,000 chart)*

A fuller description of the boundaries and vertical extent of controlled airspace (CTRs, CTAs, TMAs and Airways) is given in the UK Aeronautical Information Publication (AIP) in the ENR section. Also, *Pooley's Flight Guide* contains a useful list of Controlling Authorities and Communications Channels for all UK controlled airspace.

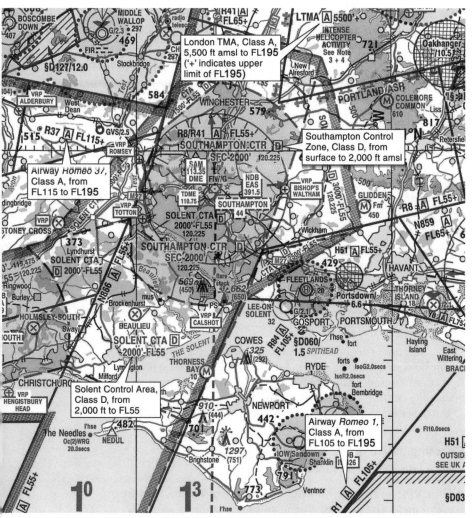

■ Figure 5-5 **Controlled airspace and its classification is shown on CAA
1:500,000 aeronautical charts**

Classification of Airspace

Each class of airspace available to VFR operations has specific
Visual Meteorological Conditions (VMC) criteria, which are
expressed in terms of minimum flight visibility and distance from
cloud. This is covered in detail in Chapter 7, *Visual Flight Rules*,
and Chapter 10, *Pilots' Licences*.

The Special VFR Clearance (SVFR)(SERA.5010)

Special VFR is an authorisation to fly within a Control Zone; subject to ATC clearance.

Except in the case of medical flights, search and rescue and fire-fighting operations, various conditions apply:

1. the pilot must remain clear of cloud and with the surface in sight;
2. the in-flight visibility must be at least 1500m or for helicopters 800m;
3. the speed must be no more than 140kts IAS; and ATC will restrict such flights;
4. day only;
5. ground visibility of at least 1500m, or 800m for helicopters;
6. cloud ceiling not less than 180m (600ft)

The UK has made some further exemptions and permissions to this basic rule: the first 3 conditions above apply and in addition:

- an aircraft shall not take off or land at an aerodrome within a control zone, or enter the ATZ or aerodrome traffic circuit when the reported meteorological conditions at that aerodrome are below the minima set out in 5) and 6) above.

The UK also permits SVFR at night.

It is important to note that the UK specific permissions and exemptions are granted for a limited period which may be revised from time to time. Therefore you should check the status and availability of these rules before relying upon them.

Further information on Special VFR is contained in AIP AD 2, ENR 1-2 and *Pooley's Flight Guide*.

Crossing an Airway

Crossing the Base of an Airway

A basic PPL holder (i.e. no IMC or Instrument Rating) may fly at right-angles across the base of an en route section of an Airway where the lower limit is defined as a flight level (and not an 'altitude', i.e. height amsl), but must not enter the Airway. This is only in weather conditions of at least VMC. For example, if the lower limit of an Airway running east–west is FL75, then the pilot may cross it by flying north or south not above FL75.

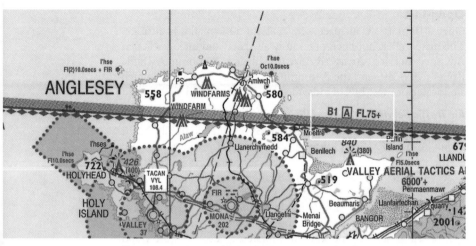

■ Figure 5-6 **Airway B1 (as shown on the half-million chart) can be crossed at right-angles at FL75 in VMC**

Penetrating an Airway

A pilot who holds a valid Instrument Rating, even in an aeroplane not fully equipped for IFR flight, may penetrate and cross an Airway in Visual Meteorological Conditions (VMC) by day provided that the pilot:

- files a flight plan either before departure or when airborne; and
- requests a *crossing clearance* from the responsible Air Traffic Control unit when at least 10 minutes from the intended crossing point, and subsequently receives that ATC crossing clearance before commencing the crossing.

Except where otherwise authorised by ATC, aircraft are required to cross an Airway by the shortest route (normally at right-angles) and to be in level flight at the cleared level on entering the Airway.

Aerodrome Traffic Zones (ATZ) in Control Zones

Aerodrome Traffic Zones exist at many aerodromes within UK Control Zones. ATZs are also established at most aerodromes outside controlled airspace, and we cover them in detail on page 85.

Uncontrolled Airspace

Uncontrolled airspace in the UK is considered to be the Open-FIR. Open-FIR includes various areas and zones (covered shortly). As far as Air Traffic Control Services are concerned, the advisory service provided in uncontrolled airspace (Class G) is less comprehensive than the control service provided in controlled airspace.

Open-FIR

Open-FIR, *Class G* airspace, covers about 50% of all UK airspace. This airspace has not been previously allocated and includes Radar Advisory Service Areas (RASAs), Military Aerodrome Traffic Zones (MATZs), and the Aerodrome Traffic Zones (ATZs) which are located at most UK aerodromes outside controlled airspace.

Air Traffic Services in Open-FIR

- A **Flight Information Service (FIS)** is available to all aircraft in both UK FIRs through "London Information" and "Scottish Information" Air Traffic Services Units. Air traffic services provided to flights in Open-FIR include:
  - information and warnings on meteorological conditions;
  - changes of serviceability in navigational and approach aids;
  - condition of aerodrome facilities;
  - alerting service for known aircraft in need of search and rescue;
  - aircraft proximity warnings;
  - other advisory information pertinent to the safety of air navigation.

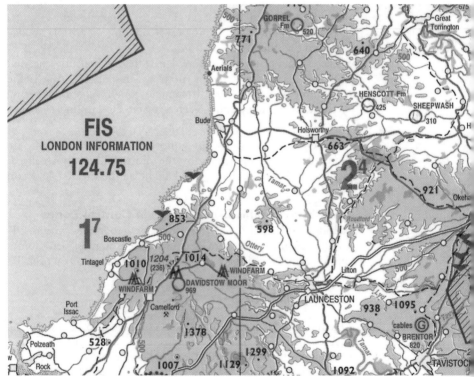

■ *Figure 5-7* **Open-FIR on a 1:500,000 chart; information (London) frequency is 124.75 MHz in this area**

- **Radar services** are also available in Open-FIR: either a *Traffic Service* or a *Deconfliction Service* provided by various Air Traffic Service Units, including those participating in the **Lower Airspace Radar Advisory Service (LARS)** – explained further in the next chapter.
- In **ATZs** and **MATZs** discrete communication frequencies are established for the responsible aerodrome authorities.

Certain Open-FIR is Regulated Airspace

Flight operations in Aerodrome Traffic Zones are regulated by Rule 11 of the Rules of the Air. Consequently, together with controlled airspace, ATZs are *regulated airspace*.

Aerodrome Traffic Zones (ATZs)

Aerodrome Traffic Zones operate at most UK civil and military aerodromes. ATZs are not allocated a specific airspace classification, but adopt the class of the airspace within which they are located.

The standard physical dimensions of an ATZ are:
- from ground level to 2,000 ft above aerodrome level (aal);
- within the area bounded by a circle of radius:
  - (i) 2 nm, where the length of the longest runway is 1,850 m or less; or
  - (ii) 2.5 nm, where the longest runway is greater than 1,850 m;
    - the centre of the circle being the mid-point of the longest runway.

NOTE Some 2 nm ATZs are expanded to 2.5 nm radius to provide at least 1.5 nm clearance from the end of all runways.

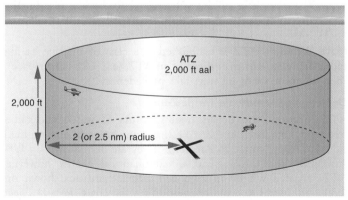

■ *Figure 5-8* **Dimensions of an Aerodrome Traffic Zone (ATZ)**

Rules to Enable Safe Flight in an ATZ (Rule 11, Rules of the Air Regs. 2015))

An aircraft must not fly within an Aerodrome Traffic Zone unless the pilot-in-command:

- has the permission of the appropriate Air Traffic Control (ATC) unit; or
- where there is no ATC unit, the pilot has obtained sufficient information from the Aerodrome Flight Information Service (AFIS) unit to enable flight within the zone to be made safely; or
- where there is no ATC or AFIS unit, the pilot has obtained information from the Air/Ground (A/G) radio station at the aerodrome to enable the flight to be made safely.

Aircraft flying in an ATZ must:

- maintain a continuous watch on the appropriate radio frequency notified for communications at the aerodrome or, if this is not possible, keep a watch for visual instructions;
- where the aircraft has radio, give position and height to the aerodrome ATC or AFIS unit or A/G radio station, as the case may be, on entering and leaving the zone; and
- make any other standard calls or requested calls.

These requirements apply at:

- a Government aerodrome at such times as are notified (usually H24, i.e. continuous);
- an aerodrome having an ATC or AFIS unit, during the hours of watch;
- a national licensed aerodrome or an EASA certified aerodrome having A/G radio communication with aircraft, during the hours of watch, and whose hours of availability are detailed in AIP AD 2.

NOTE When an ATZ is established in a class of airspace having more stringent *rules* than those of an ATZ (e.g. Class D airspace), then the more stringent rules take precedence.

Depiction of Aerodrome Traffic Zones

ATZ locations and details (radius, hours of watch and radio frequency) are listed in AIP AD 2, and any amendments notified by NOTAM (Notice to Airmen). They are also shown on UK 1:500,000 and CAA 1:250,000 aeronautical charts; however, ATZs located wholly in regulated airspace are not shown on 1:500,000 charts to avoid congestion on the chart. *Pooley's Flight Guide* lists aerodrome operating hours; usually these coincide with ATZ hours.

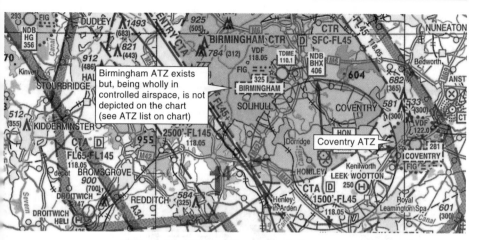

■ Figure 5-9 **ATZs outside regulated airspace are shown on the 1:500,000 chart**

CAA 1:500,000 charts have a full list of Aerodrome Traffic Zones printed on the left-hand side, together with the Air/Ground frequency of the responsible radio unit at the aerodrome.

AERODROME TRAFFIC ZONE (ATZ), is regulated airspace from the surface to 2000ft AAL within a circle centred on the notified mid-point of the longest runway, radius 2·0NM (RW≤ 1850m) or 2·5NM (RW≥1850m), where Mandatory Rules apply.
Most Government Aerodrome ATZs are H24.

ABERPORTH (EGUC)	AFIS 122·15
ANDREWSFIELD (EGSL)	AFIS or A/G 130·55
BARKSTON HEATH (EGYE)	INITIAL CALL ATC CRANWELL 119·375
BECCLES (EGSM)	A/G 134.6
BEMBRIDGE (EGHJ)	AFIS or A/G 123·25
BENSON (EGUB)	ATC 120·9
* BIGGIN HILL (EGKB)	ATC 129·4
◆ BIRMINGHAM (EGBB)	ATC 118·05
BLACKBUSHE (EGLK)	INITIAL CALL FARNBOROUGH/ODIHAM APP 125·25, AFIS or A/G 122·3
BODMIN (EGLA)	A/G 122·7
BOSCOMBE DOWN (EGDM)	ATC 126·7
BOURN (EGSN)	A/G 129·8
◆ BOURNEMOUTH (EGHH)	ATC 119·625
◆ BRISTOL (EGGD)	ATC 128·55
◆ BRIZE NORTON (EGVN)	ATC 119·0
CAERNARFON (EGCK)	ATC VALLEY 134·35, A/G 122·25
* CAMBRIDGE (EGSC)	ATC 123·6 or 122·2
◆ CARDIFF (EGFF)	ATC 125·85
CHICHESTER /Goodwood (EGHR)	AFIS 122·45
CHIVENOR (EGDC)	A/G 130·2
CLACTON (EGSQ)	A/G 135·4
COLERNE (EGUO)	ATC 122·1
COLTISHALL (EGYC)	ATC 125·9
COMPTON ABBAS (EGHA)	A/G 122·7
CONINGSBY (EGXC)	ATC 120·8
COSFORD (EGWC)	ATC 128·825
COTTESMORE (EGXJ)	ATC 130·2
* COVENTRY (EGBE)	ATC 119·25
ꞌ CRANFIELD (EGTC)	ATC 122·03
CRANWELL (EGYD)	ATC 119·375
CULDROSE (EGDR)	ATC 134·05
DENHAM (EGLD)	AFIS or A/G 130·725
DERBY (EGBD)	A/G 118·35
DUNKESWELL (EGTU)	A/G 123·475
DUNSFOLD (EGTD)	ATC 135·175

■ Figure 5-10 **Example list of ATZs from a CAA 1:500,000 chart**

Military Air Traffic Zones (MATZ)

A Military Aerodrome Traffic Zone (MATZ) is specified airspace surrounding many UK military aerodromes:

- from the surface up to 3,000 feet above aerodrome level within a radius of 5 nm; and usually
- with a stub (or stubs), width 4 nm, extending out a further 5 nm along final approach path (s) for the main instrument runway (s) between 1,000 and 3,000 ft above aerodrome level (aal).

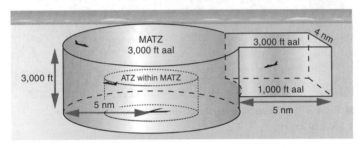

■ *Figure 5-11* **Dimensions of a typical Military Air Traffic Zone (MATZ)**

Pilots of civil aircraft wishing to penetrate a Military Air Traffic Zone are strongly advised to do so under the control of the MATZ ATC authority, in accordance with published procedures. These are detailed in AIP ENR 2-2 and *Pooley's Flight Guide*.

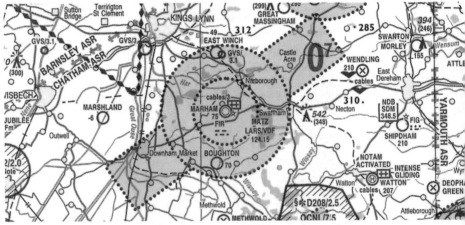

■ *Figure 5-12* **Marham MATZ, as shown on the 1:500,000 aeronautical chart**

NOTE Even if you should choose to ignore the MATZ airspace (which technically is non-regulated), there is, within the MATZ, an Aerodrome Traffic Zone (ATZ) which must be observed at all times (most are 'H24', i.e. continuous).

Summary of UK Airspace Classes

Controlled Airspace

CLASS A is allocated to the busiest airspace – Airways (except where they pass through a TMA, CTA or CTR of lower status), London and Manchester TMAs, and Cotswold, Daventry and Worthing CTAs. **Class A is not available to VFR flights.**

CLASS B airspace – is not allocated currently in the UK, and so not usually of concern to VFR pilots.

CLASS C airspace – generally allocated above FL195 (19,500 ft) and both IFR and VFR are permitted. It is not therefore usually of concern to VFR pilots, although reserved airspace exists within which VFR flight is permitted subject to specific arrangements with the appropriate air traffic services (AIP ENR.1.4).

CLASS D airspace – allocated to less-busy controlled airspace (most UK CTRs and CTAs) and the Scottish TMA above 6,000 ft amsl, including any Aerodrome Traffic Zones (ATZ) in the Class D Control Zones (AIP ENR.6-2-1-5).

VFR flights in Classes C and D airspace require appropriate flight notification to be given and an ATC clearance obtained.

CLASS E airspace – only allocated to the Scottish CTR (including ATZs in the Control Zone), the Scottish TMA at and below 6,000 ft amsl and the Belfast TMA.

Class E airspace is similar to Class D but differs from Class D in not requiring flight notification or ATC clearance, and in having a reduced traffic information service from ATC.

Uncontrolled Airspace

CLASS F Not currently allocated in the UK.

CLASS G airspace – all airspace that has not been previously allocated, and called 'Open-FIR'. Class G includes Radar Advisory Surveillance Areas (RASAs), Military Aerodrome Traffic Zones (MATZs), the Aerodrome Traffic Zones (ATZs) located at aerodromes outside controlled airspace and airspace notified for Rule 11, Rules for the Air Regulations.

Flight Information Service and Radar Services in Class G airspace are available.

For more details see AIP ENR.1.4.

VMC Criteria

Minimum weather conditions for VFR operations in the various Classes of airspace are considered in Chapter 6, *Visual Flight Rules*.

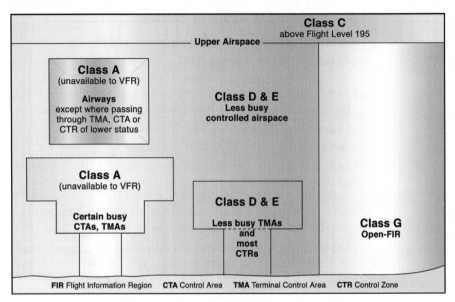

■ *Figure 5-13* **Summary of UK airspace classifications**

Flight Restrictions and Hazards

The UK Aeronautical Information Publication (AIP) contains the **Chart of United Kingdom Airspace Restrictions and Hazardous Areas** and a tabulation of the full details for each area depicted. Amendments are notified by NOTAM (Notice to Airmen) and AIC (Aeronautical Information Circular).

Aeronautical Charts also depict Airspace Restrictions and Hazards, the manner of presentation varying slightly with the chart used. Each chart will have a **legend** listing the various features and how they are depicted. Some chart *legend notes* also refer to hazardous areas.

Specific types of restriction or hazard of interest to the private pilot are given below.

Prohibited, Restricted and Danger Areas

Prohibited areas

A Prohibited Area is defined airspace in which flight is prohibited.

■ *Figure 5-14* **Prohibited Area P611, surface up to 2,200 ft (1:500,000 chart)**

Restricted Areas

A Restricted Area is defined airspace in which flight is restricted according to certain conditions.

Danger Areas

A Danger Area is defined airspace in which activities dangerous to flight may occur. They are specified in the ENR 5 section of the UK Aeronautical Information Publication (AIP) and on the **Chart of Airspace Restrictions and Hazardous Areas**, where they are shown as:

- **Solid red** outline if they are active in published hours (i.e. scheduled);
- **Pecked red** outline if they are inactive unless notified by NOTAM.

A Danger Area designated as D129/1.75 indicates that it is:

- located between 51°N and 52°N latitudes, as shown by the first number (a '0' would indicate a Danger Area that is just North of 50°N, and a '6' that it is just North of 56°N); and
- extends from the surface to 1,750 ft amsl (as shown by the '1.75'; '1–2.5' would indicate a Danger Area that extends from 1,000–2,500 ft amsl).

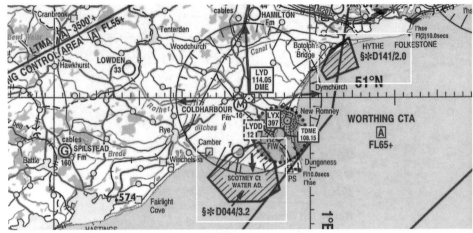

■ *Figure 5-15* **Danger Areas D044 and D141 (1:500,000 chart)**

- **On other aeronautical charts** Danger Areas may be depicted differently, and you should refer to the *legend* on the particular chart in use.

Danger Area Services available for certain Danger Areas are shown on CAA half-million (1:500,000) charts. These are the:
- **Danger Area Crossing Service (DACS)**; and
- **Danger Area Activity Information Service (DAAIS).**

The chart listings include contact frequencies for the units providing Air Traffic Service in the particular Danger Area. *Pooley's Flight Guide* also contains listings of the units providing the DACS and DAAIS.

NOTE Danger areas with identification numbers prefixed by an asterisk (*) contain airspace subject to by-laws which prohibit entry during the period of activity. See UK AIP ENR 1-1.

Some Danger Areas in the UK are known as *Weapon Range Danger Areas* (WRDA), and details are covered by a *legend note* on CAA 1:500,000 (half-million) charts. It is strongly recommended that aircraft flying in or near these areas obtain a radar service.

DANGER AREA CROSSING SERVICE (DACS) is available for certain Danger Areas. The relevant areas (identified on the chart by the prefix †) and Unit Contact Frequencies to be used are shown below. For availability of the services see UK AIP ENR 5.1.

D001	ST MAWGAN APP 126·5MHz*
D003,D004,D006A,D007,D007A,D007B,.....	PLYMOUTH MIL 121·25MHz OUTSIDE TIMES
D008, D008A, D008B, D009 & D009A	LONDON MIL VIA LONDON INFO 124·75MHz*
D006..	CULDROSE APP 134·05MHz*
D012, D013, D014, D017,	PLYMOUTH MIL 124·15MHz OUTSIDE TIMES
D021, D023, & D031	LONDON MIL VIA LONDON INFO 124·75MHz
D036..	PLYMOUTH MIL 124·15MHz SEE UNDER LIST

DANGER AREA ACTIVITY INFORMATION SERVICE (DAAIS) is available for certain Danger Areas shown on this chart (identified by the prefix §). The Nominated Air Traffic Service Units (NATSUs) to be used are shown below. See UK AIP ENR 1.1. Pilots are advised to assume that a Danger Area is _active_ if no reply is received from the appropriate NATSU.

D037, D038, D039, D040............................	LONDON INFORMATION 124·75MHz/ 124·6MHz
✳D044	LYDD INFORMATION 120·7MHz**
D060	SOLENT APP 120·225MHz
D061...	EXETER APP 128·15MHz
✳D131, D132, D133 & D133A......................	FARNBOROUGH APP 125·25MHz**
D136, D138, D138A & D138B.......................	SOUTHEND APP 128·95MHz**
✳D141	LYDD INFORMATION 120·7MHz**

■ Figure 5-16 **Excerpt of DACS and DAAIS listings on the Southern England 1:500,000 aeronautical chart**

For further information on Prohibited, Restricted and Danger areas, see AIP ENR 5.

Pilotless Aircraft

Pilotless aircraft operate and manoeuvre in certain Danger Areas. The aircraft are orange or red and may be flown by day and night in all weather conditions. These aircraft may operate up to 60,000 ft, under radar control.

Details of the Danger Areas concerned are given in AIP ENR 5-1 (primarily West Wales). Pilots should note that, because pilotless aircraft are less manoeuvrable in the landing configuration than manned aircraft, care should be taken to avoid that part of Danger Areas in which recovery of pilotless aircraft takes place. This can be ascertained by contacting the controlling authority.

Air Navigation Obstructions

Details of structures which reach a height of **300 feet above ground level** (agl) are published in AIP ENR 5-4. They are also shown on certain aeronautical charts. Obstructions which are over **500 ft agl** are lit. Those between 300 and 500 ft agl may or may not be lit.

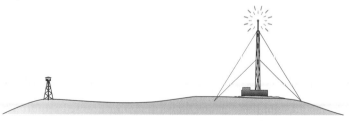

■ Figure 5-17 **Air navigation obstructions may, or may not, be lit**

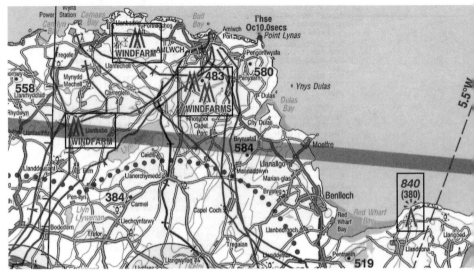

■ *Figure 5-18* **Unlit obstructions (windfarms) and a lit obstruction of**
height 840 ft amsl, 380 ft agl (1:250,000 chart)

Aerodrome Obstructions

Obstructions on or near aerodromes and which are considered
hazardous to aircraft landing or taking off are listed in the AD
section of the UK AIP and are shown on Instrument Approach
and Landing charts.

Glider Launching Sites

Glider launching may take place from aerodromes or other sites.
Pilots are warned that a winch-launched glider may carry the
cable up to a height of 2,000 ft agl before releasing it. At a few
sites this height may be exceeded. In addition, *aerotows* are
common at gliding sites, in which case the glider and tug aircraft
will be linked by a cable, the combined length of which may
extend to a maximum of 150 m horizontally.

Parachute Training Balloons

Captive balloons used for military parachute training may be
flown without notification. They will not be flown above 1,000
ft agl, and will be flown in a horizontal visibility of not less than
5 km and a separation from cloud of not less than 1,000 ft.

Parachuting Sites

Regular free-fall parachuting from up to FL150 takes place at the
sites and during the periods listed in the UK AIP. Some
Government and licensed aerodromes where regular parachuting
occurs are included in the list, but parachuting may also take place
during daylight hours at any Government or licensed aerodrome.

All parachutists are required to operate only in weather conditions which will enable them to remain clear of cloud, in sight of the surface and in a flight visibility of at least 5 km. A list of parachute dropping zones (DZs) and relevant telephone numbers and ATC frequencies for DZ activity is detailed in AIP ENR 5-5.

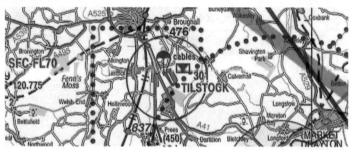

■ *Figure 5-19* **Free-fall parachuting site on 1:250,000 chart. Parachutists may be expected within a circle of 1.5 nm radius of the drop zone (DZ), up to FL150.**

Parascending

Parascending (where a parachutist is towed aloft by a winch and cable) also takes place at certain locations throughout the UK.

Because of the low-speed characteristics of parascenders, and the difficulty in seeing them in certain conditions, they are a potential hazard to other airspace users. Known parascending sites are therefore listed in the UK AIP.

Parascenders in thermals may be at heights up to the cloud base or base of controlled airspace, whichever is lower. Launch cables may be carried up to 2,000 ft agl.

Cable Launching Activities

Sites where launching by winch and cable of gliders, hang-gliders and parascending parachutes is permitted are listed in AIP ENR 5 and shown on the 1:500,000 topographical chart. Note that the cable may be carried to 2,000 ft agl, and in some cases, even higher.

Hang-Gliding Sites

Thermalling hang-gliders may be encountered at heights up to the cloud base or the base of controlled airspace, whichever is the lower. Known hang-gliding sites are listed in AIP ENR 5-5 and *Pooley's Flight Guide*.

At certain sites hang-gliders may be launched by winch or auto-tow, and cables may be carried up to 2,000 ft agl.

Microlight Flying Sites

Areas at which intensive flying by microlight aeroplanes may take place are listed in AIP ENR 5-5 and *Pooley's Flight Guide,* and are also shown on aeronautical charts (see Figure 5-21).

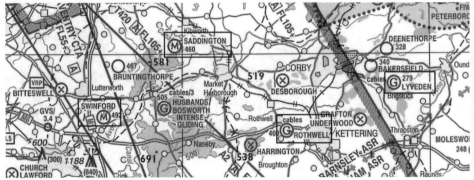

■ *Figure 5-20* **Microlight flying sites (Swinford and Saddington) and glider launching sites (Rothwell and Lyveden) on a 1:500,000 chart**

Areas of Intense Aerial Activity (AIAA) and Military Low Flying

The UK AIP gives details of areas of intense air activity and the military low flying system. Pilots should be extremely vigilant when operating in Areas of Intense Aerial Activity, keeping a very good lookout and making use of any radar service available. Avoid AIAAs if possible, entering them only if no other suitable route is available.

Military low flying occurs in many parts of the UK at heights up to 2,000 ft agl. As the **greatest concentration** is between 250 and 500 ft agl, civil pilots are strongly recommended to avoid this height band whenever possible.

Gas Venting Sites

The UK AIP ENR 1.1 lists gas venting sites together with advisory minimum altitudes for overflight. Severe turbulence may be experienced near these sites when gas venting is in progress and light aircraft pilots are strongly advised to avoid flying over such areas where possible. Gas venting sites (GVS) are indicated on charts by a magenta circle and the hazard altitude is shown in thousands of feet.

Small Arms Ranges

Ranges with a vertical hazard height of 500 ft agl do not attract UK Danger Area status, however, firing at some ranges may constitute a hazard to aircraft operating below 500 ft agl. For details see AIP ENR 5.3 and Chart of UK Airspace Restrictions (ENR 6-5-1-1).

Target Towing Trials

Aircraft towing targets on up to two thousand feet of cable may be flown in daylight, in Visual Meteorological Conditions (VMC) only, up to a height of 10,000 ft. The areas in which these trials take place are given in the UK AIP.

Bird Hazards and Sanctuaries

Bird concentration areas are shown in AIP ENR 6, together with the location of bird sanctuaries. Pilots should avoid flying below the listed *effective altitude* over bird sanctuaries and below 1,500 ft agl over any other areas where birds are known (or likely) to concentrate. Where it is essential to fly lower, bear in mind that the risk of a bird strike increases with speed.

AIP ENR 6 gives a general description of seasonal migration patterns, together with charts depicting *Bird Concentration Areas.*

Permanent warnings are published (AIP ENR 6 and *Pooley's Flight Guide)* for certain aerodromes where birds habitually present a hazard at or near the surface. **Temporary warnings** are issued by ATS Units for aerodromes and as 'Temp Nav Warnings' (TNW) when there are indications that migration or mass flocking of birds is imminent.

■ *Figure 5-21* **Minsmere bird sanctuary on the 1:500,000 chart.**
Bird sanctuaries are also shown on 1:250,000 charts.

High Intensity Radio Transmissions

AIP ENR 5 lists certain sources of high-intensity radio and radar transmissions. Flight within the specified High Intensity Radio Transmission Areas (HIRTA) may lead to interference with communication and navigational equipment, and flight within some areas could endanger health.

Royal Flights

A 'Royal Flight' is a civil or military flight over the UK carrying one or more of the principal members of the Royal Family. The special conditions applicable to such flights vary depending on whether the Royal Flight is by fixed-wing or helicopter:

- **Fixed-wing**: Royal Flights are conducted where possible within existing controlled airspace. Where this is not possible temporary controlled airspace (known as Temporary (Class D) Controlled Airspace (CAS-T)) is established along the route. Irrespective of the weather conditions, aircraft may only fly in when ATC clearance has been obtained from the controlling authorities. Details of CAS-T are promulgated by NOTAM and a Freephone telephone service is available on 08085-354802. Information on Royal Flights and CAS-T (such as for the *Red Arrows*) is updated daily. Ensure that you are fully briefed on these important matters before becoming airborne. For further information see AIP ENR 1-1 and the AIS website at www.ais.org.uk (see page 12 of this manual).

- **Helicopter**: No special ATC procedures are employed, but details are promulgated by NOTAM. You should keep a sharp lookout for the aircraft and keep well clear. In the event of getting into close proximity, however, the normal right-of-way rules apply.

Now complete: **Practice Questions - Airspace**

---

1. VFR traffic in Class D airspace may expect:

(a) *Separation from all other aircraft.*
(b) *Traffic information on VFR flights and separation from IFR aircraft.*
(c) *Traffic information on all other flights, traffic avoidance advice may be requested.*
(d) *Traffic information on IFR flights and separation from VFR flights.*

2. Controlled airspace extending from the surface of the Earth to a specified upper limit is called a:

(a) *Control Zone*
(b) *Control Area*
(c) *Aerodrome Traffic Zone*
(d) *Airway*

3. A Terminal Control Area (TCA) is a:

(a) *Control Area in the vicinity of major airports handling only arriving flights.*

(b) *Control Zone established at the confluence of ATS routes in the vicinity of one or more major aerodromes.*

(c) *Control Area established at the confluence of ATS routes in the vicinity of one or more major aerodromes.*

(d) *Control Area in the vicinity of major airports handling only departing flights.*

4. Airspace of defined dimensions annotated on an aeronautical chart with "P611/2.2" is:

(a) *A Danger Area extending from the surface to 2,200 feet.*

(b) *An area within which flight is restricted according to certain conditions.*

(c) *A Police Area extending from the surface to 22,000 feet.*

(d) *A Prohibited Area extending from the surface to 2,200 feet.*

5. A Military Aerodrome Traffic Zone (MATZ) may be established around UK military aerodromes extending from the surface to 3,000 feet and having a radius of 5 nm. One or more stubs aligned with the final approach path (s) may also be present. What are the dimensions of the stubs?

(a) *Between 2,000 and 3,000 feet, extending 5 nm from the MATZ boundary with a width of 4 nm.*

(b) *Between 1,000 and 2,000 feet, extending 4 nm from the MATZ boundary with a width of 5 nm.*

(c) *Between 1,000 and 3,000 feet, extending 4 nm from the MATZ boundary with a width of 5 nm.*

(d) *Between 1,000 and 3,000 feet, extending 5 nm from the MATZ boundary with a width of 4 nm.*

6. What are the dimensions of an ATZ surrounding an aerodrome where the longest runway is greater than 1850m?

(a) *A circle of 2 nm radius extending from the surface to 2,000 feet AAL.*

(b) *A circle of 2.5 nm radius extending from the surface to 2,000 feet AAL.*

(c) *A circle of 5 nm radius extending from the surface to 3,000 feet AAL.*

(d) *A circle of 2.5 km radius extending from the surface to 2,000 feet AAL.*

7. In order to fly within an ATZ the pilot of an aircraft equipped with a two-way radio must:

(a) *Maintain a continuous listening watch on the appropriate frequency and report the aircraft's position and heading on entering and leaving the zone.*

(b) *Report the aircraft's position, intentions and height on entering and leaving the zone.*

(c) *Report the aircraft's position and heading on entering and leaving the zone.*

(d) *Maintain a continuous listening watch on the appropriate frequency and report the aircraft's position and height on entering and leaving the zone.*

8. What is a "Special VFR" flight?

(a) *It is a VFR flight cleared by ATC to operate in a Control Area in meteorological conditions below IMC.*

(b) *It is a VFR flight cleared by ATC to operate within Controlled Airspace in meteorological conditions below VMC.*

(c) *It is a VFR flight cleared by ATC to operate in a Control Zone in meteorological conditions below VMC.*

(d) *It is a VFR flight cleared by ATC to operate in meteorological conditions below IMC.*

Answers: 1c, 2a, 3c, 4d, 5d, 6b, 7d, 8c.

Air Traffic Services

ICAO Annex 11 – Air Traffic Services

Annex 11 contains the international standards and recommended practices relating to the establishment of airspace, air traffic services units and air traffic services necessary to expedite the safe, orderly flow of air traffic.

Objectives and Need for ATS

2.2 The objectives of the air traffic services shall be to:

- prevent collisions between aircraft in the air;
- prevent collisions between aircraft on the manoeuvring area and obstructions on that area.
- expedite and maintain an orderly flow of traffic;
- provide advice and information useful for the safe and efficient conduct of flights;
- notify appropriate organisations regarding aircraft in need of search and rescue and assist such organisations as required. *Note: ATS personnel are not solely responsible for the prevention of collisions. Pilots and vehicle drivers must also fulfil their own responsibilities in accordance with Rules of the Air.*

2.4 The need for the provision of air traffic services shall be determined by considering at least the following:

- types of air traffic involved;
- density of air traffic;
- meteorological conditions an Air Traffic Control service will be provided to:
  a. all IFR flights in airspace Classes A, B, C, D and E;
  b. all VFR flights in airspace Classes A, B, C and D;
  c. all special VFR flights; and to
  d. all aerodrome traffic at controlled aerodromes.

Classification of Airspaces

We have already seen how airspace is classified. The Annex contains details of the air traffic services relating to each class of airspace as follows:

2.6 ATS airspace shall be classified and named as follows:

- **Class A.** IFR flights only permitted; all flights are subject to ATC clearance and are separated from each other.
- **Class B.** IFR and VFR flights; all flights are subject to ATC clearance and are separated from each other.
- **Class C.** IFR and VFR flights; all flights are subject to ATC clearance. IFR flights are separated from other IFR flights and from VFR flights.

VFR flights are separated from IFR flights and receive traffic information about other VFR flights and avoidance advice on request.

- **Class D.** IFR and VFR flights; all flights subject to ATC clearance. IFR flights are separated from other IFR flights and receive traffic information in respect of VFR flights. VFR flights receive traffic information about all other flights. Traffic avoidance advice is given when requested by a pilot.
- **Class E.** IFR and VFR flights; IFR flights subject to ATC clearance. IFR flights are separated from other IFR flights. All flights receive traffic information as far as is practical.
- **Class F.** IFR and VFR flights; all participating IFR flights receive Procedural or Deconfliction service and all flights may receive a Basic or traffic service if requested.
- **Class G.** IFR and VFR flights; all flights may receive one of the services available outside controlled airspace (see ATSOCAS) service if requested.

Air Traffic Services in the UK

There are many Air Traffic Service Units (ATSUs) spread throughout the UK, whose function it is to assist the passage of aircraft by providing information prior to flight and in maintaining radio contact during flight. The control of air traffic is achieved by issuing clearances and instructions with which pilots will comply.

Area Control Centre (ACC) Services

An Area Control Centre (ACC) provides the following air traffic services:

- **an Air Traffic Control Service** to aircraft operating on Airways (IFR flights);
- **a Flight Information Service** (FIS) and Alerting Service;
- **a Distress and Diversion service.**

Aerodrome Traffic Services

Air Traffic Control (ATC)

ATC at an aerodrome is responsible for the **control** of aircraft in the air in the vicinity of the aerodrome, and all traffic on the manoeuvring area. All movements on the manoeuvring area are subject to the prior permission of ATC.

The total Air Traffic Control responsibility is shared between **Aerodrome Control** and **Approach Control**. At large airports Aerodrome Control may be split between 'Tower' and 'Ground', where 'Ground' is responsible for aircraft on the manoeuvring area except runways in use and 'Tower' are responsible for aircraft on the runway as well as those in, or joining, the circuit. At smaller ATC aerodromes 'Tower' will perform both functions.

Approach Control are responsible for traffic departing the circuit, joining either VFR or IFR or operating in the vicinity of the aerodrome. The exact point at which an arriving aircraft will be transferred to Tower will vary with the type of approach being made (visual or instrument), weather or other considerations. Approach Control may be provided with or without the controller having access to radar. The normal rule is that departing aircraft contact Aerodrome Control first and arriving aircraft contact Approach Control first

Control Zones are usually staffed by controllers with access to radar. In such circumstances a 'Radar Control Service' is provided when within controlled airspace. Under a Radar Control Service pilots must comply with the clearance issued, or if this is not suitable, must request an alternative clearance before deviating from the original. Non-radio aircraft may be given instructions or information by **lamp or pyrotechnics** from the control tower and by **ground signals** in the aerodrome signals area. Lamp and pyrotechnic signals may be made to any aircraft, radio-equipped or otherwise, from a subsidiary control point such as a runway control van.

Flight Information Service (FIS)

FIS is provided at some aerodromes which do not have ATC to give information relevant to the safe and efficient conduct of flights in the ATZ. The Flight Information Service is not permitted to give instructions to aircraft in the air at any time as FIS is not a *control* service but an *information only* service. However, on the ground aircraft will be given instructions with which a pilot should comply. When FIS is provided the callsign suffix "Information" is used, e.g. "Rochester Information".

Air/Ground Communication Service

There are some aerodromes which provide neither Air Traffic Control (ATC) nor Flight Information Service (FIS) but which do have an Air/Ground Communications Service (AGCS) radio station through which aircraft and the aerodrome authority can communicate. It should be kept in mind that such facilities are usually operated by people without ATC qualifications. The callsign suffix "Radio" is used to distinguish them, for example "Nottingham Radio".

Safetycom

There are a number of active airfields within the UK which do not have an allocated VHF frequency; therefore a common frequency of 135.475 has been assigned which is known as **"safetycom"**.

Safetycom is a single common frequency, and pilots should be aware of the possibility of congestion and breakthrough. It is particularly important when using safetycom that RTF transmissions are correct and concise. Transmissions are only to be made when aircraft are below 2,000 feet above aerodrome level or below 1,000 feet above promulgated circuit height and within 10 nm of the aerodrome of intended landing. Full details are available in the *Air Pilot's Manual* volume 7 (*Communications*) or CAA Publication CAP 413.

Air Traffic Services in Open-FIR

The Lower Airspace Radar Service (LARS)

When flying in UK unregulated airspace up to FL100 within the limits of radio/radar coverage, pilots are recommended to use the Lower Airspace Radar Service (LARS). LARS is a structured national system whereby nominated civil and military ATSUs, if their primary duties permit, may provide the Traffic Service or the Deconfliction Service, on request, within approximately 30 nm of each unit. If three attempts to establish radio contact with a LARS station are made without success, it may be assumed that the station is not operating.

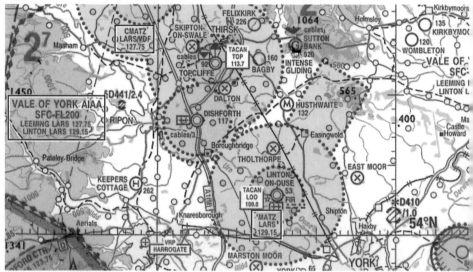

■ Figure 6-1 **LARS frequencies are shown on the 1:500,000 and 1:250,000 charts**

THE FLIGHT INFORMATION SERVICE (FIS) existed before the advent of the radar services and is still available. The service provides local information on weather, serviceability of radio navaids, aerodrome conditions and other reported traffic. In the UK the provision of a Flight Information Service are now referred to as 'Basic Service'.

THE PROCEDURAL SERVICE is a non-radar ATC service mainly used to separate IFR traffic by time and/or distance using an approach control service.

UK Flight Information Services

It is important that pilots know exactly what their responsibilities are when receiving an ATS outside controlled airspace, which service is the most appropriate for the stage of flight and what can be expected from the controller.

The "UK FIS" are fully detailed in CAP774.

General

Within Class G airspace irrespective of the service being provided **pilots are ultimately responsible for both collision avoidance and terrain clearance**. The Flight Information Services specify the varying degrees of traffic information and deconfliction instructions/advice that controllers or Flight Information Service Officers (FISOs) pass to ASSIST pilots in discharging their collision avoidance responsibilities.

The environment outside controlled airspace is shared by many users – civil and military, commercial and general aviation – and is very unpredictable in nature. It should be borne in mind that the service provided by the ATS is therefore constrained by this fact and also by the facts that: the service is not mandatory, the controller/FISO workload cannot be predicted and traffic may make sudden manoeuvres without warning even when receiving an ATS.

The services available outside controlled airspace will be:
• Basic Service
• Traffic Service
• Deconfliction Service; and
• Procedural Service

An alerting service will still be automatically provided in association with all of the UK FIS listed above.

Agreement to provide a particular service and acknowledgement of that level of service establishes a "contract" between the pilot and the controller/FISO whereby each agree to abide by the definition of that service.

Controllers will make every effort to provide the service that a pilot requests. However it should be recognised that ATS resources are finite, controller workload is variable and ATS task priorities may limit the availability of a particular service or its continued provision. Reduced traffic information may have to be applied or an alternative service may be offered. FISOs are not licensed to provide a Traffic Service, Deconfliction Service, or Procedural Service. Only the Basic Service should be requested from a FISO unit; such a unit is easily identifiable as they will use the callsign "Information".

Controllers will inform the pilot of reductions in traffic information and/or deconfliction advice with the reason and the probable duration. Some reasons may be:

* high workload (which is not always obvious from RT loading)
* areas of high traffic density
* when traffic is not displayed to the controller, for example when primary radar is not available and SSR alone is used; or
* when aircraft are operating close to the limits of radar cover

As pilots are operating outside controlled airspace any instructions issued **are not mandatory**. However the services are relying on pilot compliance as far as possible to enhance safety in Class F and G airspace for all users.

Agreements

As stated earlier pilots in receipt of a service outside controlled airspace are not mandated to follow instructions and have a high degree of autonomy to operate.

Agreements can be established between a controller (Note: not a FISO because of the limits of the FISO licence) and a pilot. An agreement may be made under a Basic or Traffic Service to ensure that a pilot follows a particular route or heading, or may restrict the flight to a certain level, level band or operating area.

Agreements are intended to facilitate the safe use of the airspace by allowing forward coordination between ATCUs on the pilot's course of action. In entering into an agreement, pilots must ensure that they are able to comply with their responsibilities in relation to the Rules of the Air and terrain clearance. Unless safety will be affected, the pilot must not deviate from the agreement without first advising and obtaining a response from the controller.

Type of Service

Pilots are to determine the appropriate service for the phase of flight and flight conditions. If a pilot does not specify the type of service required the controller will normally ask, except in the following circumstances:

* FISOs will only provide a Basic Service
* ATC Units without surveillance equipment (radar) will apply a Procedural Service to aircraft carrying out IFR departures, holding or approach procedures as a matter of routine
* IFR traffic that have planned to operate on ADR will be provided with a Deconfliction Service whenever possible.

Basic Service

The Basic Service allows a pilot maximum autonomy and is an Air Traffic Service provided to give **advice and information useful to the safe and efficient conduct of flights**. Such items may include weather information, changes in the serviceability of facilities, conditions at aerodromes or general aerial activity information.

Flight Rules and Meteorological Conditions:

- The service is available to **IFR or VFR flights**, but may not be appropriate for flight in IMC
- Controllers may identify the aircraft to aid coordination with other ATC Units, but are not obliged to inform the pilot. Identification does not imply an increased level of service or that the controller is monitoring the flight.
- **Traffic Information should not be expected.** Outside an ATZ there is no obligation for the controller/FISO to pass Traffic Information; general information may be passed to help with a pilot's situational awareness
- Regardless of whether Traffic Information is passed or not, **the pilot is responsible for collision avoidance,** unaided by the controller/FISO.

Pilot's responsibilities	Controller's responsibilities
Pilots are wholly responsible for the avoidance of other traffic unaided by the controller/FISO.	Pilots should be aware that there is no requirement for the controller/FISO to monitor the flight.
Pilots are responsible for terrain clearance at all times	Outside an ATZ there is no obligation for the controller/FISO to pass Traffic Information; general information may be passed to help with a pilot's situational awareness
Unless the pilot has entered into an agreement with a controller to maintain a particular course of action, **he/she may change heading or route without advising the controller**	
Unless the pilot has entered into an agreement with a controller to maintain a particular level or level band, **a pilot may change level without advising the controller/FISO.**	

■ Figure 6-2 **Basic service responsibilities.**

Traffic Service

The Traffic Service is a surveillance (radar) based ATS where, in addition to a Basic Service, the controller provides specific **radar derived traffic information** to assist a pilot in avoiding other traffic.

Flight Rules and Meteorological Conditions:

- The service is available to **IFR or VFR flights.** If a controller issues either a heading or level that would require flight in IMC a pilot not qualified to fly in IMC must advise the controller and request alternative instructions.
- The service can only be provided by controllers with access to radar.

Pilot's responsibilities	Controller's responsibilities
Traffic avoidance is ultimately the pilot's responsibility	Controllers **may issue headings and/or levels** for the purpose of positioning or sequencing but NOT to achieve the deconfliction minima.
The **pilot is responsible for terrain clearance.** Pilots requesting descent below the ATC Unit's terrain safe level will be reminded that he/she remains responsible for terrain clearance.	The **controller will identify the aircraft,** inform the pilot that he/she is identified and maintain the identification.
Whether Traffic Information has been passed or not, a pilot is still responsible for collision avoidance. If after receiving Traffic Information a pilot requires deconfliction advice he/she should request an upgrade to a Deconfliction Service, the controller will make all reasonable efforts to accommodate this request.	**Relevant Traffic Information will be passed** and will be updated if the traffic continues to constitute a definite hazard, or if requested by the pilot. NOTE: workload and RTF loading may reduce the controller's ability to pass Traffic Information or reduce its timeliness.
Pilots may operate under their **own navigation or the controller will provide headings** for positioning, sequencing or navigational assistance. • If a heading is unacceptable the pilot should advise the controller. • Unless safety will be compromised pilots shall not change an ATC assigned heading, or alter route without first advising and obtaining a response from the controller.	Headings will not be provided to deconflict.
A pilot may select **his/her own operating levels or he/she will be provided a level allocation** for positioning, sequencing or navigational assistance. • If an allocated level is unacceptable the pilot should advise the controller. • Unless safety will be compromised pilots shall not change an ATC assigned level, or level band without first advising and obtaining a response from the controller.	

■ Figure 6-3 **Traffic service responsibilities.**

Deconfliction Service

The Deconfliction Service is a surveillance based ATS service in addition to the basic service. The controller will provide specific radar derived traffic information and will issue headings and/or levels aimed at achieving planned deconfliction minima against all observed traffic in Class F and G airspace. Headings and levels may also be provided for positioning and/or sequencing.

The deconfliction minima are: **5 nm laterally or 3,000 feet vertically**, against unknown or uncoordinated traffic. Between aircraft working the same controller this may be reduced to **3 nm and 1000 feet** (some military units may apply 500 feet vertical separation).

CAP 774 stresses that due to controller workload or frequency congestion the ability of a controller to pass deconfliction advice may be reduced or the timeliness of the information affected. Also a reminder is included of the unpredictable nature of traffic outside controlled airspace and a caveat that achieving the minima is not guaranteed.

Flight Rules and Meteorological Conditions:
- The service can only be provided by controllers with access to radar.
- The service is available to **IFR flights.** Controllers will expect the pilot to accept headings or levels that may require flight in IMC.

Identification:
- The **controller will identify the aircraft**, inform the pilot that he/she is identified and maintain the identification.

Traffic Information:
- **Traffic Information will be passed together with headings and/or levels aimed at achieving the deconfliction minima.** Traffic Information on deconflicted traffic may also be passed to aid a pilot's situational awareness.

Deconfliction:
- Controllers will pass traffic information together with headings and/or levels aimed at achieving the deconfliction minima. **Traffic avoidance is ultimately the pilot's responsibility.** Should a pilot elect not to act on instructions he/she accepts responsibility for initiating any subsequent collision avoidance against that particular conflicting aircraft.

Terrain:
- The service is only provided at or above the ATCU's terrain safe level. If a pilot requests descent below that level a deconfliction service will no longer be provided – pilots can expect a Traffic Service instead.

NOTE If deconfliction advice is required by traffic following instrument flight procedures:

- For aircraft on departure, controllers will provide avoiding action and a terrain warning
- For aircraft on a pilot interpreted instrument approach controllers will provide avoiding action and a terrain safe level to climb to or maintain.

Pilot's responsibilities	Controller's responsibilities
Traffic avoidance is ultimately the pilot's responsibility	The **controller will identify the aircraft**, inform the pilot that he/she is identified and maintain the identification.
If a pilot elects not to act on instructions he/she accepts responsibility for initiating any subsequent collision avoidance against that particular conflicting aircraft.	Traffic Information will be passed together with headings and/or levels aimed at achieving the deconfliction minima.
	Traffic Information on deconflicted traffic may be passed to aid a pilot's situational awareness.

■ Figure 6-4 **Deconfliction service responsibilities.**

Procedural Service

A Procedural Service is an ATS where, in addition to the provision of a Basic Service, the controller provides vertical, lateral, longitudinal and time instructions, which if complied with will achieve deconfliction minima against other aircraft **participating** in the Procedural Service.

Since the service does not involve radar derived information, and as traffic does not legally need to be in contact with a procedural unit in Class F and G airspace, you should be aware that there is a high likelihood of encountering conflicting traffic without any warnings from ATC.

A Procedural Service is most commonly found at ATC Units without surveillance radar equipment at airfields with notified instrument procedures for approach, holding and departure. Pilots flying in the vicinity of aerodromes having instrument approaches outside controlled airspace are encouraged to establish RTF contact with the appropriate ATC Unit.

Flight Rules and Meteorological Conditions:

* The service is available to **IFR flights.** Controllers will expect the pilot to accept levels, radials, tracks and time allocations that may require flight in IMC.

Pilot's responsibilities	Controller's responsibilities
The **pilot is responsible for terrain clearance at all times.** If a pilot wishes to operate below the ATC unit's terrain safe level (unless the pilot is departing from an aerodrome or following a notified instrument approach procedure) the controller will issue a reminder of the terrain safe level and a reminder of his/her terrain responsibilities.	Aircraft **are not required to be identified** in order to receive a Procedural Service. Note: some procedural units may issue a squawk for Conspicuity only; this is for the benefit of adjacent radar equipped units.

The **controller may provide radials, tracks and time restrictions for the purpose of positioning, sequencing, navigational assistance or to achieve deconfliction minima**. Unless safety will be compromised a pilot must not change radials, tracks or time restrictions without first obtaining approval from the controller	The controller will provide **Traffic Information on aircraft receiving a Basic Service**, however no deconfliction advice will be issued on such traffic. **Note:** Under a Procedural Service the **controller has no ability to pass Traffic Information on traffic not in communication** with him (unless another ATS unit has advised him).
Controllers will normally provide level allocations for positioning, sequencing, navigational assistance or to achieve the deconfliction minima. **Note:** • If an allocated level is unacceptable the pilot should advise the controller. • Unless safety will be compromised pilots shall not change an ATC assigned level, or level band without first advising and obtaining a response from the controller.	**Deconfliction instructions** are provided aimed at achieving a planned deconfliction minimum **from other aircraft to which the controller is providing a Procedural Service.** Instructions will be in the form of allocated levels, radials, tracks and time restrictions or may use pilot position reports. Note: it is essential in this case that pilot position reports are accurate!

■ Figure 6-5 **Procedural service responsibilities.**

Pre-Flight Briefing Services

Aeronautical Information Services (AIS) are available to pilots preparing for a flight. Most UK aerodromes are equipped with self-briefing documents where pilots can obtain latest information which may affect their flights. British Isles En Route and Aerodrome Bulletins, together with Navigation Warning Bulletins and NOTAM information, are provided for VFR flights at the aerodromes where self-briefing facilities exist.

UK AIS is operated from a single central location from which information is made available via multi-media output. For more information, see AIP GEN 3-1. Additionally, a number of internet services exist to provide NOTAMs and other pre-flight information.

The Flight Plan

The *flight plan* is an ATC message, compiled by, or on behalf of, the aircraft commander (pilot-in-command) to a set ICAO format and then transmitted by the appropriate ATS authority to organisations concerned with the flight. It is the basis on which an ATC clearance is given for the flight to proceed.

Correct use of the CAA Flight Plan Form (form CA48) is essential – particularly in these days of automatic data processing. Incorrect completion may well result in a delay in processing and consequently a delay to the flight. Full instructions for completion of the Flight Plan Form are contained in the CAA General Aviation Safety Sense Leaflet No. 20 *Instructions for the Completion of Flight Plan Forms* and AIP ENR 1-10. An internet-based service called 'flightplanningonline' has been established using an application called AFPEX (Assisted Flight Planning Exchange.)

This provides a gateway via the internet into the AFTN and allows pilots or small aerodromes access to file their own flight plans within the UK or abroad. See also Vol. 3 of *The Air Pilot's Manual* series.

Note that a pilot intending to make a flight must in any case contact ATC (or other authority where there is no ATC) at the aerodrome of departure. This is known as **booking out** and is a separate and additional requirement to that of filing a flight plan.

Also note that where an aerodrome is notified as **Prior Permission Required** (PPR) the filing of a flight plan does *not* constitute prior permission (see page 37).

Private pilots may file a flight plan for any flight. They are advised to file a flight plan if intending to fly more than 10 nm from the coast or over sparsely populated or mountainous areas.

All pilots *must* file a flight plan for the following types of flights:

1. for all flights within controlled airspace, which are conducted in accordance with IFR;

2. for flights within Class C and D airspace conducted in accordance with VFR;

3. when the pilot wishes to receive an Air Traffic Advisory Service (Class F airspace);

4. for all flights which will cross a UK international FIR boundary;

5. for all flights at night which leave the ATZ;

6. for any flight where the destination is more that 40 km from the aerodrome of departure and the aircraft's maximum total weight authorised exceeds 5700 kg.

NOTE IFR flight in the Open-FIR, by day or night, does not, of itself, require a flight plan.

Normally flight plans should be filed at least 30 minutes before requesting taxi or start-up clearance (60 minutes in certain cases where the controlling authority is London, Manchester or Scottish Control). If this is not possible, a flight plan can be filed when airborne. If intending to enter controlled airspace, at least 10 minutes' notice must be given.

If your departure airfield does not have an Air Traffic Services Unit (ATSU), flight plans may be submitted by telephone or facsimile to designated air traffic units (normally at major airports). A responsible person should be nominated to inform the 'parent' ATSU once the flight is airborne of the time of departure. Similarly, a responsible person needs to be nominated at an arrival airfield without an ATSU. This is to ensure that alerting action will be taken if the aircraft fails to arrive.

If your 'off-blocks' (chocks) flight-planned departure time is delayed by more than 60 minutes, the flight plan should be cancelled and a new flight plan submitted (30 minutes if part of the flight enters controlled airspace).

ATC can be advised of a delay of up to 30 minutes by sending a 'Delay' (DLA) message. If a pilot who has filed a flight plan lands at an aerodrome other than the destination specified, the Air Traffic Services Unit at the specified destination must be advised within **30 minutes** of the estimated time of arrival.

Meteorology

The primary method of obtaining a pre-flight meteorological briefing in the United Kingdom is by **self-briefing**, using either:

* facilities, information and documentation routinely available or displayed in aerodrome briefing areas;or
* the Met Office's website at www.met-office.gov.uk.

For more information *see Chapter 23* of this book.

In addition to the Met Office, there are a number of commercial websites that provide weather information, but none of them should be relied on exclusively in your pre-flight planning.

NOTE Should you experience severe weather conditions (particularly if they were not forecast) you should advise the appropriate ATC unit by radio as soon as possible.

For flights outside the area of coverage of the above area forecast systems, *special forecasts* are provided by the designated Forecast Offices, as listed in the UK AIP (GEN 3-5). Requests for such forecasts should include details of the route, the period of the flight, the height to be flown and the time at which the forecast is to be collected.

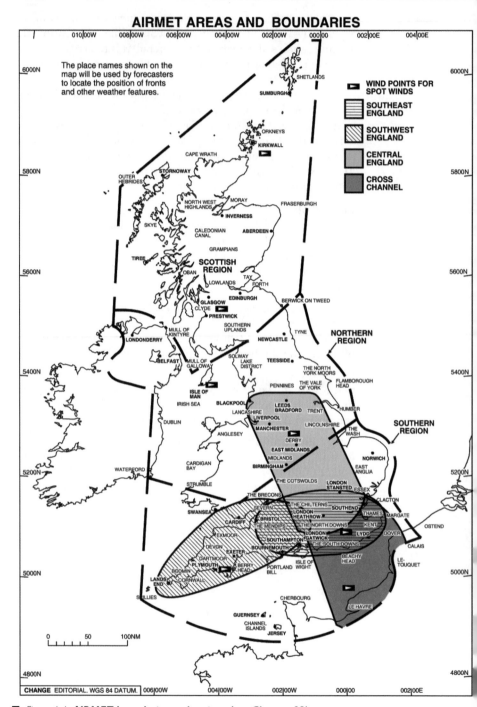

■ Figure 6-6 **AIRMET boundaries and regions (see Chapter 23)**

At least **4 hours'** notice should be given for flights over 500 nm, and at least **2 hours'** for shorter flights. At less notice the best possible service will be given in the time available, but it may be only a briefing, without documentation. A UK area forecast relevant to the flight will also have to be obtained.

Further details of areas, telephone numbers and procedures are given in AIP GEN 3-5 and *Pooley's Flight Guide.*

Regular **VOLMET** broadcasts of weather reports and trends at certain aerodromes are made on specific VHF frequencies.

Broadcasts of recorded information for certain aerodromes are made on selected VHF-NAV radio frequencies or on discrete VHF-COM radio frequencies to relieve congestion on Air Traffic Control communication frequencies. This is known as the **Automatic Terminal Information Service** (ATIS). At larger airports the ATIS may be split into arrivals and departures, each broadcast on separate frequencies.

ATIS frequencies, where the service is available, are listed in the AD section of the AIP and in the aerodrome directory of the *Pooley's Flight Guide.*

Facilitation

Facilitation is the simplification of formalities in moving aircraft across international boundaries.

Private Aircraft on International Flights

Since the completion of the European Single Market on 1 January 1993, Customs and Excise requirements vary according to whether or not the place of departure or the destination is within the European Union (EU). This is likely to change after we leave the EU on 29th March 2019.

Arrival or Departure for UK outside the EU

Broadly speaking, unless special permission has been obtained from Customs and Excise, Immigration and Police Dept., the commander of an aircraft arriving or departing the UK, from or to places outside the EU, may not do so at any place other than a designated Customs and Excise airport as listed in the UK AIP, GEN 1. For full particulars see the AIP GEN 1-2.

Arrival or Departure for UK inside the EU

Since 1993 formalities for the departure and arrival for UK have been significantly relaxed and non-designated aerodromes (even private airstrips) may be used.

However, following the revision of the Prevention of Terrorism Act 2000, any person who has arrived or is seeking to leave Great Britain by aircraft from a non-designated airfield must give a minimum of 12 hours notice in writing (24 hours in some regions) to the relevant police department. Facsimile or email is usually acceptable.

Breaches of these provisions may result in prosecution, which is punishable upon conviction by up to 3 months imprisonment, a fine of £2,500 or both.

Procedures may vary between aerodromes and advice should be sought from individual aerodrome operators as well as AIP GEN 1-2.

Flights within the Common Travel Area (Channel Islands, Republic of Ireland, Isle of Man, Northern Ireland), will normally require 24 hours' notice of arrival or departure (because of the requirements of the Prevention of Terrorism Act 2000), if your departure or arrival is from a non-designated airfield. Effectively the permission of Special Branch has to be obtained. Again, facsimile or email is normally acceptable.

NOTE The Channel Islands are regarded as places outside the EU for the purposes of arrival and departure procedures. See AIP GEN 1-2.

Eurocontrol En Route Navigation Services

Charges for en route navigation services (i.e. other than those provided in connection with the use of an aerodrome) in the London and Scottish FIRs and UIRs may be levied in respect of private aircraft. Certain flights are exempted, notably those:
- made entirely under VFR;
- starting and finishing at the same aerodrome;
- made by aircraft with a maximum total authorised weight (mass) of less than 2,000 kg.

Now complete: **Practice Questions - ATS**

1. What is an Alerting Service?

(a) A special service provided by a department of D and D.

(b) A service provided to notify the appropriate organisations of aircraft in need of Search and Rescue aid, and to assist such organisations as required.

(c) A network of civil and military stations.

(d) A service provided to notify the appropriate organisations of aircraft in need of navigational assistance.

2. Lower Airspace Radar Service (LARS) is available outside controlled airspace up to.... (i).... and within approximately..... (ii).... from a participating ATSU. It comprises the.... (iii).... Services. (UK)

(a) i) FL 80 ii) 30 nm iii) Traffic and Procedural

(b) i) FL 100 ii) 25 nm iii) Procedural and Deconfliction.

(c) i) FL 80 ii) 25 nm iii) Deconfliction and Traffic.

(d) i) FL 100 ii) 30 nm iii) Traffic and Deconfliction.

3. A Flight Information Service at an aerodrome provides:

(a) Information useful to the safe and efficient conduct of flight in a CTR.

(b) Instructions and advice to aircraft in the ATZ.

(c) Information useful to the safe and efficient conduct of flight within an ATZ.

(d) Clearances to operate within an ATZ.

4. If you receive an Air Traffic Control Clearance which you consider to be unsuitable, you should:

(a) Ignore the clearance and continue as you originally planned.

(b) Request an alternative clearance.

(c) Comply with the clearance even though it is unsuitable.

(d) Comply with as much of the clearance as you can.

5. The purpose of a Basic Service is to:

(a) *Separate aircraft outside controlled airspace.*

(b) *Give warnings of traffic using radar derived information, but the avoidance of such traffic is the pilot's responsibility.*

(c) *Deconflict aircraft outside controlled airspace, but the avoidance of such traffic is the pilot's responsibility.*

(d) *Provide information useful to the safe and efficient conduct of flight.*

6. When a flight plan has been filed and a delay has been incurred, after how long must a DLA message be sent?

(a) *30 minutes*

(b) *45 minutes*

(c) *60 minutes*

(d) *2 hours*

7. There are circumstances in which a pilot *must* file a flight plan, in addition when is it advisable to do so?

(a) *When intending to fly more than 10 km from the coast, or over sparsely populated or mountainous areas.*

(b) *When intending to fly more than 10 nm from the coast, or over sparsely populated or mountainous areas.*

(c) *When intending to transit more than one ATZ.*

(d) *When intending to land more than 40 km from the departure aerodrome.*

Visual Flight Rules (SERA.5005)

Visual reference to the outside environment both for attitude reference and to navigate the aeroplane is necessary for the visual pilot (i.e. the pilot holding a basic PPL, without either an IMC Rating or an Instrument Rating).

If visual reference is lost – for example, by inadvertently entering cloud or by flying in conditions of reduced visibility – the results may be disastrous. To avoid this, minimum flight visibility requirements and minimum distances from cloud have been established. These are known as the **Visual Flight Rules (VFR)**.

The starting point for the Visual Flight Rules is:
- **a minimum flight visibility** of 8 km; and
- **a minimum distance from cloud** of 1,500 metres horizontally and 1,000 ft vertically.

Under certain conditions these requirements are reduced, e.g. below FL100 (10,000 ft) the flight visibility minimum is reduced to 5 km.

Conditions in which flight is possible under the Visual Flight Rules are known as **Visual Meteorological Conditions (VMC).**

VMC Minima for Airspace Classes

Each airspace class (except Class A, which is unavailable in the UK to VFR flights) has VMC minima specified for VFR flights. These VMC minima are specified in SERA.5001, 5005.

VMC in Controlled Airspace

Altitude Band	Airspace Class	Flight Visibility	Distance from Cloud
At and above 3050m (10,000ft) AMSL	A*** B C D E F G	8 km	1,500m horizontally 300m (1000ft) vertically
Below 3050m (10,000ft) AMSL and above 900m (3000ft) AMSL, or above 300m (1000ft) above terrain, whichever is the higher	A*** B C D E F G	5 km	1,500m horizontally 300m (1000ft) vertically
At and below 900m (3,000ft) AMSL, or 300m (1000ft) above terrain, whichever is the higher	A*** B C D E	5 km	1,500m horizontally 300m (1000ft) vertically
	F G	5 km**	Clear of cloud and with the surface in sight

★ When the height of the transition altitude is lower than 3050m (10,000ft) AMSL, FL100 shall be used in lieu of 10,000ft.

★★ When so prescribed by the competent authority:
– a) flight visibilities reduced to not less than 1500m may be permitted for flights operating:

1. At speed of 140kts IAS or less to give adequate opportunity to observe other traffic or any obstacles in time to avoid collision; or

2. In circumstances in which the probability of encounters with other traffic would normally be low, eg. in areas of low volume traffic and for aerial work at low levels.

– b) Helicopters may be permitted to operate in less than 1500m but not less than 800m flight visibility, if manoeuvred at a speed that will give adequate opportunity to observe other traffic or any obstacles in time to avoid collision. Flight visibilities lower than 800m may be permitted for special cases, such as medical flights, search and rescue operations and fire-fighting.

★★★ The VMC minima in Class A airspace are included for guidance to pilots and do not imply acceptance of VFR flights in Class A airspace.

NOTE Under the Visual Flight Rules, the pilot is solely responsible for the safety of the flight, separation from other aircraft, terrain clearance, and for remaining at a satisfactory distance from cloud in adequate flight visibility.

VFR Flight Plan and ATC Clearance

The pilot-in-command of a VFR flight must notify flight details to the appropriate Air Traffic Control unit in **Class C** and **D airspace**, and obtain an ATC clearance for the flight. (Responsible ATC units may, however, waive this requirement, at their discretion.)

The flight plan shall contain sufficient detail to enable the ATC unit to issue a clearance and for search and rescue purposes.

While operating in the specified airspace, the pilot-in-command shall maintain a constant listening watch on the appropriate radio frequency and comply with instructions from ATC.

Exemptions to this requirement are available in the specified airspace (effectively just Class D) for:

- gliders operating with a minimum flight visibility of 8 km, and distance from cloud of 1,500 metres horizontally and 1,000 ft vertically; and
- powered aircraft without radio equipment operating during the day with 5 km or better flight visibility and at least 1,500 metres horizontally and 1,000 ft vertically from cloud, provided that the commander has previously obtained the permission of the appropriate ATC unit to make the flight.

Flights at Night

Night is defined in the Air Navigation Order as meaning the time between half an hour after sunset and half an hour before sunrise, as measured at surface level.

Flights under the Visual Flight Rules at night have been permitted in the UK, since September 2012. Generally the aircraft must not be flown below the following minima: (1) ceiling less than 450m (1500ft); or ground visibility is less than 5km.

1. If leaving the vicinity of the aerodrome, then a flight plan must be submitted;

2. Two-way radio communication should be established;

3. VMC visibility and distance from cloud as set out shall apply except in certain specific circumstances as set out in SERA.5005.

Notes on the Visual Flight Rules

In interpreting the Visual Flight Rules it is essential to remember that a pilot must at all times fly within the privileges of the licence which is held.

In the interest of safety, pilots are **advised** to select cruising levels in accordance with the *semicircular* rule as applicable, even when under VFR. However, it is perfectly acceptable, when under VFR, to fly on the regional pressure setting above 3,000 ft, especially when manoeuvring.

Now complete: **Practice Questions - VFR**

1. The criteria for VFR flight in Class D and E when operating above 3000 feet but below FL 100, are:

(a) *Flight visibility 8 km, 1500 m horizontally and 1000 feet vertically from cloud.*

(b) *Flight visibility 5 km, 1000 m horizontally and 1500 feet vertically from cloud.*

(c) *Flight visibility 5 km, 1500 m horizontally and 1000 feet vertically from cloud.*

(d) *Flight visibility 5 km, clear of cloud and in sight of the surface.*

2. For VFR flight at night, other than in a helicopter, what is the absolute minimum cloud ceiling?

(a) *1,500 feet*

(b) *1,000 feet*

(c) *2,000 feet*

(d) *500 feet*

3. Except when taking off or landing, what is the minimum level at which a night VFR flight can operate?

(a) *At least 1,000 feet above the highest obstacle within 8 nm of the aircraft.*

(b) *At least 1,500 feet above the highest obstacle within 5 km of the aircraft.*

(c) *At least 1,000 feet above the highest obstacle within 8 km of the aircraft.*

(d) *At least 1,500 feet above the highest obstacle within 5 nm of the aircraft.*

4. In the UK, "Night" is defined as being between:

(a) *The end of morning civil twilight and the beginning of evening civil twilight.*

(b) *From half an hour after sunrise until half an hour before sunset.*

(c) *From half an hour before sunset until half an hour after sunrise.*

(d) *From half an hour after sunset until half an hour before sunrise.*

5. Flying by day within sight of the surface in Class G at 130 knots below 3000 ft AMSL, the VMC minima are:

(a) *Visibility 5 km, clear of cloud.*

(b) *Visibility 1500 m, 1500 ft vertically from cloud.*

(c) *Visibility 1500 m, clear of cloud.*

(d) *Visibility 5 km, 1000 m horizontally from cloud.*

6. Special VFR is available:

(a) *Only at night.*

(b) *Within controlled airspace.*

(c) *Only within Control Zones.*

(d) *Only within Aerodrome Traffic Zones.*

7. A Special VFR clearance absolves a pilot from:

(a) *The requirement to remain 1,000 feet above the highest object within 600 m of the aircraft, but no other low flying rule.*

(b) *All of the low flying rules.*

(c) *The requirement to remain 500 feet from any person, vessel, vehicle or structure, but no other low flying rule.*

(d) *The requirement to remain 1,500 feet above the highest object within 600 m of the aircraft, but no other low flying rule.*

Instrument Flight Rules (SERA.5015)

Flight under Visual Flight Rules (VFR) is very restrictive if, for instance, a regular air service is to be achieved. For this reason, flight and navigation instruments have been developed that allow a properly trained pilot to operate in cloud and other conditions not suitable for visual flight. The rules that apply to this category of flight are known as the **Instrument Flight Rules (IFR)**.

Only two types of flight category are available in aviation: VFR or IFR.

The Minimum Height Rule

Subject to the usual low flying requirements, an aircraft operated according to the Instrument Flight Rules, both inside and outside controlled airspace, must not fly at less than 1,000 feet above the highest obstacle within 5 nm, except:

1. On a route notified for the purposes of this rule or otherwise authorised by the competent authority (this may include controlled airspace such as certain Terminal Control Areas and Airways with particular high obstacles such as a radio mast underlying them and giving less than 1000 ft clearance from the base of the controlled airspace);

2. As necessary for take-off or landing; and

3. When flying at 3,000 feet amsl or below, clear of cloud and in sight of the surface.

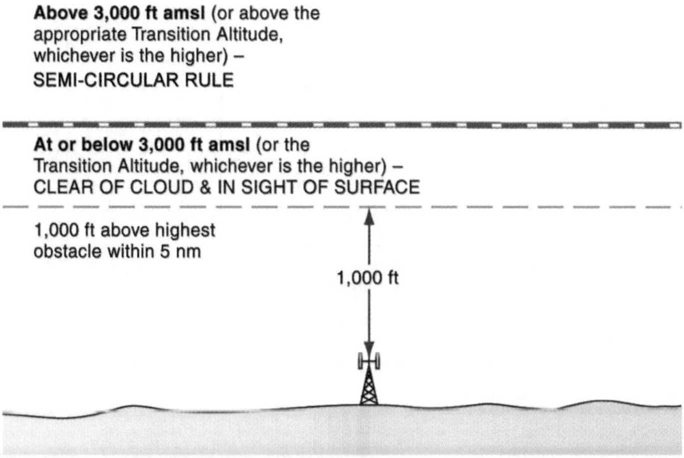

Above 3,000 ft amsl (or above the appropriate Transition Altitude, whichever is the higher) – SEMI-CIRCULAR RULE

At or below 3,000 ft amsl (or the Transition Altitude, whichever is the higher) – CLEAR OF CLOUD & IN SIGHT OF SURFACE

1,000 ft above highest obstacle within 5 nm

1,000 ft

■ Figure 8-1 **General IFR requirements**

IFR Flights Cruise at Semi-Circular Levels

In level flight above 3,000 ft amsl (or above the appropriate transition altitude, whichever is the higher), pilots must select cruising levels according to the *semicircular rule. Flight levels* are based on the standard altimeter setting 1013.2 hPa (or mb).

The semicircular rule requires an aircraft to be flown at a cruising level appropriate to its **magnetic track**, as shown below.

TABLE OF CRUISING LEVELS

TRACK*

From 000 degrees to 179 degrees						From 180 degrees to 359 degrees					
IFR Flights - Level			VFR Flights - Level			IFR Flights - Level			VFR Flights - Level		
FL	Feet	Metres	FL	Feet	Metres	FL	Feet	Metres	FL	Feet	Metres
010	1000	300	-	-	-	020	2000	600	-	-	-
030	3000	900	035	3500	1050	040	4000	1200	045	4500	1350
050	5000	1500	055	5500	1700	060	6000	1850	065	6500	2000
070	7000	2150	075	7500	2300	080	8000	2450	085	8500	2600
090	9000	2750	095	9500	2900	100	10000	3050	105	10500	3200
110	11000	3350	115	11500	3500	120	12000	3650	125	12500	3800
130	13000	3950	135	13500	4100	140	14000	4250	145	14500	4400
150	15000	4550	155	15500	4700	160	16000	4900	165	16500	5050
170	17000	5200	175	17500	5350	180	18000	5500	185	18500	5650
190	19000	5800	195	19500	5950	200	20000	6100	205	20500	6250
210	21000	6400	215	21500	6550	220	22000	6700	225	22500	6850
230	23000	7000	235	23500	7150	240	24000	7300	245	24500	7450
250	25000	7600	255	25500	7750	260	26000	7900	265	26500	8100
270	27000	8250	275	27500	8400	280	28000	8550	285	28500	8700
290	29000	8850	-	-	-	300	30000	9150	-	-	-
310	31000	9450	-	-	-	320	32000	9750	-	-	-
330	33000	10050	-	-	-	340	34000	10350	-	-	-
350	35000	10650	-	-	-	360	36000	10950	-	-	-
370	37000	11300	-	-	-	380	38000	11600	-	-	-
390	39000	11900	-	-	-	400	40000	12200	-	-	-
410	41000	12500	-	-	-	430	43000	13100	-	-	-
450	45000	13700	-	-	-	470	47000	14350	-	-	-
490	49000	14950	-	-	-	510	51000	1550	-	-	-
etc.	etc.	etc.				etc.	etc.	etc.			

*Magnetic track, or in polar areas at latitudes higher than 70 degrees and within such extensions to those areas as may be prescribed by the competent authorities, grid tracks as determined by a network of lines parallel to the Green Meridian superimposed on a polar stereo graphic chart in which the direction towards the North Pole is employed as the Grid North.

■ *Figure 8-2* **IFR cruising levels**

An aeroplane operating under the Instrument Flight Rules may cruise at a different level from those specified above when complying with instructions given by an ATC unit or with notified holding procedures.

Flight Plan and ATC Clearance

SERA.5020 applies to IFR flights within controlled airspace.

1. In order to comply with the Instrument Flight Rules, before any flight within controlled airspace the aircraft commander must file a flight plan (irrespective of whether IMC or VMC exist) and obtain an ATC clearance based upon it. The flight must be made in accordance with the clearance and with the notified holding and approach procedures at the destination unless otherwise instructed by ATC.

2. A pilot flying IFR in controlled airspace must follow:

   - the terms of the Air Traffic Control clearance and any further instructions given by ATC;
   - the published instrument holding and approach procedures for the destination aerodrome;

   however, the pilot may cancel IFR (and therefore switch to VFR), provided that:

   > the pilot can maintain VMC whilst in controlled airspace; and
   > the pilot informs ATC accordingly, asking them to cancel his or her flight plan.

3. ATC must be told as soon as possible if, to avoid immediate danger, any departure has to be made from the requirements of this rule.

4. Except when the flight plan has been cancelled, an aircraft commander must inform ATC when the aircraft lands within or leaves controlled airspace.

Position Reports (SERA.5025)

An aircraft under IFR which flies in or intends to enter controlled airspace must report its time, position and level at such reporting points or at such intervals of time as may be notified or directed by ATC.

TYPICAL POSITION REPORT	
Aircraft identification	Golf Alpha Echo Sierra Echo
Position and time	Wicken four seven
Level	Flight level four zero
Next position and estimate	Marlow five seven

Now complete: **Practice Questions - IFR**

1. The minimum height to fly under IFR is:

(a) 1000 feet AGL.
(b) 1500 feet above the highest obstacle within 10 nm of track.
(c) 1000 feet above the highest obstacle within 5 nm of track.
(d) 1000 feet above the highest fixed obstacle within 600 m.

2. In order to fly IFR within controlled airspace a pilot must do which of the following?

(a) Obtain an ATC clearance.
(b) Land at least 40 km away.
(c) File a flight plan and obtain an ATC clearance based upon it.
(d) File a flight plan, fly in IMC and follow a specified route to leave controlled airspace.

3. When a position report is required the correct format is:

(a) Ground station call sign, Position, Level, Next Reporting Point and ETA.
(b) Aircraft call sign, Position, Level, Next Reporting Point and ETA.
(c) Ground station call sign, Position, Time, Exit Point and ETA.
(d) Aircraft call sign, Position, Time, Level, Next Reporting Point and ETA.

Answers: 1c, 2c, 3d.

Registration and Airworthiness

Registration and Marking of Aircraft

ICAO Annex 7

Aircraft Nationality and Registration Marks

Annex 7 contains standards and definitions adopted by ICAO to define the minimum requirements for the display of aircraft nationality and registration marks.

Nationality and Registration Marks to be Used

2.1 The nationality and registration mark shall consist of a group of letters and/or numbers (e.g. G-AGOH, N7207V).

2.2 The nationality mark shall appear before the registration mark in the group. When the first character of the registration mark is a letter it shall be preceded by a hyphen (e.g. F-BUDG).

2.5 The registration mark shall be letters and/or numbers, and shall be assigned by the State of Registry.

Location of Nationality and Registration Marks

3.1 The nationality and registration mark shall be painted on, or permanently affixed to, the aircraft. The marks shall be kept clean and visible at all times.

3.2 On balloons, the marks shall appear on each side, near the widest part of the balloon, above either the rigging band or the basket cable attachment points. On other lighter-than-air aircraft, the marks shall be visible from the sides and from the ground.

3.3 On heavier-than-air aircraft the marks shall appear once on the lower surface of the wing, on the left-hand side unless they extend across the whole wing structure. The tops of the letters and/or numbers shall be toward the leading edge of the wing, and the mark shall be positioned midway between the leading and trailing edge.

The marks shall also appear on both sides of the fuselage, between the wings and tail surface, or on the upper halves of the vertical tail surfaces. When located on a single vertical tail surface the marks shall appear on both sides.

Dimensions of Nationality and Registration Marks

4.1 On lighter-than-air aircraft, the height of the marks shall be at least 50 centimetres.

4.2 For heavier-than-air aircraft, the height of the marks on the wings shall be at least 50 centimetres. On the fuselage or vertical tail surfaces the marks shall be at least 30 centimetres high.

Lettering for Nationality and Registration Marks

5.1 Letters shall be Roman capitals, without ornamentation. Numbers shall be Arabic, without ornamentation. The width of each character (except for the letter I and the number 1) shall be two-thirds of the height of a character. In other words, the character shapes cannot be 'stretched' too much in height as to make them difficult to read. The characters should be formed from solid lines, in a contrasting colour to the background.

Identification Plate

Aircraft shall carry an identification plate inscribed with its nationality or common mark and registration mark. The plate shall be made of fireproof metal or other suitable fireproof material, and shall be secured to the aircraft near the main entrance.

Registration of Aircraft in the UK
(ANO Articles 24, 25 and 26; Schedule 4)

To all intents and purposes, the private pilot must not fly in the UK unless the aircraft is registered, either in the UK or elsewhere, and displays the appropriate registration markings.

United Kingdom
Civil Aviation Authority

Certificate of Registration of Aircraft

Certificate Number G-KILT/R1

1 Nationality or Common Mark and Registration Mark	2 Manufacturer and Manufacturer's Designation of Aircraft	3 Aircraft Constructor's Serial Number
G - KILT	Gulfstream American Aviation Corporation, USA Gulfstream AA5A	AA5A-0893

4 Name of Registered Owner or Charterer

■ *Figure 9-1* **Part of a Certificate of Registration**

■ *Figure 9-2*
Registration markings

In applying for registration, the aeroplane must be properly described according to the General Classification of Aircraft specified in Schedule 4 of the Air Navigation Order (ANO).

It is the responsibility of **owners** (and part-owners) to inform the CAA in writing of any change in the particulars shown on the original application for registration of an aircraft, e.g. change of ownership or part-ownership, its destruction or permanent withdrawal from use.

Non-EASA Gliders and hang-gliders need not be registered. In some circumstances, a powered aeroplane need not be registered, e.g. experimental or test aeroplanes, and aeroplanes undergoing certification testing, or carrying out a demonstration flight.

If a pilot does fly an unregistered aircraft, the pilot is accountable for any other offences against the ANO made during the flight, just as if the aircraft were registered.

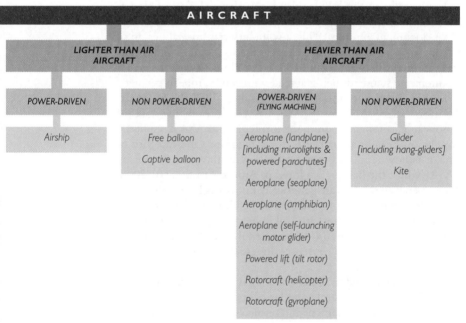

■ *Figure 9-3* **The general classification of aircraft**

Airworthiness and Equipment

Airworthiness of Aircraft (ICAO Annex 8)

Annex 8 describes the broad standards of airworthiness to be adopted by national authorities. These standards are the minimum basis by which a Certificate of Airworthiness issued by one state can be recognised by another State. This ensures that when aircraft fly over the territory of other States, they comply with international minimum airworthiness standards, which are agreed by all contracting States. This ensures a universal standard of safety and protection to aircraft, people and property in all countries.

ANO Part 4 Chapter 3, Schedule 3 and EC Regulation 216/2008

These ICAO standards of airworthiness are the minimum and many individual States include differences in detail which they consider necessary.

Historically, in the UK legislation on airworthiness of aircraft has been contained in the Air Navigation Order (ANO) and other CAA documents. In the 1990s, a voluntary transitional period of European harmonisation (standardisation of regulations /requirements between countries) led to close airworthiness and maintenance standards being agreed with our European partners.

Under direction of the European Council (EC), the European Aviation Safety Agency (EASA) has taken over the task of European harmonisation from the former JAA. EASA has split the population of light aircraft into two categories. One category of aircraft is now regulated in accordance with the rules set out by EASA, whilst the balance are listed in Annex 2 to EC.216/2008. Thus aircraft in the UK are generically known as EASA aircraft or Annex 2 aircraft. Most older aircraft and all home built aircraft fall under Annex 2 and they are still subject to the airworthiness provisions set out in the ANO. However, they will either be issued with EASA Certificates of Airworthiness (CofA) or CAA issued Permits to Fly (PtoF).

A CofA is required in respect of each aircraft determined to be airworthy, following careful consideration of design, construction, materials, essential equipment and results of flying trials and other tests.

Under UK regulations for Annex 2 aircraft, a CofA is issued for 3 years after which point it must be renewed, but a CofA in respect of EASA aircraft is non-expiring and is maintained in force by an annual issue/extension of an Airworthiness Review Certificate (ARC). See Figure 9-5.

NOTE The CofA is considered invalid if the aircraft is modified, repaired or maintained (in other than an approved manner). This would in turn invalidate the aircraft's insurance.

A **Flight Manual (or Pilot's Operating Handbook – POH)** forms part of the aircraft's list of equipment and should be available to the pilot at all times. In the case of foreign manufactured aircraft, the CAA may attach supplements to the original Flight Manual expanding or amending the manner in which the aircraft should be operated.

In general, a pilot may only fly within the UK in an aircraft that has a current CofA valid under the law of the country in which it is registered and then only according to the conditions specified; e.g. to tow a glider legally, the aircraft must be approved to do so (Article 87).

In some circumstances, an aircraft that does not have a current CofA may be required to fly; e.g. to perform flight tests necessary for the issue or re-issue of a CofA. With regard to EASA aircraft, EASA issue a Permit to Fly and this system is administered by the CAA. For Annex 2 aircraft (excluding home built and other aircraft whose airworthiness is administered by the Light Aircraft Association – for whom separate rules apply) a suitably licensed type-rated engineer may issue a PtoF under 'A' conditions in ANO Schedule 3.

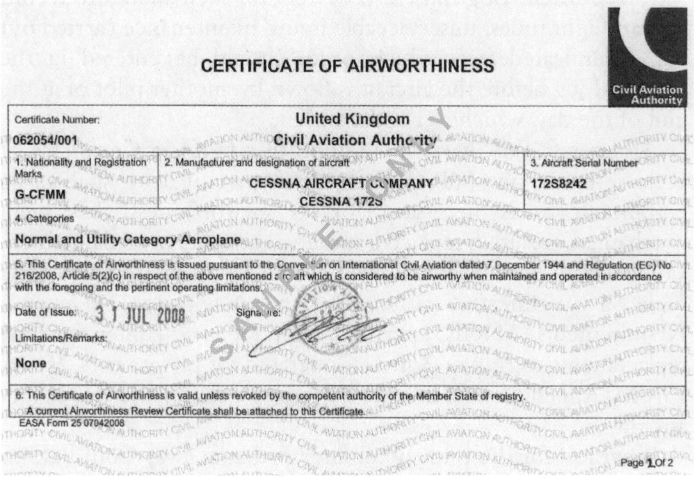

CERTIFICATE OF AIRWORTHINESS

Civil Aviation Authority

Certificate Number: 062054/001

United Kingdom
Civil Aviation Authority

1. Nationality and Registration Marks: G-CFMM

2. Manufacturer and designation of aircraft: CESSNA AIRCRAFT COMPANY CESSNA 172S

3. Aircraft Serial Number: 172S8242

4. Categories: Normal and Utility Category Aeroplane

5. This Certificate of Airworthiness is issued pursuant to the Convention on International Civil Aviation dated 7 December 1944 and Regulation (EC) No 216/2008, Article 5(2)(c) in respect of the above mentioned aircraft which is considered to be airworthy when maintained and operated in accordance with the foregoing and the pertinent operating limitations.

Date of Issue: 31 JUL 2008 Signature:

Limitations/Remarks: None

SAMPLE ONLY

6. This Certificate of Airworthiness is valid unless revoked by the competent authority of the Member State of registry.
A current Airworthiness Review Certificate shall be attached to this Certificate.

EASA Form 25 07042008

Page 1 Of 2

■ *Figure 9-4* ***The Certificate of Airworthiness***

Maintenance (ANO Articles 44-48 and EC Regulation 216/2008)

EASA aircraft must be maintained to a Light Aircraft Maintenance Programme (LAMP). Annex 2 aircraft (excluding those administered by the LAA) will normally be maintained under a Light Aircraft Maintenance Schedule (LAMS). In addition, for Annex 2 aircraft, an annual Certificate of Maintenance Review (CMR) must be in force if the aircraft is used for anything other than private uses.

Under the CAA system it was relatively easy to determine whether the aircraft was restricted to private operations by the wording on the CofA. Furthermore, many private owners were keen to exercise the privileges permitted by the regulations allowing them to carry out certain maintenance on their own aircraft. Whilst this is still permitted for Annex 2 aircraft, the owner/operator of an EASA aircraft must seek the agreement of the appropriate Continuing Airworthiness Management Organisation (CAMO) before carrying out any maintenance himself.

Additionally, the onus is on the operator of an aircraft to make decisions regarding the eligibility of the aircraft for any form of commercial activity (including rental and flying training). The CAMO will be able to provide information to assist this decision.

A **Technical Log** must also be kept for such aircraft to record aircraft flight times, unserviceable items, maintenance carried out etc. Technical defects which occur should be entered in the technical log before the aircraft is flown by another pilot or at the end of the day, whichever is the earlier.

An aircraft must have, in addition to a CofA, a Certificate of Release to Service (CRS) if it (or any part of it, or such of its equipment as is necessary for its airworthiness) has been overhauled, repaired, replaced, modified or otherwise maintained. Only certain persons are allowed by the ANO or EASA to issue such a certificate, although Air Navigation (General) Requirements (ANGRs) permit certain repairs, maintenance and replacements to Annex 2 aircraft operated for private uses. EASA Part M, Appendix VIII lists the permitted maintenance for EASA aircraft.

Provision for the pilot of an aircraft that is away from base to confirm that a minor adjustment to a control has been satisfactorily performed and to sign the second part of a Duplicate Inspection certificate is restricted to Annex 2 aircraft only.

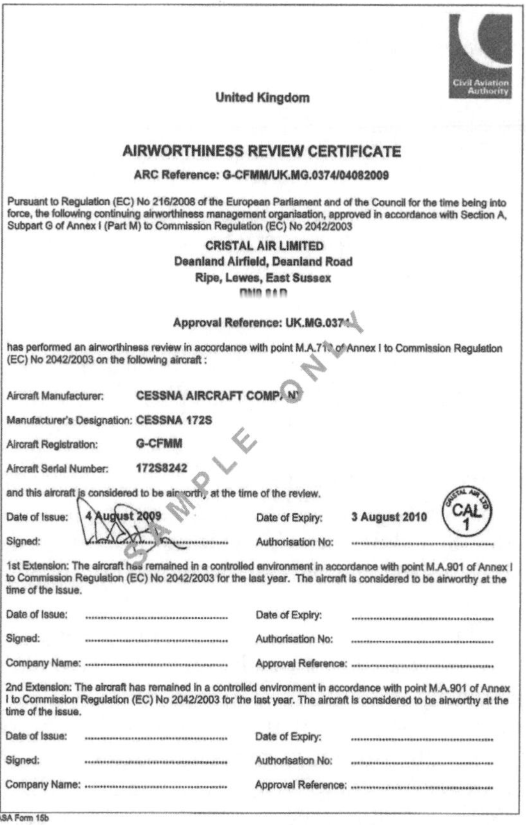

Civil Aviation Authority

United Kingdom

AIRWORTHINESS REVIEW CERTIFICATE

ARC Reference: G-CFMM/UK.MG.0374/04082009

Pursuant to Regulation (EC) No 216/2008 of the European Parliament and of the Council for the time being into force, the following continuing airworthiness management organisation, approved in accordance with Section A, Subpart G of Annex I (Part M) to Commission Regulation (EC) No 2042/2003

CRISTAL AIR LIMITED
Deanland Airfield, Deanland Road
Ripe, Lewes, East Sussex
[illegible]

Approval Reference: UK.MG.037[illegible]

has performed an airworthiness review in accordance with point M.A.71[illegible] of Annex I to Commission Regulation (EC) No 2042/2003 on the following aircraft :

Aircraft Manufacturer: **CESSNA AIRCRAFT COMPANY**

Manufacturer's Designation: **CESSNA 172S**

Aircraft Registration: **G-CFMM**

Aircraft Serial Number: **172S8242**

and this aircraft is considered to be airworthy at the time of the review.

Date of Issue: **4 August 2009** Date of Expiry: **3 August 2010**

Signed: .... Authorisation No: ....

SAMPLE ONLY

CRISTAL AIR LTD CAL 1

1st Extension: The aircraft has remained in a controlled environment in accordance with point M.A.901 of Annex I to Commission Regulation (EC) No 2042/2003 for the last year. The aircraft is considered to be airworthy at the time of the issue.

Date of Issue: .... Date of Expiry: ....

Signed: .... Authorisation No: ....

Company Name: .... Approval Reference: ....

2nd Extension: The aircraft has remained in a controlled environment in accordance with point M.A.901 of Annex I to Commission Regulation (EC) No 2042/2003 for the last year. The aircraft is considered to be airworthy at the time of the issue.

Date of Issue: .... Date of Expiry: ....

Signed: .... Authorisation No: ....

Company Name: .... Approval Reference: ....

EASA Form 15b

■ *Figure 9-5* ***Airworthiness Review Certificate***

Engine and Propeller Logbooks (ANO Article 226 and Schedule 7). In addition to the previously mentioned documents, the *operator* is required to keep:

- an Aircraft Logbook;
- an Engine Logbook;
- a Variable-Pitch Propeller Logbook (if applicable).

All logbooks have to be preserved for two years after the particular aircraft, engine or propeller has been destroyed or permanently withdrawn from use.

Temporary Loss of Airworthiness (ICAO Annex 8)

PART II, 6.1 If an aircraft is not maintained in an airworthy condition as defined by the appropriate requirements it cannot be flown until it is restored to an airworthy condition.

PART II, 6.2 If an aircraft is damaged, the State of Registry shall determine whether such damage renders the aircraft no longer airworthy.

If an aircraft is damaged in the territory of another State, that State is entitled to prevent the aircraft from flying, provided it notifies the State of Registry immediately. Should the State of Registry consider that the damage sustained makes the aircraft not airworthy, it shall prohibit the aircraft from flying until it is restored to airworthiness. However, in exceptional circumstances it may allow the aircraft to fly under limiting conditions, without fare-paying passengers, to an aerodrome where repairs can be made. The State in which the aircraft was damaged (that prevented further flight in the first place) shall allow such a flight to be made.

On the other hand, if the State of Registry considers that the damage sustained (in another State) is such that the aircraft is still airworthy, the aircraft shall be allowed to resume its flight.

Mass and Balance (ANO Article 43)

An important part of the Certificate of Airworthiness is the **Aircraft Weight Schedule**, which approves certain weight limitations and specifies the allowable range for the position of the centre of gravity (CG).

ANO Article 43 requires that an aeroplane must be weighed at its basic weight (or other approved weight) and have the position of its centre of gravity determined at that weight. A Weight Schedule must then be prepared by the operator. Following the next occasion when the aircraft is officially weighed for the purposes of this Article and a new Weight Schedule prepared, the earlier Weight Schedule should be preserved for a period of 6 months, even though it has expired.

Fly within the CofA Specifications

Operating the aircraft outside the conditions specified in the CofA (which includes the Flight Manual) may seriously degrade the safety of the flight and render the CofA invalid, e.g. flying a non-permitted operation or manoeuvre or exceeding *weight and balance* limitations. In addition to the safety issues, this has very serious legal implications, making the pilot liable to a fine or imprisonment, rendering the insurance policies invalid and invalidating any warranties or guarantees on the aircraft and its equipment.

A pilot should always operate an aeroplane within the specifications of its CofA.

Aircraft Limitations and Information (ICAO Annex 8)

PART II, 8 Each aircraft shall be provided with a Flight Manual, placards, or other documents describing any limitations within which the aircraft is considered airworthy, and any other information necessary for the safe operation of the aircraft.

Operating Limitations and Information

PART III, 9.1 Any operating limitations which must be complied with under the Certificate of Airworthiness, and any other information necessary for the safe operation of the aircraft, shall be made available in a Flight Manual or on placards or markings etc.

PART III, 9.2 Where there is a risk of exceeding operating limitations in flight, they shall be defined such that the flight crew can determine, by reference to the instruments available to them, when the limitations are reached.

Loading limitations shall include all limiting masses (weights), centres of gravity positions, mass (weight) distributions and floor loadings.

Airspeed limitations shall include all speeds that are limiting in relation to structural integrity and flying qualities (e.g. V_{NE}). Various aeroplane configurations shall be taken into account in identifying these speeds (e.g. V_{FE}).

Powerplant limitations shall include all those established for the various powerplant components installed in the aeroplane.

Equipment and systems limitations shall include all those established for the various equipment and systems installed in the aeroplane.

Miscellaneous limitations shall include any other limitations necessary to the safe operation of the aeroplane.

PART III, 9.3 Loading information shall include the empty mass of the aeroplane, together with a definition of the condition of the aeroplane at the time of weighing, the corresponding centre of gravity position, and the reference point (s) and datum line (s) to which the CG limits are related.

NOTE 'Empty mass' usually excludes crew and payload, usable fuel and drainable oil; but it includes all fixed ballast, unusable fuel, undrainable oil, engine coolant and hydraulic fluid.

Operating procedures, both normal and emergency, that are unique to the aircraft shall be described. These shall include engine-failure procedures.

Handling information: unusual or significant aeroplane characteristics, including stall speeds or minimum steady flight speeds, shall be described.

PART III, 9.5 An aeroplane Flight Manual shall be available to the crew. It shall identify clearly the specific aeroplane or series of aeroplanes for which it is written and contain at least the limitations, procedures and information mentioned above.

PART III, 9.6 Markings and placards on instruments, equipment, controls, etc., shall include any limitations or information necessary to the crew during flight.

Electrical Systems

PART IV, 8 Aircraft electrical systems shall be designed and installed to ensure that they will perform their intended function under any foreseeable operating conditions.

Equipment of Aircraft
(ANO Part 5 Articles 77 and 78, Schedules 5 & 6)

Many aircraft are lavishly equipped, but there is a certain minimum standard specified in the ANO below which an aeroplane should not be flown (general aircraft equipment being detailed in ANO Schedule 5, and radio communication and radio navigation equipment being detailed in Schedule 6).

Pilots must be familiar with the minimum equipment requirements for their particular operation: e.g. when carrying out aerobatic manoeuvres, a suitable safety harness or safety belt must be fitted; when night flying in helicopters, parachute flares must be carried; an unserviceable attitude indicator (artificial horizon) may not render the aeroplane unserviceable, whereas an unserviceable clock may do so.

Noise Certification

A Noise Certificate is required for every propeller-driven aeroplane with an all-up weight of 9,000 kg or less, all helicopters and microlight aeroplanes, and every other subsonic aeroplane which at maximum authorised weight requires a take-off distance of more than 610 metres. Certain short take-off and landing (STOL) aeroplanes are exempt.

Insurance

Aircraft insurance may be considered in three parts: Passenger, Third Party and the Hull (the aircraft's value). Since 30 April 2005 the regulations require all aircraft operating within the EU to have minimum levels of insurance cover in respect of passenger and third-party liability.

While there is no legal requirement in the UK to insure an aircraft hull, flying an uninsured aircraft could lead to you being substantially out of pocket, even bankrupt, if you suffer an accident.

As part of your pre-flight check you should ensure that the certificate of insurance is present and valid for the type of flight intended. Although it is the responsibility of the owner or operator to arrange for insurance cover, you should remember that you, as pilot-in-command, are responsible under Articles 69 and 75 of the ANO for ensuring that the flight may be safely and legally conducted. The existence of insurance cover does not exempt you from observing the requirements of the ANO and your licence privileges.

If you hire an aircraft from an ATO or DTO it is likely that proper and adequate insurance will be in place, although beware, there may be an 'excess' that you would have to pay in the event of an accident. The excess is likely to be between £1,500 – £2,000 depending on the type of aircraft, however, some clubs operate a scheme to self-insure the excess by contributing a small amount to a pooled kitty (which obviously will have to be replenished by further contributions if it has to be drawn on following someone else's accident).

If you wish to land at a military airfield, you may have to arrange additional third party cover up to £7,500,000 or pay a premium on top of the landing fee. This is because typical light aviation insurance policies normally only provide cover of £1,000,000–£3,000,000 of third party liability, and all that military hardware is rather expensive if you accidentally run into it on landing! These limits have recently been raised considerably by new European legislation requiring all aircraft to carry higher minimum insurance cover.

You may find a number of exclusions in your insurance policy, so do check it carefully. Typically your insurer may not cover you for landing at unlicensed strips, or perhaps for aerobatics. You may also find that there is a 'pilot warranty' clause requiring a minimum number of hours total time or experience on type. Be careful of this as insurers are well-known for refusing to pay out on claims arising from accidents where the pilot has fewer hours than specified in the pilot warranty. If you are not the owner you could then face a claim personally by the owner, in addition to any third party claims! If in doubt, check with your insurance broker.

Now complete: **Practice Questions - Registration & Airworthiness**

1. A Certificate of Airworthiness (C of A) would cease to be valid:

(a) *After 5 years.*
(b) *If the aircraft, or its equipment, is overhauled, modified or repaired in a non-approved manner.*
(c) *Outside the State of Registry.*
(d) *If the airframe hours exceed the maximum allowed in any twelve month period.*

2. As well as a C of A, an aircraft must have a Certificate of Release to Service. This will be issued:

(a) *By the operator at the start of each day.*
(b) *Only after major rebuilding or reconstruction of any part of the airframe.*
(c) *If it has been overhauled, repaired, modified or otherwise maintained.*
(d) *By the owner and signed off by the pilot.*

3. Following the preparation of a new Weight Schedule:

(a) *The preceding one must be kept for 6 months.*
(b) *The old one may be destroyed after 3 months.*
(c) *All expired Weight Schedules must be retained.*
(d) *The preceding one should be kept for 1 year.*

4. Any defects requiring maintenance which are encountered during a flight should be recorded by the pilot:

(a) *On the Certificate of Maintenance Review.*
(b) *In the Aircraft Technical Log.*
(c) *On the Certificate of Release to Service.*
(d) *On any handy scrap of paper which should be left in the aircraft.*

5. Before any flight, the legal responsibility to ensure that all of an aircraft's maintenance documentation is current rests with the:

(a) *Aircraft Owner*
(b) *Aircraft Operator*
(c) *Chief Engineer*
(d) *Pilot*

6. The Pilot's Operating Handbook:

 (a) *Must be kept in a secure location at the aircraft's home base.*
 (b) *Is part of the aircraft's equipment list and must be available to the pilot at all times.*
 (c) *Is only required for training aircraft.*
 (d) *Must be carried in the aircraft if landing away.*

Answers: 1b, 2c, 3a, 4b, 5d, 6b.

Pilots' Licences

EASA Part-FCL

The EASA rules came into force in the UK on 17 September 2012. These requirements are implemented by a directly-applicable European Rule, Regulation 1178/2011, as amended by Regulation 290/2012, known jointly as 'the EASA Aircrew Regulation'. This consists of the Regulation itself and 7 annexes, including Annex I (Part-FCL), which replaces JAR-FCL 1 and 2, and Annex III (Part-MED), which replaces JAR-FCL 3.

The new rules replace and override the equivalent national legislation in the Air Navigation Order for pilots of aircraft to which the legislation applies. However, the ANO will still have to provide for some aspects of licensing, e.g. to cover non-EASA aircraft, and will continue to apply to all UK national licences.

EASA Aircraft

All civil aircraft registered in the Member States of the EU are 'EASA aircraft', unless:

- they are carrying out activities on behalf of the State, such as military, customs or police; or

- they are within the categories set out in Annex II to the Aircrew Regulation, mainly such types as microlights, home builds and historic aircraft.

Licences Under EASA Part-FCL

Part-FCL makes provisions to grant licences and ratings that are equivalent to those previously issued under JAR-FCL (the Joint Airworthiness Authorities-now defunct), which are ICAO-compliant and thus recognised worldwide. All JAR-FCL licences automatically became EASA licences. Part-FCL also provides for a Light Aircraft Pilot Licence (LAPL), which is similar to the UK NPPL(A): this does not comply with ICAO, but is valid throughout Europe for EU-registered aircraft. All Part-FCL licences are non-expiring 'lifetime' licences, although their use depends upon the validity of the associated ratings and medical certificates.

PART-FCL TERMINOLOGY

Category (of aircraft)
A grouping of similar aircraft according to specified basic characteristics, e.g. aeroplane, helicopter, glider, free balloon.

Class rating
Approval to fly a single-pilot aeroplane that does not require a type rating.

Conversion (of a licence)
The issue of an EASA Part-FCL licence on the basis of a licence issued by a Member State.

Dual instruction time
Flight time or instrument ground time during which a person is receiving flight instruction from a properly authorised instructor.

Flight time
The total time from the moment that an aircraft first moves under its own or external power for the purpose of taking off until the moment it comes to rest at the end of the flight.

Flight time as student pilot-in-command (SPIC)
Flight time during which the flight instructor will only observe the student acting as pilot-in-command and shall not influence or control the flight of the aircraft.

Instrument time
Instrument flight time or instrument ground time (i.e. attained in a simulator).

Instrument flight time
Time during which the pilot is controlling an aircraft solely by reference to the flight instruments.

Instrument ground time
Time during which a pilot is receiving instruction in simulated instrument flight in synthetic training devices (STDs).

Multi-crew cooperation
The functioning of flight crew as a team of cooperating members led by the pilot-in-command.

Multi-pilot aeroplanes
Aeroplanes certificated for operation with a minimum crew of at least two pilots.

Night
The period between the end of evening civil twilight and the beginning of morning civil twilight, or such other period between sunset and sunrise as may be prescribed by the appropriate Authority.
Note: Night is defined in the UK as 30 minutes after sunset until 30 minutes before sunrise.

Other training devices
Training aids other than flight simulators; flight training devices or flight and navigation procedures trainers that allow training where a complete flight deck environment is not necessary.

Private pilot
A pilot who holds a licence that does not permit him to be paid for flying aircraft, excluding instruction or examination activities.

Professional pilot
A pilot who holds a licence that permits him to be paid for flying aircraft.

PART-FCL TERMINOLOGY

Proficiency checks
Demonstrations of skill to revalidate or renew ratings, including oral examinations as necessary.

Rating
An entry in a licence stating special conditions, privileges or limitations pertaining to that licence.

Renewal
(e.g. of an **expired** rating or approval) The reinstatement of the privileges of the rating or approval for a further specified period, subject to certain requirements.

Revalidation
(e.g. of an **existing** rating or approval) Permission granted that allows the holder of a rating or approval to exercise the privileges of the rating or approval for a further specified period, subject to certain requirements.

Single-pilot aeroplanes
Aeroplanes certificated for operation by one pilot.

Skill tests
Demonstrations of skill for the issue of a licence or rating, including oral examinations as required.

Solo flight time
Flight time during which a student pilot is the sole occupant of an aircraft.

Touring motor glider (TMG)
A motor glider with a Certificate of Airworthiness issued or accepted by an EU member State that has an integrally mounted, non-retractable engine and a non-retractable propeller. It shall be capable of taking off and climbing under its own power according to its Flight Manual.

Type (of aircraft)
Aircraft of the same basic design, including all modifications except those that result in a change of handling, flight characteristics or flight crew complement.

Type rating
A rating that permits the holder to fly a specific aeroplane type. A type rating is **not** included in a class rating.

Student Pilots

A student pilot may begin training without a licence under the supervision of a suitably qualified flight instructor. During the course of training for a PPL(A), a student pilot may (without a licence) act as pilot-in-command (PIC) and fly solo if the following conditions are complied with.

• The student pilot is at least 16 years of age.
• The student pilot holds a Part-MED Class 1 or Class 2 medical certificate from an Authorised Medical Examiner (AME) and complies with any restrictions on it (e.g. a requirement to wear spectacles);
• No other person is carried in the aircraft; and
• The student pilot is authorised and supervised by a suitably qualified flight instructor.

Medical Requirements: EASA Part-MED

Before applying for a licence and before exercising the privileges of a licence, the applicant or licence holder must have passed a medical examination made by an Authorised Medical Examiner (AME). Part-MED applies to EASA Part-FCL licences and provides for Class 1, Class 2 and LAPL medical certificates.

• For a PPL (A), PPL (H), PPL (As), SPL or BPL, a Class 2 (or Class 1) medical certificate is required.
• For any LAPL, the LAPL medical certificate (or a Class 1 or Class 2) is required.

Validity of Medical Certificates

The periods of validity for Class 2 medical certificates are as follows:

MEDICAL CERTIFICATE VALIDITY – CLASS 2	
Age	**Validity**
less than 40 years	60 months
40 to 49 years	24 months
50 years or over	12 months

Note 1 *This certificate is valid for its time period even if the applicant enters the next age group. However, a Class 2 or LAPL certificate issued prior to the pilot's 40th birthday (normally validity 5 years) will not be valid after he/she reaches 42, and one issued prior to reaching 50 will not be valid after he/she reaches 51.*

Note 2 *Professional pilots are required to hold a Class 1 medical certificate, which is more stringent.*

Note 3 *Pilots may renew their medical certificates up to 45 days before the expiry date. The validity period will commence from the expiry date of the previous medical certificate. An initial medical certificate is valid from the date of the medical assessment.*

LAPL Medical

The LAPL medical can be issued by an AME, or, provided that the applicant does not have any significant medical history, a General Practitioner (GP). The requirements are less stringent than for Class 2 and an examination may not be required.

LAPL medical certificates are valid for a period of:

- 60 months until the licence holder reaches the age of 40. A medical certificate issued prior to reaching the age of 40 shall cease to be valid after the licence holder reaches the age of 42; and
- 24 months after the age of 40.

In all cases, it is the licence-holder's responsibility to ensure that renewals are made within the appropriate time limits if licence privileges are to be maintained.

A pilot is not entitled to act as flight crew if he/she knows or suspects that he/she is medically unfit for it. The pilot must therefore seek advice from an AME or Aeromedical Centre (AeMC) immediately.

Conditions include:

- undergoing a surgical operation or invasive procedure;
- frequent use of medication;
- suffering a significant injury or illness;
- pregnancy;
- admission to a hospital or medical clinic;
- first requiring corrective lenses.

In all cases, the AME or AeMC will decide whether the licence-holder is fit to resume the exercise of his or her privileges.

Self-Declaration

It is now possible to make a self-declaration in certain circumstances where you meet the medical requirements of a DVLA Group 1 Ordinary Driving Licence. The details for this are set out in Form SRG 1210 on the CAA website and the form must be completed and submitted on-line to the CAA.

ANAESTHETICS A pilot should not exercise the privileges of his or her licence after receiving a local anaesthetic for at least 12 hours after the event (such as a dental visit requiring an injection for tooth extraction or filling), and at least 48 hours, after a general anaesthetic.

BLOOD OR BONE MARROW DONATION Twenty-four hours should elapse between giving blood and flying. In the case of bone marrow donation involving a general anaesthetic, 48 hours should elapse before flying.

PREGNANCY Once certified as fit, flying is permitted up to the 26th week of pregnancy, but a pilot should ground herself and seek medical advice if she feels unwell during this period.

The Granting of a Private Pilot's Licence (PPL)

The CAA only grants a PPL when it is satisfied that the applicant is a fit person to hold the licence and is qualified by reason of knowledge, experience, competence, skill, physical fitness and mental fitness. The minimum age for holding a Private Pilot's Licence is 17 years.

Training must be carried out at an Approved Training Organisation (ATO) or Declared Training Organisation (DTO): the use of Registered Facilities for PPL training will cease on 7 April 2019.

In addition to holding a valid medical certificate, a PPL applicant must produce evidence to the CAA that he/she has, within an 18-month period from the date of the first examination, passed:

* nine ground examinations: (1) Air Law, (2) Operational Procedures; (3) Navigation; (4) Meteorology; (5) Aircraft General Knowledge; (6) Principles of Flight; (7) Human Performance and Limitations; (8) Flight Performance and Planning; and (9) Communications. The exams must be passed within 6 sittings (a sitting is 10 consecutive days); once completed the examination credit is valid for a further two year period for the purpose of licence issue.
* a practical examination in Radiotelephony;
* a solo navigational cross-country flight of at least 270 km (150 nm) with two intermediate full stop landings at aerodromes other than the aerodrome of departure; and
* a flight test, (skill test) which will also involve an oral examination: Aircraft (Type)

The EASA Private Pilot's Licence is not valid until it is signed in ink by the holder. It is then valid for life.

NOTE Under the UK ANO, an EASA PPL (A) is also valid with the same privileges for non-EASA aircraft within the same class.

EASA PPL RATINGS A PPL includes one or more ratings specifying the aircraft class or type that the holder may fly (provided that the rating is current) and any additional privileges that he/she has obtained. It is possible to obtain an EASA PPL from any member State and then obtain ratings in another member State, although the ratings must be entered on the licence by the State of licence issue. If the licence holder wishes to transfer the licence to another state for administrative convenience, he/she will have to show *'normal residency'*. This means the place where he/she resides and/or works for more than 185 days each year. The pilot must also transfer his/her medical records. The CAA will not accept applications from anyone whose medical records are not held in the UK.

The Privileges Accorded to a Private Pilot

A holder of a PPL(A) may fly as *pilot-in-command* (PIC) (often stated as *'aircraft commander'*) or as co-pilot of aeroplanes or Touring Motor Gliders (TMGs) engaged in non-commercial operations, provided that:
- his/her licence includes a valid rating for the type or class of aircraft to be flown;
- he/she holds a valid Class 1 or Class 2 Medical certificate.

Notwithstanding the above, a PPL(A) holder with instructor or examiner privileges may receive remuneration for:
- the provision of flight instruction for the LAPL(A) or PPL(A);
- the conduct of skill tests and proficiency checks for these licences; or for
- the ratings and certificates attached to these licences.

COMMERCIAL OPERATIONS AND COST-SHARING Commercial operation means any operation of an aircraft, in return for remuneration or other valuable consideration, which is available to the public or performed under a contract between an operator and a customer, where the customer has no control over the operator. Currently, an EASA PPL(A) holder may not fly for the purpose of 'commercial operations', which includes towing a glider or dropping persons by parachute. However, EASA has recently agreed that PPL holders may receive payment to drop parachutists or tow gliders at clubs or organisations whose goal is training towards a licence or promoting aviation. It has also been agreed that cost-sharing between pilot and passengers on private flights in aircraft certified for up to 6 persons may be permitted, provided that the cost is shared between all of them, including the pilot.

NOTE Since 8 April 2018, a PPL holder requires a Sailplane [glider] Towing Rating in order to tow gliders.

Visual Flight Rules (VFR) *(see also Chapter 7)*

The current rules on VFR flight are those as defined by EASA, which replace and override any national rules in the Air Navigation Order for aircraft that come within the scope of the EASA regulation. There is no longer any requirement for a PPL holder to have the surface in sight at all times, unless he/she is below 3,000 ft. This is sometimes referred to as 'VFR on top', although the term has no official meaning in the UK.

Minimum visibility for VFR flights:
In controlled airspace (Class D and E):
- At and above 10,000 ft (3050 m): flight visibility (i.e. visibility forward from the cockpit) of at least 8 km; distance from cloud of 1,500 m horizontally and 1,000 ft (300 m) vertically.

- Below 10,000 ft: flight visibility of at least 5 km; distance from cloud of 1,500 m horizontally and 1,000 ft (300 m) vertically.
- A Special VFR (SVFR) flight in a control zone shall not be commenced when the visibility is less than 1,500 m.

In uncontrolled airspace (Class G):
- At and above 10,000 ft (3050 m): flight visibility of at least 8 km; distance from cloud of 1,500 m horizontally and 1,000 ft (300 m) vertically.
- Below 10,000 ft: flight visibility of at least 5 km; distance from cloud of 1,500 m horizontally and 1,000 ft (300 m) vertically.

If at 3,000 ft or below:
- Any aircraft: clear of cloud and with the surface in sight in a flight visibility of 5km.
- Helicopters flying at a speed which, having regard to visibility, is reasonable: clear of cloud and with the surface in sight in a flight visibility of 1500m.

NOTE VFR flights are not permitted in Class A controlled airspace. There is no Class B airspace in the UK and Class C only exists at FL195 and above.

The EASA Private Pilot Licence for Helicopters - PPL(H)

Privileges and requirements

The privileges of a PPL(H) holder are to act without remuneration as PIC or co-pilot of helicopters engaged in non-commercial operations, except that if the holder has instructor or examiner privileges, he/she may receive remuneration for:
- the provision of flight instruction for the LAPL(H) or PPL(H);
- the conduct of skill tests and proficiency checks for these licences;
- the ratings and certificates attached to these licences.

Applicants for a PPL(H) must complete a training course at an ATO, consisting of:
- 45 hours of flight instruction on helicopters (5 of which may be in an approved flight simulator), including:
  - (i) 25 hours of dual flight instruction; and
  - (ii) 10 hours of supervised solo flight time, including 5 hours of solo cross-country flight time with one cross-country flight of 185 km (100 NM), with full stop landings at two aerodromes different from the aerodrome of departure.

35 of the 45 hours must be completed on the same type of helicopter as the one used for the skill test. In addition, the

applicant must pass 9 theoretical exams in the same subjects as for the PPL(A).

Applicants for a PPL (H) who hold an LAPL(H) must complete, at an ATO:

- 5 hours of dual flight instruction; and
- 1 supervised solo cross-country flight of at least 185 km (100 NM), with full stop landings at 2 aerodromes different from the aerodrome of departure.

Applicants who hold a PPL for another aircraft category (except balloons) receive credit of 10% of their total flight time as PIC up to a maximum of 6 hours.

NOTE 1 There is no EASA licence for gyrocopters, which are non-EASA aircraft.

NOTE 2 Non-EASA helicopter type ratings cannot be added to an EASA licence, for which a pilot will require a UK national licence. A list of EASA helicopter types is available on the website, www.easa.europa.eu, under the Certification section.

Carriage of Passengers – Recency Requirements – PPL(A) and (H)

In order to carry passengers, the pilot-in-command must have made at least three take-offs, approaches and landings within the preceding 90 days, in an aircraft of the same type or class

If passengers are to be carried at night, at least one of the three take-offs, approaches and landings within the preceding 90 days must have been made at night (unless the pilot holds a current Instrument Rating).

The Flight Radiotelephony Operator's Licence

This is a UK national requirement - to operate radio-equipped UK-registered EASA and non-EASA aircraft, a private pilot must hold a Flight Radiotelephony Operator's Licence (FRTOL), although student pilots have a dispensation. A written and practical classroom test is required to attain the licence; your training organisation will guide you on this. The licence can be a stand-alone licence or can be added to a flight crew licence. An applicant for a PPL must pass the Communications paper before applying for his/her pilot's licence, but the practical test can be taken after the licence has been issued. Refer also to Volume 7 of *The Air Pilot's Manual, Radiotelephony (Communications),* for more details.

EASA Class Ratings and Maintaining a Rating

A PPL includes one or more ratings specifying the class or type of aircraft class that the holder may fly and any additional privileges that he or she has obtained, provided that a valid and appropriate Certificate of Revalidation is held.

If a class or type rating has lapsed, an applicant must take refresher training at an ATO, to be determined by the ATO on a case-by-case basis, taking into account the experience of the applicant, the complexity of the aircraft and the amount of time since the expiry of the rating. For further details, see *Acceptable Means of Compliance and Guidance Material to Part-FCL* at www.easa.europa.eu.

For PPL holders, aircraft are sub-divided into the following class rating groups:
- single-engine piston aeroplane (land)
- multi-engine piston aeroplane (land)
- single-pilot aeroplane (sea) (single or multi-engine).

Single Engine Piston Aeroplanes (Land)

Normally the first class rating to be obtained, this includes virtually all single-engine piston aircraft regardless of weight.

The EASA PPL(A) requires a minimum of 45 hours training, including at least 25 hours dual instruction and 10 hours solo flight. Solo flight time must include 5 hours of cross country flying including one flight of at least 150 nm (270 km) with two intermediate full-stop landings at different airfields away from the departure field. The applicant may fly solo from the age of 16, but the PPL will not be issued until he/she is 17. In general, all training towards the issue of the initial PPL(A) should be carried out on the same category of aircraft. There are some exceptions as set out below in the text.

Holders of a pilot licence for another category of aircraft (except balloons) will be credited with 10% of their total flight time as PIC, up to a maximum of 10 hours, towards a PPL(A). However, this credit cannot be used to replace the 10 hours supervised solo cross country requirement. Training must be conducted at an Approved Training Organisation (ATO) or Declared Training Organisation (DTO)(or registered facility until 7 April 2019).

NOTE Pilots who wish to fly more complicated aircraft with variable-pitch propellers, retractable undercarriages, turbo or supercharged engines or pressurised cabins must undergo differences training with a flight instructor and record it in their logbook. Tailwheel aircraft also require differences training if you learnt on a nosewheel/tricycle undercarriage aircraft.

Similarly, differences training will be required to operate single lever power control (SLPC) aircraft and those with 'glass' cockpits. (See AIC P070/2010.) Pilots who train for licences on these variants of aircraft will also require differences training to operate conventional aeroplanes.

To maintain the SEP (Land) class rating, the holder must: either:

1. within the 3 months preceding the expiry date of the rating, pass a proficiency check in the relevant class of aircraft with an examiner; or

2. within 12 months preceding the expiry date of the rating, complete 12 hours of flight time in the relevant class of aircraft, including;

   - 6 hours as PIC;
   - 12 take offs and 12 landings; and
   - a training flight of at least 1 hour with a FI or CRI-this flight may be completed in up to 3 separate flights with the same FI or CRI.

Alternatively, applicants may be exempt from the training flight if they have passed in an aeroplane, a skill test or proficiency check for any class, type, instrument or mountain rating or an assessment of competence for any flight instructor, class rating instructor or instrument rating instruction certificate included in the applicant's aeroplane pilot licence.

3. Following completion of these requirements, the rating should be endorsed on the applicant's licence by an examiner or suitable qualified instructor.

Multi-Engine Piston (Land)

This class rating is normally added to an existing single-engine class rating and includes virtually all single-pilot multi-engine piston aircraft of this class, irrespective of the aircraft's weight.

The applicant must have at least 70 hours 'pilot-in-command' experience (aeroplanes), before the issue of the rating. The multi-engine course, which must be conducted at an Approved Training Organisation (ATO), comprises a minimum of 2½ hours of two-engine flight, 3½ hours asymmetric flight training and 7 hours of theoretical knowledge of multi-engine operation. In addition, a multiple-choice written examination relating to the specific aircraft type and general multi-engine operations must be passed. The applicant must pass a skill test within 6 months of starting the training course.

To maintain this rating, applicants must complete:

- a proficiency check with a flight examiner within the 3 months preceding the expiry date of the rating; and
- at least ten route sectors during the preceding 12 months (a route sector is defined as a flight comprising take-off, departure, cruise of at least 15 minutes, arrival, approach and landing); or
- one route sector with a flight examiner, which may be flown during the proficiency check.

Should the rating expire before meeting the revalidation requirements, then the applicant must take refresher training as required at an ATO and pass a proficiency check with an examiner.

Single-Pilot Aeroplane (Sea) – Single or Multi-Engine

The training course for an SEP (Sea) Rating includes theoretical knowledge, 8 hours of dual flight instruction, if the applicant holds the land version of the relevant rating, or 10 hours if he/she does not hold such a rating. There is also a theoretical knowledge test (verbal for the single engine rating, or a written, multiple-choice exam for the multi-engine) and a skill test.

Type Ratings

A type rating requirement is established for aeroplanes of significant complexity of handling characteristics that require additional flying (or simulator) training. Type ratings are established for all types of single-pilot, single-engine or multi-engine turbo propeller (or jet) aeroplanes or for any aeroplane requiring two or more pilots. A list of specific EASA type ratings is available at **www.easa.europa.eu** under Certification. Type ratings are valid for 12 months.

Night Rating (Aeroplanes, TMGs and Helicopters)

The Night Rating entitles the holder to exercise the privileges of his or her licence in VFR conditions at night.

Instrument Meteorological Conditions (IMC) Rating (Aeroplanes)

The IMC Rating is a UK national rating that entitles holders to act as pilot-in-command of an aeroplane without being subject to all of the flight visibility restrictions stated earlier.

EASA has agreed with the CAA that UK-issued JAA and national licences that contained an IMC rating issued prior to 8 April 2014, which are converted to EASA licences, will retain the privileges of the IMC indefinitely. This will appear on a Part-FCL licence as IR (Restricted) and will only be valid in UK airspace. The European Commission has also agreed that the CAA may continue to issue the IMC rating until April 2019.

The holder of a PPL(A) with an IMC Rating may:
- accept an IFR clearance in Class D or E airspace;
- fly when the aeroplane is taking off or landing at any place if the flight visibility below cloud is at least 1,500 m.

He/she may not act as PIC in IMC:
- outside UK territorial airspace, unless written permission is obtained from another State;

- in controlled airspace in circumstances requiring compliance with the Instrument Flight Rules (except in Class D and E as above)

Instrument Rating (Aeroplanes)
The privileges of a holder of an IR(A) are to fly aeroplanes under the Instrument Flight Rules with a minimum decision height of 200 feet (60 m).

Instrument Rating (Helicopters)
This allows the holder to fly helicopters under the Instrument Flight Rules with a minimum decision height of 200 feet (60 m).

Other EASA Ratings
EASA has also introduced an Aerobatic Rating, Sailplane Towing and Banner Towing Ratings and a Mountain Rating. See CAP 804 for more details.

EASA Flight Instructor Certificate (FI)
The privileges of the EASA Flight Instructor Certificate are to carry out instruction for EASA licences and ratings, as defined in the specific instructor certificate privileges.

FI - Restricted Privileges
An FI with restricted privileges is limited to conducting flight instruction under the supervision of an FI and shall not have the privilege to authorise student pilots to conduct first solo flights and first solo cross-country flights.

The EASA Private Pilot Licence for Airships - PPL (As)

Privileges and Requirements
The privileges mirror those for the PPL(A). Training must be completed at an ATO and consists of 35 hours of instruction, of which 5 may be in a Flight Simulation Training Device (FSTD), and must include:
(a) 25 hours of dual instruction, including:
  – 3 hours of cross-country flight training, including 1 flight of at least 35nm;
  – 2 hours instrument instruction;
(b) 8 take-offs and landings; and
(c) 8 hours of supervised solo flight.
Applicants must also pass 9 theoretical knowledge exams as for the PPL(A) above.

The EASA Sailplane Pilot Licence - SPL

This licence entitles the holder to fly Sailplanes (i.e. gliders) and Powered Sailplanes (i.e. Self-Launching Motor Gliders or SLMGs). It is not valid for Touring Motor Gliders unless a TMG rating is included.

Privileges and Requirements

The minimum age for an SPL is 16. The holder may act as PIC of gliders and SLMGs, but must have completed 10 hours' flight time or 30 launches following licence issue in order to carry passengers. To undertake commercial operations, a licence holder must be at least 18, with 75 hours' flight time or 200 launches after licence issue, and must pass a proficiency check with an examiner. 15 hours' flight training is required, which must be completed at an ATO and include:

- 10 hours of dual flight instruction;
- 2 hours of supervised solo flight;
- 45 launches and landings; and
- 1 cross-country flight of at least 50nm (solo) or 55nm (dual).

Applicants must pass a skill test, and the privileges of the licence are limited to the launch method included in the test. They must also pass exams in the 9 subjects as for the PPL(A) above. Holders must also comply with recency requirements, i.e. within the last 24 months have completed:

- 5 hours' flight time as PIC, including 15 launches; and
- 2 training flights with an instructor.

Alternatively, they may pass a proficiency check with an examiner, or perform the required hours and launches either with an instructor or solo under supervision.

NOTE No licence is required for a private flight in a non-EASA glider under the ANO. Holders of an EASA SPL with commercial privileges may also fly commercially in non-EASA gliders.

The EASA Balloon Pilot Licence - BPL

Privileges and Requirements

The minimum age for a BPL is 16. The holder may act as PIC on balloons and hot-air airships, in the class or group of balloons (see note below) in which the skill test was taken. For commercial operations, the minimum age is 18, and the holder must have completed 50 hours' flight time and 50 take-offs and landings as PIC and pass a proficiency check with an examiner. A BPL holder with instructor or examiner privileges may receive remuneration for instruction and conducting skill tests and proficiency checks.

16 hours' flight training at an ATO is required, to include:

- 12 hours of dual flight instruction;
- 10 inflations; and
- 1 supervised solo flight of at least 30 minutes.

A skill test and exam passes in 9 subjects (as for the PPL(A) above) are also required. The privileges of the licence are limited to non-tethered flights, until the holder has completed at least 3 tethered instruction flights.

Holders must also comply with recency requirements, i.e. within the last 24 months have completed:

- 6 hours' flight time as PIC, including 10 take-offs and landings; and
- 1 training flight with an instructor in a balloon of the appropriate class.

A further 3 hours and 3 take-offs and landings within 24 months is required for each additional class of balloon. A proficiency check with an examiner can be substituted for the experience requirements.

In order to carry passengers, the pilot must have completed, within the preceding 180 days:

- 3 flights as pilot flying, including 1 in a balloon of the relevant class or group; or
- 1 flight in a balloon of the relevant class or group with a suitably qualified instructor.

NOTE As well as classes, balloons are also divided into 4 groups, depending on their size, from Group A (with an envelope capacity of up to 3400 m³) to Group D (> 10,500 m³). A licence holder must gain additional experience to extend his/her privileges to another class or group.

The EASA Light Aircraft Pilot Licence - LAPL

This is a new licence for aeroplanes, helicopters, sailplanes and balloons. It allows the holder to fly for leisure (no remuneration is permitted), within Europe only. In all cases, applicants must have a valid medical certificate (Part-MED Class 1, 2 or LAPL). The minimum age is 17 for aeroplanes and helicopters, or 16 for sailplanes and balloons. Training must be completed at an ATO and the applicant must pass 9 theory exams and a skill test.

Holders of an LAPL(A) (aeroplanes) or LAPL(H) (helicopters) may only fly aircraft with a maximum certified take-off weight (MTOW) of less than 2000 kg, and may carry no more than 3 passengers.

The Light Aircraft Pilot Licence for Aeroplanes - LAPL(A)

This enables the holder to act as PIC on single-engine piston land aeroplanes or TMGs. Passengers can only be carried after a further 10 hours' flight experience following licence issue. Training required is:

- 15 hours of dual instruction; and
- 6 hours of supervised solo flight, including 3 hours of cross-country flight training and 1 flight of at least 80nm with a landing at another aerodrome.

Recency requirements are 12 hours PIC in the preceding 24 months, including 12 take-offs and landings and an hour of dual training with an instructor, or alternatively a proficiency check. To fly an aircraft of a different class or variant a further 3 hours' training is required, including 10 dual and 10 solo take-offs and landings, and a skill test.

The Light Aircraft Pilot Licence for Helicopters - LAPL(H)

The training required is 40 hours of flight instruction, of which 35 must be on the type of helicopter to be used in the skill test, and must include:

- 20 hours dual, and
- 10 hours solo, including 5 hours of solo cross-country flight with 1 flight of at least 80nm landing at another aerodrome.

To remain current, the holder must have flown for 6 hours as PIC, including 6 take-offs and landings and an hour of dual training with an instructor, in the preceding 12 months. Alternatively he/she can take a proficiency check with an examiner. The pilot is limited to the type that he/she flew in the skill test unless he/she completes a further 5 hours' training on type, including 15 dual and 15 solo take-offs and landings, and a skill test.

The Light Aircraft Pilot Licence for Sailplanes [Gliders] - LAPL(S)

The holder may act as PIC on sailplanes, and can carry passengers after a further 10 hours' flight time or 30 launches after licence issue. Training required is 15 hours of flight instruction, including:

- 10 hours of dual instruction;
- 2 hours supervised solo flight;

- 45 launches and landings; and
- 1 cross-country flight of at least 50nm (solo) or 55 nm (dual).

The holder must undergo further training in order to use a launch method other than that used in the skill test.
Currency is maintained by:
- 5 hours flight in the preceding 24 months, including:
  - i) 15 launches, and
  - ii) 2 flights with an instructor
In the case of TMGs, the requirement is:
- 12 hours PIC in the preceding 24 months, including:
  - i) 12 take-offs and landings, and
  - ii) 1 hour's dual training flight with an instructor

Alternatively, the pilot can complete a proficiency check in either case.

The Light Aircraft Pilot Licence for Balloons - LAPL(B)

The holder may act as PIC on hot-air balloons or airships with a maximum envelope capacity of 3400 m³, or gas balloons with a maximum envelope capacity of 1200 m³, carrying no more than 3 passengers.
Training required is 16 hours of flight instruction, including:
- 12 hours of dual instruction;
- 10 inflations and 20 take-offs and landings; and
- 1 supervised solo flight of at least 30 minutes.

The holder is restricted to non-tethered flights until he/she has completed 3 tethered instruction flights.
The recency requirement is, within the last 24 months:
- 6 hours PIC, and
- 1 hour's dual training flight with an instructor.

UK PPL VALIDITY PERIOD
The old style pre 2001 UK PPL has no expiry date, although, for the holder to exercise its privileges, it must be revalidated periodically in the same way as an EASA PPL with a Certificate of Revalidation, which is valid for 24 months in the case of aeroplanes (SEP/TMG).
     A UK PPL could be used to fly EASA aircraft that come within the scope of the LAPL (i.e. weighing less than 2,000 kg and with not more than 4 occupants) until June 2018. Now the EU rules have been fully implemented, so anyone wanting to fly

an EASA aircraft must convert his or her licence to a EASA Part-FCL licence.

Reinstatement of the UK CAA PPL

When JAR-FCL was implemented in the UK, the CAA stopped issuing new UK licences that were equivalent to JAR licences, and therefore training for the UK CAA PPL ceased. However, a problem now arises when an EASA licence-holder qualifies for a type rating on a non-EASA aircraft. Consequently the ANO has been amended so that UK equivalents to EASA PPLs (and ATPLs and CPLs) can again be issued where necessary to enable the pilot to exercise the privileges of such a rating using his/her UK licence.

NOTE 1 This problem does not occur with aeroplane class ratings, as the CAA has further changed the ANO so that an EASA licence with the appropriate class rating is valid for non-EASA aircraft within that class: for example, the holder of an EASA PPL(A) with an SEP rating does not need a national licence in order to fly a Tiger Moth.

NOTE 2 The holder of an existing UK licence who only ever wants to fly non-EASA aircraft may continue to do so, and in this respect is unaffected by the EASA rules (as long as the aircraft is not being flown for the purpose of commercial transport).

Converting an Existing UK CAA PPL to EASA

UK-issued licences that were fully compliant with JAR-FCL automatically became EASA licences. For an existing UK CAA PPL(A) that does not fully comply, and provided that it was issued before 17 September 2012, the criteria to convert it to an EASA PPL(A) are as follows:

• the holder must have at least 70 hours' flying experience on aeroplanes; and
• he/she shall demonstrate the use of radio navigation aids to the satisfaction of a Chief Flying Instructor or Examiner.

The criteria for this and other non-compliant licences to be converted to EASA licences are detailed in Annex II to the Aircrew Regulation.

Obtaining a New UK CAA PPL

The new UK PPL will be a non-expiring lifetime licence. The requirement to obtaining one is either:

• to hold the equivalent EASA licence in accordance with Part-FCL and comply with the requirements of the rating; or
• to comply with the requirements of Part-FCL for the category of licence and comply with the requirements of the national rating. (Note, however, that if such a UK licence is issued after

the implementation date for the Aircrew Regulation, it will not be possible to convert it to an EASA licence at a later date.)

The UK PPL for Aeroplane, Helicopters, Balloons and Airships

The privileges of these UK licences are defined in Part A of Schedule 8 to the ANO 2016.

Licence holders may fly UK-registered, non-EASA aircraft of the relevant class or type. They must have a valid Part-MED medical certificate or declaration, as appropriate.

NOTE Unlike the holder of an EASA PPL(A), the holder of a UK PPL(A) may NOT fly out of sight of the surface, unless he/she holds an IMC or IR.

UK PPL(G) – Gyroplanes.

There are no ICAO standards for gyroplanes and therefore this licence is not recognised by ICAO. See ANO Schedule 7. The licence holder must not fly out of sight of ground or water, or by sole reference to instruments. Applicants must have a valid EASA Part-MED Class 1, 2 or LAPL medical certificate or an NPPL medical declaration.

The UK National Private Pilot's Licence (NPPL) with an SSEA/SLMG Rating

The UK NPPL for Simple Single Engine Aeroplanes (SSEA), microlights and Self-Launching Motor Gliders (SLMG) will continue in existence with a few changes to take EASA rules into account. The CAA is introducing an NPPL(H) for helicopters, which may be issued for holders of the LAPL(H) or those who have fulfilled the requirements, and a Part-MED certificate will be required.

The NPPL was introduced in 2002 with support from the CAA and various industry bodies. The NPPL is administered by the National Pilots Licensing Group Limited with delegated authority from the CAA.

The NPPL(A) with SSEA/SLMG Rating

The NPPL is a simpler form of licence than the EASA PPL and the minimum requirements for its issue are as follows:

- 22 hours of dual training, including 1 hour of instrument appreciation.
- 10 hours of solo flight, including one solo cross-country flight in which two full-stop landings at two aerodromes other than the aerodrome of departure shall be made.

The theoretical knowledge requirements for the NPPL are to pass the 9 Part-FCL exams for the PPL(A).

A Navigation Skill Test (NST) and a General Skill Test (GST), each of a minimum of one hour duration, shall be passed; the NST prior to the solo qualifying cross-country flight. Minimum age for first solo is 16, for licence issue is 17.

The minimum medical requirement is an NPPL medical declaration, or a Part-MED Class 1, 2 or LAPL medical.

Unless differences training has been completed and signed off in the pilot's logbook, the holder of an NPPL may not:
• pilot an aeroplane with more than 4 persons on board;
• pilot an aircraft fitted with features such as retractable undercarriage or variable-pitch propeller.

Note also the following limitations:
• The licence is limited to day VFR conditions.
• The privileges of the NPPL are restricted to UK airspace.
• An NPPL holder may not fly an aircraft with a maximum continuous cruising speed in excess of 140 kt IAS.
• The maximum take off weight must not exceed 2,000 kgs.
The NPPL (SSEA) is issued with a lifetime validity.
The flying training must be conducted at an organisation acceptable to the CAA.

Full details of the NPPL syllabi of flying training, flight tests and theoretical knowledge requirements can be found on the NPPL website, **www.nationalprivatepilotslicence.co.uk** or **www.aopa.co.uk**.

The NPPL Licence is valid for life, and the associated ratings are valid for 24 months. The revalidation requirements are to complete either a General Skill Test or 12 hours flight time, including 8 hours as PIC, 12 take-offs and landings and 1 hour with an instructor. Six of those hours must be completed in the 12 months preceding the expiry date.

The UK NPPL(A) with a Microlight Rating

Microlights are classified as follows:
• single-seat
• two-seat
• three-axis
• weight-shift

Microlight aircraft are designed to carry not more than two people and have a maximum authorised total weight not exceeding:
• 300 kg for a single-seat landplane;
• 450 kg for a two-seat landplane;
• 330 kg for a single-seat amphibian or floatplane.
• 495 kg for a two-seat amphibian or floatplane;
Microlights are limited to a wing loading not exceeding 25 kg per square metre and/or a stalling speed (V_{S0}) of 35 kt calibrated airspeed.

A minimum of 25 hours of instruction including 10 hours of solo flight is required before licence issue. However, a restricted licence is available after 15 hours of training of which 7 hours must be solo. The restricted licence limits the holder to flight within an 8 mile radius of the departure airfield.

Microlight aircraft are operated on a Permit to Fly and no aerial work is permitted other than instruction.

The NPPL (Microlight) is issued with a lifetime validity. Applicants may obtain either an 'unrestricted' licence or a 'restricted' licence (which includes operational limitations).

Applicants for an NPPL (Microlight) are currently required to pass theoretical knowledge examinations in the following subjects:

1. Aviation Law, Flight Rules and Procedures

2. Human Performance and Limitations

3. Navigation

4. Meteorology

5. Aircraft (General)

The minimum medical requirement is an NPPL medical declaration, or a Part-MED Class 1, 2 or LAPL medical.

Full details of the NPPL (Microlight) syllabi of flying training, flight tests and theoretical knowledge requirements can be found on the website of the British Microlight Aircraft Association, **www.bmaa.org.**

The validity of microlight rating attached to an NPPL is maintained in the same way as the SSEA/SLMG.

Medical Requirements: UK Licences

The minimum medical requirements for UK (i.e. non-EASA) licences are as follows:

MINIMUM MEDICAL REQUIREMENTS FOR UK LICENCES	
Licence	**Medical Certificate Required**
UK NPPL(A) (SSEA, SLMG or Microlight)	UK Medical Declaration
UK NPPL(H)	EASA Part-MED Certificate (contact CAA for further details)
UK PPL(A)	EASA Part-MED Class 2
UK PPL(H)	EASA Part-MED Class 2
UK PPL(G)	UK Medical Declaration
UK PPL(BA)	UK Medical Declaration

NOTE 1 An EASA Part-MED LAPL, Class 1 or Class 2 Medical Certificate is valid in place of the UK Medical Declaration.

NOTE 2 Existing JAR-FCL 3 Medical Certificates, and those issued in accordance with JAR-FCL 3, will be deemed to be EASA Part-MED Certificates.

Personal Flying Logbooks

A personal flying logbook in a suitable format (this may include computerised versions in certain circumstances) must be kept by qualified pilots and those flying to obtain or renew a licence. The following particulars shall be recorded:

- the name and address of the licence holder;
- the details of the licence;
- the details of each flight made as a member of a flight crew or for the purpose of obtaining or renewing a licence, including:
  - the date and places at which the holder embarked and disembarked and the time spent during the flight in either of the capacities mentioned (flight time being from when the aircraft first moves under its own power until the moment it comes to rest after landing);
  - the type and registration marks of the aircraft;
  - the capacity in which the holder acted in flight (with a flight instructor on board, the time is logged as *dual;* when solo or pilot-in-command, the time is logged as *in command*);
  - details of any special conditions including night flying, instrument flying and in particular the training exercises specified in the PPL qualifying requirements;
  - particulars of any test or examination undertaken whilst in flight;
  - particulars of flight simulator tests.
    - > A helicopter is deemed to be in flight from the moment it first moves under its own power for the purpose of taking off until the rotors are next stopped.
    - > Particulars of any test or examination undertaken whilst in a flight simulator shall be recorded in the logbook, including:
  - the date;
  - the type of simulator;
  - the capacity in which the holder acted; and
  - the nature of the test or examination.

It is worth noting that there is an offence in the ANO of intentionally damaging, altering or mutilating entries in a logbook or licence. There is evidence of the CAA successfully prosecuting pilots for such offences (which amount to forgery). The penalty may be a fine or even imprisonment.

Your logbook is a valuable legal document and is your only proof of the true record of your flying so you should take care of it. It is worth photocopying the pages from time to time in case you do lose it, since in such a case the CAA will require you to make a witness statement certifying its loss and to attempt to reconstruct the hours claimed.

NOTE The *commander* of an aircraft is required to produce his or her logbook within a reasonable time after being requested to do so by an authorised person, for up to 2 years from the date of the last entry.

Now complete: **Practice Questions - Pilots' Licences**

1. A pilot suffers a significant injury and is unfit to function as flight crew. What action should the pilot take?

(a) *The medical remains current and the pilot can resume flying when feeling better.*
(b) *The pilot must immediately seek advice from their GP.*
(c) *The medical is deemed suspended; the pilot must not act as a crew member for 20 days.*
(d) *The pilot must immediately seek advice from their AME.*

2. A Part-FCL PPL holder must have a valid Medical Certificate in order to exercise the privileges of the licence. The medical must be either:

(a) *Class 1 or 2.*
(b) *Class 2 or 3.*
(c) *Class 2.*
(d) *An HGV medical certificate or a certificate issued by a GP.*

3. Under EASA Part-FCL, a single pilot single-engine class rating is valid for:

(a) *13 months.*
(b) *2 years.*
(c) *3 years.*
(d) *1 year.*

4. Before carrying passengers a PPL(A) and (H) holder shall have made 3 take-offs and 3 landings in the same class or type of aircraft within:

(a) *The preceding 45 days.*
(b) *The preceding 90 days.*
(c) *The preceding calendar month.*
(d) *The preceding 60 days.*

5. Which of the following is a method to re-validate a single engine piston class rating?

(a) *Pass a proficiency check flight with a flight examiner within 12 months preceding the expiry date of the rating.*
(b) *Complete 12 hours of flight time including 6 take-offs and landings, and complete a 2 hour training flight with an instructor within the 6 months preceding the expiry of the rating.*
(c) *Complete a 2 hour training flight with a flying instructor in 6 months preceding the expiry of the rating.*
(d) *Complete 12 hours of flight time including 6 hours PIC and 12 take-offs and landings, and complete a 1 hour training flight with an instructor within the 12 months preceding the expiry of the rating.*

6. A Part-MED Class 2 medical is valid for:

(a) *60 months until the licence holder reaches the age of 50.*
(b) *24 months after the licence holder reaches the age of 50.*
(c) *60 months until the licence holder reaches the age of 40.*
(d) *24 months until the licence holder reaches the age of 40.*

7. A pilot should not exercise the privileges of their licence for at least…. (i)…. following a local anaesthetic and at least…. (ii)…. Following a general anaesthetic. Which answer correctly fills the blanks?

(a) *i) 24 hours ii) 12 hours.*
(b) *i) 12 days ii) 24 days.*
(c) *i) 12 hours ii) 48 hours.*
(d) *i) 24 days ii) 12 days.*

8. EASA permits a PPL holder and their passengers to share the cost of a flight, but under what conditions?

(a) *The cost of a private flight may be shared if the aircraft carries a maximum of 4 people and the pilot may be excluded.*

(b) *The cost of a private flight may be shared if the aircraft carries a maximum of 6 people and the pilot may be excluded.*

(c) *The cost of a private flight may be shared if the aircraft carries a maximum of 6 people and the pilot must pay a share.*

(d) *The cost of a private flight may be shared if the aircraft carries a maximum of 4 people and the pilot must pay a share.*

9. Which of the following aircraft could a LAPL holder fly?

(a) *MTOW 1,900 kg and 4 seats.*
(b) *MTOW 2,500 kg and 6 seats.*
(c) *MTOW 2,500 kg and 4 seats.*
(d) *MTOW 1,900 kg and 6 seats.*

Operation of Aircraft

NOTE This section does not contain all of the subject matter required for the examination on Operational Procedures (see Volume 6, Human Performance and Limitations and Operational Procedures).

Ops Procedures (UK ANO)

The ICAO standards and recommended practices for the international operation of general aviation aircraft contained in Annex 6 differ in some parts from the ANO's requirements. Therefore we set out those parts of the ANO regarding operation of aircraft first, followed by the relevant procedures relating to international flights which might be made by PPL holders (page 178).

NOTE The EASA Air Operations Regulation is set out as Commission Regulation (EU) No.965/2012 and the references below are to parts of the Guidance Material to Annex VII (Part-NCO). By virtue of article 270 of the Air Navigation Order, the CAA is designated as the competent authority for the purpose of the EASA Air Operations Regulation, which came into force on 28 October 2014.

Pre-Flight Actions

Pre-Flight Actions of the Pilot-in-Command (Part NCO. GEN.105 and ANO Articles 69 and 75)

The pilot-in-command must be satisfied before each flight:
- that the flight can be made safely, taking into account the latest information available as to route and aerodromes to be used, weather reports and forecasts available, and options open if the flight cannot be completed as planned;

- that equipment (including radio) required by regulation is carried and working and that appropriate maps and charts and navigational equipment are carried;

- that the aircraft is fit for the flight and has a valid Airworthiness Review Certificate or Certificate of Maintenance Review where required;

- that any load is safe in terms of weight, distribution and security;

- that enough fuel, oil, coolant and ballast (if appropriate) is carried, including a margin for safety;

- that, with regard to its performance, the aircraft is capable of safely taking off, reaching and maintaining a safe height and making a safe landing at the intended destination. (In very approximate terms, a 10% increase in weight will increase the **take-off distance required** by 20%; a tailwind component of 10% of the take-off speed – usually about 5 knots – will increase take-off distance required by 20%; a 10°C rise in temperature or 1,000 ft rise in elevation will increase take-off distance required by about 10%. Precise consideration, of course, requires reference to the take-off and landing charts or tables for your particular aeroplane);

- that all required pre-flight checks have been carried out.

Passenger Briefing (ANO Article 73)

Before taking off on any flight, the pilot-in-command must brief the passengers on the position and method of use of:
- emergency exits;
- safety belts or safety harnesses; and
- oxygen equipment and life jackets (when they are required to be carried).

In Flight

Authority of the Commander of Aircraft (ANO Article 244)

Everyone on board must obey all lawful commands which the aircraft commander gives for the purpose of the safety of the aircraft and of people or property carried, or for the safety, efficiency or regularity of air navigation.

Crew Composition (ANO Article 66)

An aircraft must not fly unless the crew composition meets the legal requirements of the country of registration.

Pilots to Remain at Controls (ANO Article 70)

The commander of a flying machine or glider is responsible for ensuring that:
- one pilot is at the controls at all times in flight;
- both pilots are at the controls during take-off and landing if the aircraft is required to carry two pilots under the Order;
- each pilot at the controls wears a safety belt or a safety harness.

NOTE A harness must be worn during take-off and landing when one is required to be provided.

Method of Carriage of Persons

No one must be in or on any part of an aircraft in flight not designed for the accommodation of people, nor be in or on any object (other than a glider or flying machine) towed or attached to an aircraft in flight, except for temporary access to any part of an aircraft:
- for the purpose of taking action necessary for the safety of the aircraft or of any person, animal or goods on board;
- in which cargo or stores are carried and which is designed to enable a person to have access during flight.

Smoking in Aircraft (ANO Article 243)

Notices indicating when smoking is prohibited in any part of an aircraft must be exhibited so as to be visible from each passenger seat and obeyed.

It is good airmanship to observe *no smoking* during take-off, landing and low flying, although smoking is not specifically prohibited at any time except when the 'no smoking' sign is displayed. The pilot has the authority to ban smoking at all times, bearing in mind that cigarette smoke in the cockpit may impair performance and cause distress to certain people.

Drunkenness in Aircraft (ANO Article 242)

A person shall not enter an aircraft when drunk, or be drunk on any aircraft. A person must not, when acting as a crew member or being carried for the purpose of so acting, be under the influence of drink or a drug to such an extent as to impair his/her capacity so to act. Although no exact times are specified in the ANO, it is reasonable for a pilot not to fly until at least 8 hours after any alcohol has been imbibed and, if excessive amounts have been consumed, for this time to be considerably extended.

NOTE Alcohol has been a contributing factor to a number of aircraft accidents. It is well established that even small amounts of alcohol in the blood produce a significant and measurable deterioration in the performance of skilled tasks. EU-OPS specifies a maximum blood alcohol limit of 20 milligrams per 100 millilitres of blood. This is a quarter of the maximum UK legal driving limit.

Acting in a Disruptive Manner (ANO Article 245)

Following publicity in the media about 'air rage', an offence was introduced in ANO 2000: "A person shall not use threatening or abusive or insulting language towards a member of the crew, nor shall they behave in a threatening, abusive, insulting or disorderly manner towards a crew member, nor interfere intentionally with the performance of the duties of the crew."

Endangering the Safety of Aircraft, Persons or Property (ANO Articles 240 and 241)

A person must not, recklessly or negligently, either act in a manner likely to endanger an aircraft or anyone in it, or cause or permit an aircraft to endanger anyone or any property; e.g. a person deliberately damaging an aeroplane or a pilot flying excessively low, carrying inadequate fuel, etc., would be in contravention of this Article.

Operation of Radio in Aircraft (ANO Article 79)

Anyone operating an aircraft's radio equipment must hold an appropriate radiotelephony (R/T) licence (see Chapter 10). The radio equipment itself must be licensed and operated only in accordance with the conditions of that licence.

Flight Recording Systems (ANO Article 231 and Schedule 5)

Although this article will not usually apply to a private pilot, aeroplanes over 5,700 kg and helicopters over 2,700 kg maximum take-off weight authorised are required, in certain circumstances, to carry and operate flight recording systems, and to preserve the records from them for a specified time.

Towing Gliders (ANO Article 87)

An aircraft in flight may not tow a glider unless its Certificate of Airworthiness includes an express provision that it may. The Article also specifies safety requirements with regard to signals, take-off techniques, and length and condition of tow-ropes. Part SPO gives the EASA requirements for these types of activity.

Towing, Picking Up and Raising of Persons and Articles (ANO Article 88)

An aircraft in flight may not tow, pick up or raise anything unless expressly permitted by its Certificate of Airworthiness. The Article also contains specific requirements concerning the several types of activity which fall under its heading, e.g. banner-towing and loads slung from helicopters. Part SPO gives the EASA requirements for these types of activity.

Dropping of Articles and Animals (ANO Article 89)

Articles and animals whether or not attached to a parachute must not be dropped, projected or lowered so as to endanger people or property and should not be dropped, projected or lowered in other circumstances without **written CAA approval**, except for certain articles in certain situations, e.g. dropping a life-raft to save lives, or jettisoning of items to lighten the load in an emergency.

Pilots involved in crop-spraying operations are directed to Article 91 and the requirement to obtain an *Aerial Application Certificate*. Also, if the Certificate of Airworthiness for a helicopter expressly allows it, then the lowering of any person, animal or article to the surface is permitted.

Dropping of Persons (ANO Article 90) – Parachuting

Except for escaping in an emergency, no one must drop to the surface or jump from an aircraft in flight without the **written permission of the CAA** and then only in such a manner as not to endanger people or property. In the case of parachuting, the Certificate of Airworthiness of the aircraft must include a provision that it may be so used and the aircraft must be operated in accordance with the Parachuting Manual which the holder of a *CAA Permission to Drop* has to maintain.

Carriage of Weapons and Munitions of War (ANO Article 98)

No weapon may be carried on board an aircraft unless:
• the consent of the operator is obtained;
• the weapon is unloaded in the case of a firearm; and
• the weapon is carried in a part of the aircraft not accessible to passengers.

Munitions of war (including weapons, ammunition, explosives or noxious substances) shall not be carried without the written permission of the CAA and then only in accordance with any conditions relating thereto.

Carriage of Dangerous Goods (ANO Article 97 and The Air Navigation (Dangerous Goods) Regulations 2002)(Part NCO. GEN.140)

The Secretary of State can classify certain articles and substances as **dangerous goods** (see page 206 for definition). As a pilot, you should be aware that goods which may be fairly innocuous at ground level and/or in the open air, may be very dangerous in flight where atmospheric pressure is reduced and persons are restricted to the confined space of the aircraft cabin.

Many dangerous goods are not permitted in aircraft and those permitted to be carried by air are subject to special conditions of handling, loading, packing, labelling and documentation. Classification lists and conditions are published in the form of regulations made from time to time by the Secretary of State.

As a common-sense practice, private pilots should make a habit of checking the items carried by passengers in their aircraft for obviously dangerous items, such as certain types of matches and lighters, any compressed gases, corrosives or flammable substances. Examples include aerosol hairsprays, batteries, camping gas cylinders and fire lighters, all of which might be carried on that weekend camping trip! As a general rule, *if in doubt, leave it out!*

In addition, the use of a mobile telephone on board an aircraft can interfere seriously with its navigational equipment. Even in stand-by mode, mobile phones emit signals periodically. Not only is there an adverse effect on safety, but the use of mobile telephones in an aircraft is a breach of the telephone user's licence. Therefore the commander of an aircraft should ensure that all mobile telephones are switched off prior to engine start.

Part NCO.GEN.125 deals with the carriage of Portable Electronic Devices and their operation on board an aircraft.

Rules of the Air (ANO Article 249)

This Article is the legal basis for the specific UK *Rules of the Air and Air Traffic Control Regulations, and variations from SERA (see Chapter 2).* Article 114 also lists when the Rules of the Air may be departed from, and to what extent.

Balloons, Kites, Airships, Gliders and Parascending Parachutes (ANO Articles 92 and 93)

There are specific limitations for the flying of captive balloons and kites with regard to the method of mooring, location and height. A captive balloon or kite shall not be flown:

- at a height of more than 60 metres agl (above ground level);
- within 60 metres of any vessel, vehicle or structure;
- within 5 km of an aerodrome.

A balloon, either captive or free, exceeding 2 metres in any linear dimension (including any basket, etc.) must not be flown in controlled airspace notified for the purposes of this restriction.

An airship shall not be moored.

A glider or parascending parachute shall not be launched by winch and cable, or by ground tow, to a height of more than 60 metres above ground level.

NOTE Each of these limitations may be varied by request and with written permission of the CAA, subject to conditions which will accompany the permission.

Documentation and Records

Documents to be Carried (ANO Article 229 and Schedule 10)(Part NCO. GEN.135)

On a non-commercial flight, the documents to be carried are:
- the aircraft's radio licence;
- the Certificate of Airworthiness (CofA);
- flightcrew licence (s);
- a copy of the loadsheet;
- one copy of the Airworthiness Review Certificate in force;
- the Technical Log (if any and if required);
- the Certificate of Registration (if the flight is international, i.e. beyond the bounds of the UK, Channel Islands and Isle of Man);
- a copy of the notified procedures to be followed if the aircraft is intercepted, and the visual signals for use in such circumstances (this applies to international flights only); and
- although not always a requirement, it is good practice to carry the insurance documents.

NOTE 1 The requirement to carry full documentation a non-commercial flight is **waived** when it is intended to take off and land at the **same aerodrome** and remain **within UK airspace**. Also, with the CAA's approval, a Flight Manual need not be carried if an Operations Manual, which contains the specified information, is carried.

NOTE 2 A **private** flight need only carry the first five documents listed above if international air navigation is involved, but for flights totally within the confines of the UK, Channel Islands and the Isle of Man no documents need be carried.

NOTE 3 The requirement to carry insurance documents is mandatory in Spain, and a translation of the insurance certificate must be available in Spanish.

Production of Documents (ANO Article 235)

The commander of an aircraft shall, within a reasonable time after being requested to do so by an authorised person (a constable, or anyone authorised by the Secretary of State or the CAA in a manner appropriate to the case), produce:

- the Certificates of Registration and Airworthiness in respect of the aircraft;
- the licence (s) of its flight crew and the personal flying logbooks (for up to two years after the date of the last entry in any book); and
- such other documents that the aircraft should carry when in flight.

Offences in Relation to Documents & Records (ANO Article 256)

It is an offence to:

- use a forged, altered, revoked or suspended document issued under the Order, or to use one to which you are not entitled;
- lend a document issued under the Order, or otherwise allow it to be used by anyone else, with intent to deceive;
- forge or render illegible any logbook or record required by the Order, or to make a false entry or material omission, or to destroy it during the period for which it is required to be preserved (all entries in such documents must be made in ink or indelible pencil).

NOTE The CAA can revoke or vary any licence or document that it has issued.

Operation of SSR Transponders

The airborne component of the ATC secondary surveillance radar (SSR) system is known as the **transponder**, and there are requirements prescribed in the ANO and AIP ENR 1-6-0 for carriage of SSR transponder equipment.

The three capabilities of transponders are:

- Mode A – capable of selecting 4,096 4-digit codes; and
- Mode C – 4,096 codes, with the capability of transmitting the aircraft's altitude (read from a suitable linked altimeter known as an *encoding altimeter).*
- Mode S – newer technology with improved functionality, including improved quality and integrity of aircraft detection. Mode S provides almost 17 million unique aircraft addresses and the aircraft's identity is automatically reported to the controller.

Mandatory Requirements

- A transponder operating on Mode A (at least) is required in the Scottish TMA between 6,000 ft amsl and FL100.
- Mode A and Mode C with altitude reporting is required for:
  - the whole of UK airspace at and above FL100; and
  - in UK controlled airspace notified for the purposes of ANO Schedule 6 (sub-paragraph 2(1)(a)) below FL100 when operating under Instrument Flight Rules (IFR), except when receiving a 'crossing service'. (The ANO Schedule 5 notified airspace is listed in AIP ENR 1-4.)
- Certain TMZs (Transponder Mandatory Zones) have been designated in busy airspace close to control zones. In these areas aircraft not equipped with transponders are unlikely to gain admittance.

Gliders are exempt from the above requirements.

In airspace where the use of transponders is *not* mandatory, pilots should *squawk* (the term for using a transponder code) the Conspicuity Code (see below) except when remaining within the confines of an aerodrome traffic pattern below 3,000 ft agl.

NOTE Mode S is required for IFR traffic in designated TMA and en route airspace such as airways.

Transponder Codes

The conspicuity code 7000 (and Mode C if so equipped) shall be used for normal operations *at and above FL100* except:
- when receiving a service from an ATSU or ADU requiring a different transponder code setting; or
- when circumstances require the use of one of the special purpose codes (see below).

Below FL 100, pilots should select the conspicuity code and Mode C, except as above. Special-purpose codes are reserved for various purposes as described in the table below.

SPECIAL-PURPOSE TRANSPONDER CODES	
Code 7700	to indicate an emergency condition (except that, if the aircraft is already transmitting a code and receiving an air traffic service, that code will normally be retained)
Code 7600	to indicate a radio failure
Code 7500	to indicate unlawful interference
Code 7000	conspicuity code for normal operations
Code 2000	when entering UK airspace from an adjacent region where transponder operation has not been required
Code 7004	a special code to indicate that training, practising or displaying of aerobatics is taking place
Code 0033	a special code to be selected 5 minutes before parachute dropping begins and until the parachutists are estimated to have reached the ground

Mode C (if so equipped) should be operated with all of the above codes.

NOTE When selecting the conspicuity code 7000, pilots should be careful not to activate a special-purpose code (7700, 7600 or 7500) inadvertently.

For further reading on transponder operations, see AIP ENR 1-6-2, and Vol. 7 of *The Air Pilot's Manual*.

Airprox Reporting Procedure

When a pilot considers that the safety of his or her aircraft may have been endangered by the proximity of another aircraft, within UK airspace, the incident must be reported as an *Airprox*.

An initial report should be made by radio to the Air Traffic Service Unit (ATSU) with which the aircraft is in communication. If it is impossible to report by radio, a report should be made by telephone or other means to any ATSU, but preferably to an Air Traffic Control Centre (ATCC) immediately after landing. Reports made by telephone or radio must be confirmed within seven days online on CA Form 1094 or military pilots in accordance with MAA RA1410.

AIP ENR 1-14 contains information on Airprox Reporting.

International Flights (ICAO Annex 6)

The following extracts from Annex 6 cover matters particularly relevant to PPL holders making international flights.

General

3.1. The pilot-in-command shall comply with the relevant laws, regulations and procedures of the States in which the aircraft is operated.

3.2. The pilot-in-command shall be responsible for the operation and safety of the aeroplane and for the safety of all persons on board, during the flight.

3.3. Should an emergency situation occur which endangers the safety of the aeroplane or people, and requires the pilot to take action which violates local regulations or procedures, the pilot shall notify the appropriate authority as soon as possible. Some States may require the pilot to submit a report on the violation, normally within ten days.

3.4. In the event of an accident involving the aeroplane which results in serious injury or death or substantial damage to the aeroplane or property the pilot-in-command shall be responsible for notifying the appropriate authority as quickly as possible.

3.5. ICAO recommends that the pilot-in-command should carry on board the aeroplane essential information on search and rescue services in the areas over which the aeroplane will be flown.

Adequacy of Operating Facilities

4.1. The pilot in command shall not begin a flight unless he/she has ascertained that the aerodrome facilities, communication facilities and navigation aids required are adequate for the safe operation of the aeroplane.

Aerodrome Operating Minima

4.2. The pilot-in-command shall not fly below the operating minima specified for an aerodrome, except with State approval.

Briefing

4.3.1 The pilot-in-command shall ensure that crew members and passengers are briefed on the location and use of:
* seat belts;
* emergency exits;
* life jackets;
* oxygen equipment;
* any other emergency equipment, including passenger briefing cards.

4.3.2 The pilot-in-command shall ensure that everyone on board is familiar with the location and use of emergency equipment carried for collective use, such as life rafts.

Aeroplane Airworthiness and Safety Precautions

4.4.1 The pilot-in-command shall not begin a flight unless he/she is satisfied that:

- the aeroplane is airworthy, registered and has the appropriate certificates on board;
- the instruments and equipment in the aircraft are appropriate to the expected flight conditions;
- necessary maintenance has been completed;
- the aeroplane's weight and balance will be within safe limits for the flight;
- cargo is correctly stowed and secured;
- the aeroplane's operating limitations, as described in the Flight Manual, will not be exceeded.

NOTE ICAO recommends that the pilot-in-command should have sufficient information on climb performance to be able to determine the climb gradient that can be achieved during the departure phase in the prevailing conditions.

Limitations Imposed by Weather Conditions

4.6.1 Flights to be conducted under the visual flight rules shall not be commenced unless current weather reports and forecasts indicate that visual meteorological conditions exist along the flight-planned route.

4.6.3 Flights shall not be continued towards the planned destination aerodrome unless current weather reports indicate conditions at that aerodrome, or at least one alternate destination aerodrome, are at or above specified minima.

4.6.4 Aeroplanes on approach to land shall not exceed aerodrome operating minima, except in emergency situations.

4.6.5 A flight may not be conducted in known or expected icing conditions unless the aeroplane is equipped to cope with such conditions.

Fuel and Oil Supply

4.8.1 A flight may not be commenced unless the aeroplane carries sufficient fuel and oil to complete the flight safely, considering the weather conditions and any expected delays.

In-flight Emergency Instruction

4.11 In an in-flight emergency, the pilot-in-command shall ensure that passengers and crew are instructed in appropriate emergency action.

Weather Reporting by Pilots

4.12 If weather conditions are encountered that are likely to affect the safety of other flights, they should be reported as soon as possible.

Hazardous Flight Conditions

4.13 *Hazardous flight conditions encountered in-flight such as volcanic ash and dust-storms, other than those associated with weather conditions, should be reported as soon as possible.*

Instruction – General

4.17. *An aeroplane may be taxied on the movement area of an aerodrome only if the person at the controls:*
* *has been authorised by the owner, lessee or agent to do so;*
* *is fully competent to taxy the aeroplane;*
* *is qualified to use the radio if radio communications are required;*
* *has received instruction from a competent person in aerodrome layout, routes, signs, marking, lights, ATC signals and instructions, phraseology and procedures and is able to conform safely to the operational standards required for the safe movement of aeroplanes at the aerodrome.*

Refuelling with Passengers on Board

4.18.1 ICAO recommends that aircraft should not be refuelled while passengers are boarding, on board, or leaving the aircraft, unless it is attended by the pilot-in-command or another qualified person who is able to organise an evacuation of the aircraft should it be necessary.

Aeroplane Performance and Operating Limitations

5.1 *An aeroplane shall be operated:*
* *in compliance with its airworthiness certificate;*
* *within the operating limitations prescribed by the certificating authority of the State of registry.*

5.2 *Placards, listings and instrument markings containing operating limitations prescribed by the State of registry shall be displayed in the aeroplane.*

Aeroplane Instruments and Equipment

6.1 In addition to the minimum equipment necessary to satisfy the Certificate of Airworthiness, an aeroplane shall carry the instruments, equipment and documents appropriate to the planned flight.

6.2 An aeroplane shall be equipped with instruments that will enable the flight crew to control the flightpath of the aeroplane, carry out any required procedural manoeuvre, and observe the operating limitations of the aeroplane in the expected flight conditions.

6.1.3 *Aeroplanes shall be equipped with:*
* *an accessible first-aid kit;*
* *a safe portable fire extinguisher in the cockpit and in each passenger compartment if separate from the cockpit;*

- a seat or berth for each person on board over a minimum age determined by the State of registry;
- *a seat belt for each seat and restraining belts for each berth;*
- *the following manuals, charts and information:*
    - *the Flight Manual and other necessary related documents;*
    - *suitable aeronautical charts for the planned route and any diversions that could reasonably be anticipated;*
    - *procedures and visual signals for pilots-in-command of intercepted aircraft (for UK pilots, this is the CAA's General Aviation Safety Sense Leaflet No. 11: see also pages 31–34 of this text);*
- *spare fuses for replacement of those accessible in flight.*

VFR Flights

6.2 *Aeroplanes operating on VFR flights shall be equipped with:*
- *a magnetic compass;*
- *an accurate timepiece that indicates the time in hours, minutes and seconds;*
- *an altimeter;*
- *an airspeed indicator;*
- *additional instruments or equipment that may be prescribed by the appropriate authority.*

Flights over Water

6.3.2 *All single-engined landplanes when flying over water beyond gliding distance from land should carry one life-jacket or equivalent flotation device for each person on board, stowed in an easily accessible position for its intended user.*

NOTE *Landplanes above includes amphibious aircraft operated as landplanes.*

6.3.3 *All aeroplanes on extended flights over water shall be equipped as follows:*
- *When over water and more than 50 nautical miles from land suitable for an emergency landing:*
    - *one life-jacket or equivalent flotation device for each person on board, stowed in an easily accessible position for its intended user.*
- *When over water and more than 100 nautical miles from land suitable for an emergency landing in the case of single-engined aeroplanes, and more than 200 nautical miles in the case of multi-engined aeroplanes capable of continuing flight with one engine inoperative:*
    - *live-saving rafts capable of carrying all persons on board, stowed for ready access in an emergency, provided with appropriate life-saving equipment;*
    - *equipment for making pyrotechnic distress signals.*

Flights over Designated Land Areas

6.4 *Aeroplanes flying over land areas designated by the State as being areas in which search and rescue would be especially difficult, shall be equipped with appropriate signalling devices and life-saving equipment.*

Now complete: **Practice Questions - Operation of Aircraft**

1. As pilot in command you must:

   (a) *File a flight plan.*
   (b) *Brief passengers on the use of seat belts, harnesses and emergency exits.*
   (c) *Secure the POH in a baggage compartment within the aircraft.*
   (d) *Obtain an Air Traffic Control clearance.*

2. Below FL100 it is recommended that suitably equipped aircraft squawk 7000 with altitude. What are the exceptions to this?

   (a) *When transiting controlled airspace.*
   (b) *When a discrete code has been assigned by ATC or when squawking a special purpose or a monitoring code.*
   (c) *When the visibility is greater than 10 km.*
   (d) *When the AGCS operator has advised that the information is corrupted.*

3. The transponder code used to indicate radio failure is:

   (a) *7700*
   (b) *7500*
   (c) *7000*
   (d) *7600*

4. The final authority over the operation of an aircraft and the safe conduct of a flight belongs to:

   (a) *The pilot-in-command.*
   (b) *The aircraft owner.*
   (c) *The person manipulating the controls.*
   (d) *The aircraft operator.*

5. On over water flights, single engine land planes should carry life rafts when their distance from land suitable for making an emergency landing is more than:

(a) 100 km
(b) 200 km
(c) 100 nm
(d) 200 nm

Distress, Urgency, Safety and Warning Signals

Distress Signals

If a pilot feels that the aeroplane is in grave and imminent danger and wants immediate help, then the following signals, either together or separately, before a message will alert others to the fact.

Radiotelephony (R/T or RTF): on the frequency in use or on the emergency service frequency 121.5 MHz "Mayday Mayday Mayday", followed by the message, e.g.

> **Mayday Mayday Mayday**
> London Centre (or name of station addressed)
> Golf Alpha Bravo Charlie Delta
> Engine has failed
> Making a forced landing
> Five miles north of the field
> Three thousand feet and descending
> Heading two eight zero
> Student pilot

NOTE Although not an international (ICAO) requirement, inclusion of pilot qualification in an emergency message enables the controller to plan a course of action best suited to the pilot's ability.

Student pilots are recommended to use the term 'Student' when flying solo and also when transmitting an emergency message on a military frequency to indicate to the controller their lack of experience. This will ensure that instructions issued should be able to be followed by the pilot without any difficulty.

VISUAL SIGNALLING can be made with lights, pyrotechnics or flares to indicate **distress:**
- S-O-S in Morse code: *dit-dit-dit dah-dah-dah dit-dit-dit;*
- a succession of pyrotechnic single reds fired at short intervals; or
- a red parachute flare.

SOUND SIGNALLING (other than radiotelephony) can be used to indicate **distress:**
- S-O-S in morse code: *dit-dit-dit dah-dah-dah dit-dit-dit;*
- a continuous sound, with any apparatus.

Urgency and Safety Signals

The following signals, either together or separately before a message, mean that an aircraft is in difficulties which compel it to land, but the pilot considers that he/she does not need immediate assistance:

- a succession of white pyrotechnics;
- repeated switching of landing lights ON and OFF;
- repeated switching of navigation lights ON and OFF (in a manner distinguishable from normal flashing navigation lights).

The following, either together or separately, mean that the aircraft has an **urgent** message to transmit concerning the safety of a ship, aircraft, vehicle or other property, or of a person on board or within sight of the aircraft from which the signal is given:

RADIOTELEPHONY (R/T OR RTF) on the frequency in use or on the emergency service frequency 121.5 MHz, "Pan-Pan Pan-Pan Pan-Pan", e.g.

> *Pan-Pan Pan-Pan Pan-Pan*
> *Cranfield Approach*
> *Golf Bravo Charlie Delta Echo*
> *An aircraft has force-landed two miles south of Olney*
> *Occupants appear safe and have evacuated the aircraft*

VISUAL SIGNALLING X-X-X in Morse code:

> *"dah-dit-dit-dah dah-dit-dit-dah dah-dit-dit-dah"*

SOUND SIGNALLING (other than by radio): X-X-X in Morse:

> *"dah-dit-dit-dah dah-dit-dit-dah dah-dit-dit-dah"*

Use of Transponder

In a radar environment, make use of your transponder to indicate an emergency (Code 7700), a radio failure (Code 7600), or unlawful interference/hijack (Code 7500).

If Mode C (altitude-reporting) is available on your transponder, it should be selected.

Danger Areas

The Danger Area Crossing Service (DACS) and Danger Area Activity Information Service (DAAIS) are available for certain UK Danger Areas. Full details are included in AIP ENR 5, and CAA 1:500,000 aeronautical charts include a list of the Danger Areas covered by each service, including the relevant Air Traffic Service Unit to contact. *Pooley's Flight Guide* also contains information on these Services.

DANGER AREA CROSSING SERVICE (DACS) is available for certain Danger Areas. The relevantareas(identified on the chart by the prefix †) and Unit Contact Frequencies to be used are shown below. For availability of the services see UK AIP RAC 5-3, column 5.

D001	ST MAWGAN APP 126·5MHz*
D003 & D004	PLYMOUTH MIL 121·25MHz or LONDON MIL VIA LONDON INFO 124·75MHz
D006	CULDROSE APP 134·05MHz*
D006A, D007, D007A, D007B, D008, D008A, D008B, D009 & D009A	PLYMOUTH MIL 121·25MHz*

DANGER AREA ACTIVITY INFORMATION SERVICE (DAAIS) is available for certain Danger Areas shown on this chart (identified by the prefix §). The Nominated Air Traffic Service Units (NATSUs) to be used are shown below. See UK AIP RAC 5-1. Pilots are advised to assume that a Danger Area is active if no reply is received from the appropriate NATSU.

D015	BOURNEMOUTH TWR 125·6MHz
✳D026	LONDON INFORMATION 124·75MHz
D036, D037, D038, D039, D040, D041, D048, D049, D053, D053A, D054, D055, D056, D057, D058 & D059	LONDON INFORMATION 124·75MHz/124·6MHz /125·475MHz

■ *Figure 12-1* **Example of DACS and DAAIS information on a** **CAA 1:500,000 aeronautical chart**

NOTE Pilots who realise that they have inadvertently entered a Prohibited Area should leave the area as quickly as possible without descending, even if no radio instruction is received.

Low Fuel Situations on Aircraft Inbound to UK

If a pilot wishes to alert ATC to the need for a priority landing because his/her fuel state is becoming critical, the pilot should declare an emergency using Mayday or Pan, to ensure priority handling.

A pilot should only make such a call if he/she believes the aircraft to be in danger, and the seriousness of the emergency call should reflect the actual fuel state.

Pilots should plan to arrive overhead their destination aerodrome with at least enough fuel to:
• make an approach to land;
• carry out a missed approach;
• fly to an alternate aerodrome and carry out the subsequent approach and landing; and
• hold at an alternate aerodrome for 45 minutes.

Note that this recommendation is a bare minimum only. It is good airmanship to carry more fuel than this to allow for unforeseen circumstances.

Now complete: **Practice Questions - Chapter 12**

1. The states of emergency are:

(a) *Mayday and pan pan.*
(b) *Difficulty and urgency.*
(c) *Distress and urgency.*
(d) *Mayday and distress.*

2. In the first instance which frequency should be used for transmitting a MAYDAY?

(a) *121.5 MHz.*
(b) *The civil or military frequency in use at the time.*
(c) *The nearest MATZ.*
(d) *Any local emergency frequency.*

3. What does DACS stand for?

(a) *Danger Area Clearance Service.*
(b) *Danger Area Crossing Service.*
(c) *Danger Area Confliction Service.*
(d) *Danger Area Confirmation Service.*

4. What would it mean if you saw an aircraft's landing light signalling "XXX" in Morse code?

(a) *That the aircraft was in distress and experiencing grave and/or imminent danger.*
(b) *That the aircraft was in distress and the pilot required immediate assistance.*
(c) *That an urgency situation existed and the pilot is concerned for the safety of the aircraft.*
(d) *That an urgency situation existed and the pilot required immediate assistance.*

Answers: 1c, 2b, 3b, 4c.

Search and Rescue (SAR)

Search and Rescue in the UK

Search and Rescue in the event of a mishap is controlled by a Rescue Coordination Centre (RCC), who will act upon reports received from any source. A joint civil/military response may result. The types of service, responsible authorities and procedures are contained in AIP GEN 3-6.

A continuous listening watch is held on the aeronautical emergency VHF frequency 121.5 megahertz, so, if a pilot is unable to transmit a Mayday (Emergency), Pan-Pan (Urgency) or 'Lost' call on the frequency that he/she is already using, then a call on 121.5 MHz should be made.

Alerting Service

An Alerting Service is available for all aircraft that are known by the Air Traffic Services to be operating within the UK Flight Information Regions (FIRs). The responsibility for initiating action normally rests with the Air Traffic Services Unit (ATSU) which was last in communication with the aircraft in need of SAR assistance or which receives such information from an external source.

Autotriangulation on 121.5 MHz

Most of the United Kingdom land mass to the east and south of Manchester above 3,000 ft amsl, and down to 2,000 ft amsl in the vicinity of the London airports, is covered by a position-fixing service which operates on 121.5 MHz. The system utilises DF (direction-finding) bearing information and provides almost instantaneous aircraft position-fixing. It is activated simply by the pilot calling on the emergency frequency (121.5).

Emergency Transponder Codes

In an emergency it is a good idea to select the appropriate transponder *special purposes* code:
- **Code 7700** – indicates an emergency condition (except that if already transmitting a code and receiving an air traffic service, that code will normally be retained).
- **Code 7600** – indicates a radio failure.
- **Code 7500** – indicates unlawful interference with the planned operation of the flight (unless circumstances warrant use of Code 7700).

Mode C (altitude reporting), if fitted, should be operated with all of the above codes.

SAR Watch Procedures

Aircraft desirous of a constant SAR watch can **file a flight plan** with Air Traffic Control. This is advised if:
- flying more than 10 nm from the coast;
- flying over remote or hazardous areas *(remote areas* include northern Scotland and almost all of the west coast down to Cornwall);
- flying an aircraft not fitted with a suitable radio.

If an aircraft is expected at an aerodrome, the pilot must inform the Air Traffic Control Unit or other Authority at that aerodrome as quickly as possible of:
- any change in intended destination; and/or
- any estimated delay in arrival of 45 minutes or more.

These requirements are contained in SERA and the UK implementing rules, which are intended to apply to delays prior to departure caused by technical problems, weather deterioration, late passengers, etc., say for a flight for which a flight plan has already been submitted.

If a pilot decides whilst en route **not** to land at the planned destination, but at another airfield, then he/she must inform ATC at the original destination (or request that they be informed) prior to his or her **planned ETA plus 30 minutes** at that field, otherwise SAR action will commence.

Search and Rescue (ICAO Annex 12)

NOTE Annex 12 applies to the establishment, maintenance and operation of search and rescue services in the territories of ICAO contracting States and over the high seas, and to the coordination of SAR services between States.

SAR Service Provision

2.1 States shall provide search and rescue service within their territories 24 hours a day. This service shall be provided regardless of the nationality of an aircraft (or its occupants) in distress.

SAR Regions

2.2 States shall define regions within which they will provide search and rescue service. These regions will not overlap those of other States.

SAR Services Units

2.3 States shall establish a rescue coordination centre in each search and rescue region.

Cooperation

3.1 States shall coordinate their search and rescue organisations with those of neighbouring States.

3.2 States shall arrange for aircraft, ships and local services and facilities that are not part of the SAR organisation to help with search and rescue and to assist the survivors of aircraft accidents.

Dissemination of information

3.3 States shall publish all information necessary for the entry of rescue units of other States into their territories.

Information about Emergencies

5.1 Any authority or any part of the SAR organisation that believes an aircraft is in an emergency shall give immediately all available information to the appropriate rescue coordination centre.

Rescue coordination centres shall, on receipt of information concerning aircraft in emergency, evaluate the situation and determine the extent of action required.

When information on aircraft in danger is received from sources other than air traffic services units, the rescue coordination centre shall determine which emergency phase applies and invoke the appropriate procedures.

In addition, ICAO recommends that States should encourage anyone who observes an accident or who believes an aircraft is in danger to inform immediately the appropriate rescue coordination centre.

Procedures for Rescue Coordination Centres during Emergency Phases

5.2 UNCERTAINTY PHASE. During the uncertainty phase, the rescue coordination centre shall cooperate with air traffic services units and other bodies to ensure that incoming reports are evaluated quickly.

ALERT PHASE. When the alert phase is invoked, the rescue coordination centre shall immediately alert SAR units and initiate any necessary action.

DISTRESS PHASE. When an aircraft is believed to be in distress, the rescue coordination centre shall:
- initiate action by SAR units;
- determine the position of the aircraft, estimate the degree of uncertainty of this position, and accordingly determine the extent of the area to be searched;
- notify the operator;
- notify adjacent rescue coordination centres if it seems likely that their help will be required;
- notify the appropriate air traffic services unit of information received from other sources;

- request at an early stage that aircraft, ships and coastal stations not included in the SAR organisation assist the operation by:
  - maintaining a listening watch for transmissions from the aircraft in distress or from an emergency locator transmitter;
  - assisting the aircraft in distress as far as practicable;
  - informing the rescue coordination centre of any developments;
- formulate and update when necessary a plan for the SAR operation, and make that plan available to appropriate authorities;
- notify the State of Registry of the aircraft;
- notify the appropriate accident investigation authorities.

These actions shall be carried out in the above order unless circumstances dictate otherwise.

Procedures for Pilots at Accidents

5.8.1 If a pilot-in-command observes another aircraft or surface craft in distress, he/she shall, unless unable or considers it unnecessary:
- keep in sight the craft in distress for as long as necessary;
- if his or her position is not known with certainty, take steps to determine it precisely;
- report to the rescue coordination centre or air traffic services unit as much of the following information as possible:
  - type of craft in distress, its identification and condition;
  - its position, expressed in either geographical coordinates, or in distance and true bearing from a distinctive landmark or from a radio navigation aid;
  - time of observation (in hours and minutes UTC);
  - number of people seen;
  - whether people have abandoned the craft in distress;
  - number of persons afloat;
  - apparent physical condition of survivors;
- act as instructed by the rescue coordination centre or the air traffic services unit.

5.8.1.1 If the first aircraft to reach an accident scene is not a SAR aircraft it shall take charge of on-scene activities of all other subsequently arriving aircraft until the first SAR aircraft arrives.

If, in the meantime, such aircraft is unable to establish communication with the appropriate rescue coordination centre or air traffic services unit, it shall, by mutual agreement, hand over to a capable aircraft until a SAR aircraft arrives.

5.8.2 When an aircraft has to direct a surface craft to the location of an aircraft or surface craft in distress, it shall do so by transmitting precise instructions by any means at its disposal.

Procedures for Pilots Intercepting Distress Transmissions

5.9 When the pilot-in-command of an aircraft intercepts a distress signal and/or message, he/she shall:

- record the position of the aircraft if given;
- if possible take a bearing on the transmission;
- inform the appropriate rescue coordination centre or air traffic services unit of the distress transmission, giving all available information;
- at his or her discretion, while awaiting instructions, proceed to the position given in the transmission.

Search and Rescue Signals

If an aeroplane makes a forced landing, the survivors should, if it is deemed necessary, make a call on the radio if it is still functioning, or use some or all of the following methods of attracting attention when search aircraft or surface craft are seen or heard.

1. Fire distress flares or cartridges.

2. Use some object with a bright flat surface as a heliograph to flash sunlight at the searching craft.

3. Flash a light.

4. Fly anything in the form of a flag and, if possible, make the international distress signal by flying a ball, or something resembling a ball, above or below it.

5. Blow whistles.

6. Deploy fluorescent markers to leave a trail in the sea.

7. Lay out the following ground–air visual signals (as appropriate), forming the symbols as large as possible (at least 2 or 3 m long) with materials which contrast with the background. These are the standard international signals.

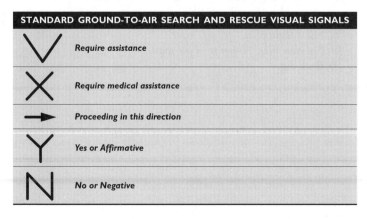

STANDARD GROUND-TO-AIR SEARCH AND RESCUE VISUAL SIGNALS	
V	*Require assistance*
X	*Require medical assistance*
→	*Proceeding in this direction*
Y	*Yes or Affirmative*
N	*No or Negative*

The following air-to-ground signals by aircraft mean that the ground signals have been understood:
- during daylight hours:
  - rocking the aircraft's wings;
- during darkness:
  - flashing the aircraft's landing lights on and off twice, or if not so equipped, switching its navigation lights on and off twice.

Lack of the above signal indicates that the ground signal is not understood.

Now complete: **Practice Questions - SAR?**

---

1. In search and rescue operations, what does the following sign mean 'V'?

  (a) Require medical assistance.
  (b) Proceeding in the direction indicated.
  (c) Request instructions.
  (d) Require assistance.

2. An Alerting Service is:

  (a) A special department of D and D.
  (b) A service provided to notify the appropriate organisations of aircraft in need of search and rescue aid, and to assist such organisations as required.
  (c) A network of civil and military stations.
  (d) A service provided to notify the appropriate organisations of aircraft in need of navigational assistance.

3. A pilot wanting a constant SAR watch is advised to:

  (a) Call 123.1 MHz.
  (b) File a flight plan.
  (c) Fly more than 10 nm from the coast.
  (d) Book out.

4. For SAR purposes when is it advisable that a pilot files a flight plan?

(a) *When a pilot wishes to enter controlled airspace and will fly more than 20 nm from the coast.*

(b) *When intending to fly more than 20 nm from the coast, over congested areas or when the aircraft does not have a suitable radio.*

(c) *When intending to fly more than 10 nm from the coast, over remote areas or when the aircraft does not have a suitable radio.*

(d) *When the entire flight will be conducted outside controlled airspace and will fly more than 10 nm from the coast.*

Accident Investigation Regulations

Accident Investigation in the UK

An accident must be notified if, between the time when anyone boards an aircraft with the intention of flight, and such time as all have left it:
- anyone is killed or seriously injured while in or on the aircraft, or by direct contact with any part of the aircraft (including any part which has become detached from it) or by direct exposure to jet blast, except when the death or serious injury is from natural causes, is self-inflicted or is inflicted by other persons or is suffered by a stowaway hiding outside the areas normally available in flight to the passengers and crew; or

- the aircraft incurs damage or structural failure, other than:
  - engine failure or damage, when the damage is limited to the engine, its cowling or accessories;
  - damage limited to propellers, wingtips, aerials, tyres, brakes, fairings, small dents or punctured holes in the aircraft skin:

- unless it adversely affects its structural strength, performance or flight characteristics and which would normally require major repair or replacement of the affected component;

- the aircraft is missing or is completely inaccessible.

When a notifiable accident occurs the aircraft commander (or, if he/she is killed or incapacitated, the operator) must notify:
- the Chief Inspector of Air Accidents by the quickest available means; and
- the local police authority, when the accident occurs in or over the UK.

- It is the responsibility of the authority of a state in which an accident takes place, to commence any investigation.

Purpose of Accident Investigations
The sole purpose of an accident investigation is to determine the cause and to ensure that steps are taken or recommendations are made to prevent recurrence of the same type of accident. The accident investigators have no remit to attach blame or apportion liability for an accident. It is the duty of the commander of an aircraft to assist the accident investigators in their inquiries.

The legal responsibility for implementing the safety recommendations of the investigation falls on the CAA. In order to eliminate 'blame' and to encourage reporting, a Confidential Human Factors Reporting Programme (CHIRP) is in operation.

There is a separate system for confidential reporting of general aviation accidents. The reports (GA Feedback) are available online at **www.chirp.co.uk.**

The CHIRP Charitable Trust
Centaur House
Ancells Business Park
Ancells Park
Fleet, GU51 2UJ.
Tel: +44(0) 1252 378947.
Freephone: 0800 772 3243.

Aircraft Accident and Incident Investigation (ICAO Annex 13)

NOTE The aptly numbered Annex 13 describes the procedures for ICAO States to follow during the investigation of aircraft accidents and incidents. These procedures are intended to facilitate prompt and efficient reporting of aircraft accidents by competent experts and to encourage cooperation among such experts of different States. Furthermore, States are urged to distribute accident information for the benefit of safety in air navigation worldwide. In a nutshell, the philosophy is to allow everyone to learn from the mistakes of others.

When investigating an accident, the investigator is entitled to:
• visit the scene of the accident;
• examine the wreckage;
• obtain witness information and suggest areas of questioning;
• have access to all relevant information and evidence;
• participate in off-scene investigations such as component examinations, tests and simulations;
• make submissions regarding the investigation.

Now complete: **Practice Questions - Accident Investigation**

1. Which of the following would be classed as an aircraft accident?

   (a) *A person on the ground is seriously injured after being hit by a component that has become detached from a light aircraft in flight.*
   (b) *A main tyre bursting on landing.*
   (c) *An aerial becomes detached.*
   (d) *A bird strike which slightly dents the leading edge of a wing.*

2. Who is responsible for starting the investigation into an aircraft accident?

   (a) *The Authority of the State in which the accident occurred.*
   (b) *The EASA investigation Department.*
   (c) *The aircraft owner or operator.*
   (d) *The local police.*

3. An air accident occurring in the UK must be reported by the quickest means available to (UK):

   (a) *The CAA and AAIB.*
   (b) *The CAA and the Chief Inspector of Air Accidents.*
   (c) *The Chief Inspector of Air Accidents and the local police.*
   (d) *The Chief Inspector of Police and the CAA.*

4. Which of the following would be classed as an aircraft accident?

   (a) *During landing the propeller tips are slightly damaged.*
   (b) *An engine failure in the circuit. Damage is confined to the engine and the aircraft makes a successful forced landing on the runway.*
   (c) *A person is seriously injured on the apron by the wingtip of a taxiing aircraft.*
   (d) *An aircraft under tow damages another parked aircraft.*

5. A person on the ground is seriously injured after being hit by a component that has become detached from an aircraft in flight. The event is:

   (a) *An aircraft incident.*
   (b) *A reportable occurrence.*
   (c) *A crime.*
   (d) *An aircraft accident.*

ICAO Annex Terminology

The following summarises terms used in the ICAO Annexes pertinent to the EASA. You should be familiar with these terms because they are used in the PPL examinations.

See also the Part–FCL terminology on page 381.

ICAO ANNEX TERMINOLOGY

Accident
Event associated with the operation of an aircraft in which the aircraft sustains significant damage, causes significant damage, or causes personal injury. Specifically, an event that occurs between the time any person boards the aircraft with the intention of flight and the time all persons have disembarked, where:

- a person is fatally or seriously injured as a result of:
  - being in the aircraft; or
  - being in direct contact with any part of the aircraft, including parts that have fallen off the aircraft; or
  - direct exposure to jet blast;

Note: Exceptions are when the injuries are from natural causes, self-inflicted or inflicted by other persons, or when the injuries are to stowaways hiding outside the areas normally available to passengers and crew (such as cargo bays).

- the aircraft sustains damage or structural failure which:
  - jeopardises the structural strength, performance or flight characteristics of the aircraft; or
    would normally require major repair or replacement of the affected component;

Note: Exceptions are engine failure or damage (when the damage is limited to the engine, its cowlings or accessories), damage limited to propellers, wing tips, antennae, tyres, brakes, fairings, small dents or puncture holes in the aircraft skin.

- the aircraft is missing or is completely inaccessible.

Note: An aircraft is considered to be missing when the official search has been terminated and the wreckage has not been found.

Advisory airspace
Airspace of defined dimensions, or a designated route, within which air traffic advisory service is available.

Advisory route
Designated route along which air traffic advisory service is available.

Aerial work
Aircraft operations where aircraft are used for specialised purposes, such as agriculture, construction, fish-spotting, photography, surveying, search and rescue etc.

Aerodrome
Defined area of land or water used for the arrival, departure and surface movement of aircraft.

ICAO ANNEX TERMINOLOGY

Aerodrome beacon
An aeronautical beacon used to indicate the location of an aerodrome from the air.

Aerodrome control service
Air traffic control service to aerodrome traffic.

Aerodrome control tower
A unit established to provide air traffic control services to aerodrome traffic.

Aerodrome elevation
The elevation (height above sea level) of the highest point of the landing area at the aerodrome.

Aerodrome identification sign
A sign at an aerodrome that indicates the name of the aerodrome from the air.

Aerodrome reference point
Designated geographical location of an aerodrome.

Aerodrome traffic
All traffic on the manoeuvring area of an aerodrome and all aircraft flying in the vicinity of an aerodrome.

Note: An aircraft is considered to be 'in the vicinity of an aerodrome' when it is in, entering, or leaving an aerodrome traffic circuit.

Aerodrome traffic circuit
The specified path to be flown by aircraft operating in the vicinity of an aerodrome.

Aeronautical beacon
An aeronautical ground light visible from all directions, either continuously or intermittently, to indicate the location of a particular point on the surface of the earth.

Aeronautical fixed service (AFS)
A telecommunication service between specified fixed points provided primarily for the safety of air navigation and for the regular, efficient and economical operation of air services.

Aeronautical ground light
A light provided to aid air navigation (not a light on an aircraft).

Aeronautical Information Publication (AIP)
A document issued by a State that contains permanent aeronautical information essential to air navigation.

Aeronautical station
A land (or sea) station in the aeronautical mobile service.

Aeronautical telecommunication service
A telecommunication service provided for any aeronautical purpose.

Aeroplane
A power-driven heavier-than-air aircraft that derives its lift from aerodynamic reactions on fixed aerofoils, i.e. fixed-wing.

Airborne collision avoidance system (ACAS)
Aircraft system based on secondary surveillance radar (SSR) transponder signals which indicates to a pilot potential conflicting aircraft that are equipped with SSR transponders. ACAS operates independently of any ground-based equipment.

ICAO ANNEX TERMINOLOGY

Aircraft
Any machine that can support itself in the atmosphere, by means other than the reactions of air against the earth's surface.

Aircraft identification
A group of letters, numbers or a combination thereof which makes up the callsign of an aircraft.

Aircraft observation
A meteorological observation made from an aircraft in flight.

Aircraft proximity
A situation where minimum safe separation distances between aircraft in flight have been compromised.

Aircraft stand
A designated area on an aerodrome apron for the parking of aircraft.

Air-ground communication
Two-way radio communication between aircraft in flight and ground (or sea) stations.

AIRMET information
Information issued by a met office about weather conditions or expected weather conditions that may affect the safety of aircraft. Such information is in addition to previously issued forecasts.

AIRPROX
Code word used in an air traffic incident report to designate aircraft proximity.

Airship
A power-driven lighter-than-air aircraft.

Air-report
A report from an aircraft in flight containing specific information on position, operation and meteorological conditions.

Air-taxiing
Movement of a helicopter above the surface of an aerodrome, normally in ground effect and at a groundspeed of less than 20 knots.

Air traffic
All aircraft in flight or operating on the manoeuvring areas of aerodromes.

Air traffic advisory service
A service provided within advisory airspace to ensure separation in so far as practical between aircraft operating on IFR flight plans.

Air traffic control clearance
Authorisation for an aircraft to proceed under conditions specified by an air traffic control unit. This term is often abbreviated to 'clearance'.

Air traffic control instruction
A directive issued by air traffic control that requires a pilot to take a specific action.

Air traffic control service
A service provided to (a) expedite the flow of air traffic and (b) to prevent collisions between aircraft in flight and on the manoeuvring area, and between aircraft and ground obstructions.

Air traffic control unit
Aerodrome control tower, area control centre or approach control service.

ICAO ANNEX TERMINOLOGY

Air traffic service
Flight information service, alerting service, air traffic advisory service or air traffic control service.

Air traffic services airspaces
Airspaces of defined dimensions, alphabetically designated (Classes A to G), within which specific types of flights may operate and for which specific air traffic services and rules of operation apply.

Air traffic services unit (ATSU)
Air traffic control unit, flight information centre or air traffic services reporting office.

Airway
A corridor-shaped control area equipped with radio navigation aids.

Alerting service
Service which notifies appropriate organisations of aircraft that require search and rescue aid.

Alert phase
Where concern is registered regarding the safety of an aircraft and its occupants.

Alternate aerodrome
An aerodrome to which an aircraft may proceed if it becomes either impossible or inadvisable to proceed to or land at the intended destination aerodrome. Alternate aerodromes include the following:

• En-route alternate: an aerodrome at which an aircraft would be able to land after experiencing an abnormal or emergency condition while en route.

• Destination alternate: an alternate aerodrome to which an aircraft may proceed if it becomes either impossible or inadvisable to land at the intended destination aerodrome.

Note: The departure aerodrome may also be an en-route or destination alternate aerodrome for the flight.

Altitude
The vertical distance of a point from mean sea level.

Approach control office
A unit established to provide air traffic control service to controlled flights arriving at, or departing from, one or more aerodromes.

Approach control service
Air traffic control service for arriving or departing controlled flights.

Approach sequence
The order in which two or more aircraft are cleared to approach to land at an aerodrome.

Appropriate ATS authority
The authority designated by a State as being responsible for providing air traffic services in its territory.

Appropriate authority
(a) Regarding flight over the high seas: the relevant authority of the State of Registry; (b) Regarding flight over the territory of a State: the relevant authority of the State that has sovereignty over the territory being overflown.

Apron
An area on an aerodrome where aircraft can be parked for the loading and unloading of passengers, mail or cargo, refuelling or maintenance.

ICAO ANNEX TERMINOLOGY

Area control centre
Unit which provides air traffic control service to controlled flights in control areas under its jurisdiction.

Area control service
Air traffic control service for controlled flights in control areas.

Area navigation (RNAV)
A navigation method where aircraft may operate on any flightpath within the coverage of station-referenced navigation aids or within the limits of self-contained aids, or both. Such systems avoid the need to overfly ground-based radio navigation aids.

Area navigation route
An ATS route for aircraft using area navigation.

Assignment, assign
Distribution of frequencies to stations or SSR codes to aircraft.

ATIS
Automatic terminal information service: continuous repetitive broadcast of current routine aerodrome information to arriving and departing aircraft.

ATS route
A route (airway, advisory route, arrival or departure route etc.) used as necessary for the provision of air traffic services.

Balloon
A non-power-driven lighter-than-air aircraft.

Blind transmission
A radio transmission from one station to another where the transmitter cannot hear the receiver, but believes that the transmission can be received.

Broadcast
An 'all stations' transmission of air navigation information.

Cloud ceiling
The height above ground or water of the lowest layer of cloud below 20,000 ft covering more than half the sky.

Clearance limit
The point to which an aircraft is granted an air traffic control clearance.

Clearway
A defined rectangular area at the upwind end of a runway that is suitable for the initial climb-out of aeroplanes. Will be under the control of the aerodrome authority.

Control area
A controlled airspace extending upwards from a specified height above the earth's surface.

Controlled aerodrome
An aerodrome at which a control service to aircraft is provided.

Note: This does not necessarily imply that the aircraft is within a control zone.

Controlled airspace
An airspace of defined dimensions within which air traffic control services are provided to IFR and VFR flights.

ICAO ANNEX TERMINOLOGY

Controlled flight
Any flight subject to air traffic control clearances.

Control zone
A controlled airspace extending upwards from the earth's surface to a specified upper limit.

Cruise climb
An aeroplane cruising technique resulting in a net gain in altitude as the aeroplane mass decreases.

Cruising level
A level maintained during a significant portion of a flight.

Dangerous goods
Articles or substances that are capable of posing significant risk to health, safety or property when they are transported by air.

Declared distances
Declared distances at aerodromes are agreed by the relevant authority – in the UK this is the CAA, and the distances are published in the Aerodrome section of the AIP.

- **Take-off run available (TORA)**. The length of runway declared available and suitable for the ground run of an aeroplane taking off.

- **Take-off distance available (TODA)**. The length of the take-off run available plus the length of the clearway, if provided.

- **Accelerate-stop distance available (ASDA)**. The length of the take-off run available plus the length of the stopway, if provided.

- **Landing distance available (LDA)**. The length of runway declared available and suitable for the ground run of an aeroplane landing.

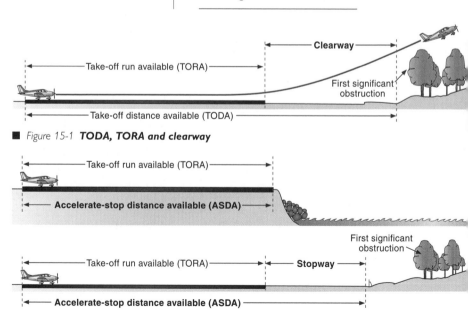

■ Figure 15-1 **TODA, TORA and clearway**

■ Figure 15-2 **Accelerate-stop distance (ASDA)**

ICAO ANNEX TERMINOLOGY

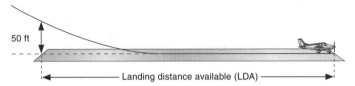

■ *Figure 15-3* **Landing distance available (LDA)**

Distress phase
Where it is reasonably certain that an aircraft and its occupants require immediate assistance or are threatened by grave or imminent danger.

Ditching
The forced landing of an aircraft on water.

Elevation
The vertical distance between a point on the earth's surface and mean sea level.

Emergency phase
Generic term meaning either uncertainty phase, alert phase or distress phase.

Estimated elapsed time
Estimated time required to proceed from one significant point to another.

Estimated off-block time
Estimated time at which the aircraft will move 'off chocks' to begin movement towards take-off.

Estimated time of arrival (ETA)
For VFR flights, the estimated time at which the aircraft will arrive over the destination aerodrome.
For IFR flights, the estimated time at which the aircraft will arrive over a point defined by radio navigation aids, from which an instrument approach procedure will begin

(if the destination aerodrome does not have an associated navigation aid, ETA is the time at which the aircraft will arrive over the aerodrome).

Expected approach time
The time at which ATC expects an arriving aircraft that has been instructed to hold will leave the holding pattern to complete its approach for a landing.

Filed flight plan
A flight plan as submitted to an ATS unit without subsequent changes.

Fireproof material
A material capable of withstanding heat as well as, or better than, steel

Flight crew member
A licensed crew member charged with duties essential to the operation of an aircraft during flight.

Flight Information centre
A unit that provides flight information service and alerting service.

Flight information region
An airspace of defined dimensions within which flight information service and alerting service is provided.

Flight information service
Service which provides advice and information useful to the safe and efficient conduct of flights.

ICAO ANNEX TERMINOLOGY

Flight level
A surface of constant atmospheric pressure which is related to a specific pressure datum, 1013.2 mb (hPa), and is separated from other such surfaces by specific pressure intervals. Flight levels are expressed in hundreds of feet, e.g. FL180 = 18,000 ft.

Flight Manual
A manual, associated with the Certificate of Airworthiness, containing limitations within which the aircraft is to be considered airworthy, and instructions and information necessary to the pilot for the safe operation of the aircraft. An aircraft Flight Manual is written by the manufacturer (e.g. Piper), approved by the State of Manufacture (in the US approval is given by the FAA) and supplemented if necessary by the State of Registration (for instance, by the UK CAA). The Flight Manual forms part of the Certificate of Airworthiness.

Flight plan
Specified information provided to air traffic services units about an intended flight or portion of a flight.

Flight time
The total time from the beginning of the take-off roll until the moment the aircraft stops at the end of a flight.

Note: This definition of flight time is synonymous with the terms 'block to block' or 'chock to chock'.

Flight visibility
Visibility forward from the cockpit of an aircraft in flight.

Forecast
A description of the expected weather conditions over a specified period of time for a particular area.

General aviation operation
An aircraft operation other than a commercial air transport flight or an aerial work operation.

Glider
A non-power-driven heavier-than-air aircraft that derives its lift from aerodynamic reactions on fixed aerofoils.

Ground visibility
Visibility at an aerodrome, as reported by a meteorological observer.

Gyroplane
A power-driven heavier-than-air rotorcraft that derives its lift from aerodynamic reactions on a freely-rotating rotor in the vertical axis. Powered by a propeller on the longitudinal axis.

Hazard beacon
An aeronautical beacon used to indicate a danger to air navigation.

Heading
The direction in which an aircraft is pointing, usually expressed in degrees from north (either true, magnetic or compass).

Height
The vertical distance between a point and a specified datum (such as sea level or ground level).

Heavier-than-air aircraft
An aircraft that derives its lift mainly from aerodynamic forces.

ICAO ANNEX TERMINOLOGY

Helicopter

A heavier-than-air rotorcraft that derives its lift and control from one or more power-driven rotors on substantially vertical axes.

Heliport

An aerodrome or a defined area on a structure for the landing, taking off and surface movement of helicopters.

Holding bay

A defined area at an aerodrome where aircraft can be held or bypassed without disrupting the flow of other traffic.

Holding point

A specified location, around which an aircraft flies a standard pattern until cleared to proceed with the flight.

Identification beacon

An aeronautical beacon that flashes a coded signal such that its location can be identified.

IFR flight

A flight made under the Instrument Flight Rules.

IMC

Instrument Meteorological Conditions.

Incident

An occurrence, other than an accident, which affects or could affect the safety of an aircraft operation.

Instrument Meteorological Conditions (IMC)

Meteorological conditions expressed in terms of visibility, distance from cloud, and ceiling, less than the minima specified for visual meteorological conditions.

Investigation

A process conducted for the purpose of accident investigation which includes the gathering and analysis of information, the drawing of conclusions, including the determination of causes and, when appropriate, the making of safety recommendations.

Landing area

The area on an aerodrome used for the landing or take-off of aircraft.

Level

A generic term relating to the vertical position of an aircraft in flight – referring to either height, altitude or flight level.

Lighter-than-air aircraft

An aircraft that is supported in flight mainly by its buoyancy in the air (e.g. a hot-air balloon).

Location indicator

A four-letter code assigned to the location of an aeronautical fixed station (could be either an aerodrome or a met station).

Manoeuvring area

The part of an aerodrome used for the taxiing, take-off and landing of aircraft, excluding aprons.

Marker

An object displayed above ground level to indicate an obstacle or boundary, e.g. the orange-and-white striped wedge-shaped markers that delineate an aerodrome boundary.

ICAO ANNEX TERMINOLOGY

Marking
A symbol or group of symbols displayed on the surface of the movement area to convey aeronautical information, e.g. the double white cross used to indicate gliding is in progress.

Meteorological information
Meteorological report, analysis, forecast or other statement relating to existing or expected weather conditions.

Meteorological office
An office that provides a meteorological service for international air navigation.

Meteorological report
A statement of observed weather conditions at a specific place at a specific time.

Mode (SSR)
Mode of operation of SSR transponder, e.g. Mode C (altitude reporting) or Mode A.

Movement area
The part of an aerodrome used for the taxiing, take-off and landing of aircraft, including the manoeuvring area and apron(s).

Night
The hours between the end of evening civil twilight and the beginning of morning civil twilight or such other period between sunset and sunrise as may be prescribed by the appropriate aviation authority.

Non-instrument runway
A runway for the use of aircraft using visual approach procedures only.

Non-radar separation
Separation distances between aircraft when position information is obtained from sources other than radar.

NOTAM
Notice to Airmen, which contains urgent information concerning the establishment, condition or change in any aeronautical facility, service, procedure or hazard.

Obstacle
Any fixed or mobile object (or part thereof) located on the surface movement area of an aerodrome that extends above a defined height.

Operator
A person, organisation or enterprise engaged in or offering facilities in aircraft operations.

Pilot-in-command
The pilot responsible for the operation and safety of an aircraft during flight time.

Pressure altitude
An atmospheric pressure expressed in terms of altitude which corresponds to that pressure in the standard atmosphere (i.e. 1013.2 hPa set in altimeter subscale).

Primary radar
Radar system that uses reflected radio signals.

Primary surveillance radar
Radar surveillance system that uses reflected radio signals.

ICAO ANNEX TERMINOLOGY

RADAR
Radio detection system which provides information on range, position and elevation of objects.

Radar approach
An approach to land where the final approach phase is directed by a radar controller.

Radar clutter
Unwanted signals displayed on a radar screen, caused by interference, static etc.

Radar contact
When the radar position of a particular aircraft is seen and identified on a radar display.

Radar control
Where radar information is used directly in the provision of air traffic control.

Radar controller
An air traffic controller qualified to use radar information.

Radar display
Electronic display (screen, monitor) which uses radar information to depict the position and movement of aircraft.

Radar identification
When the position of a particular aircraft is seen on a radar display and positively identified by the air traffic controller.

Radar monitoring
Use of radar to provide aircraft with information on their deviations from planned flightpath and deviations from air traffic control clearances.

Radar separation
Separation distances used when aircraft position information is provided by radar sources.

Radar service
A service provided by means of radar.

Radar unit
Part of an air traffic services unit that uses radar.

Radar vectoring
Where a radar controller issues heading instructions to aircraft, based on radar information.

Radio direction-finding station
A radio station that determines the relative direction of other transmitting stations.

Radiotelephony
A form of radio communication used mainly for the exchange of speech information.

Reporting point
A geographic location at which the position of an aircraft in flight can be reported.

Rescue coordination centre
Unit responsible for organising search and rescue operations within a certain area.

Rescue unit
A group of people trained and equipped to perform search and rescue operations.

Rotorcraft
A power-driven heavier-than-air aircraft that is supported in flight by reactions of air on one or more rotors.

ICAO ANNEX TERMINOLOGY

Runway
A defined rectangular area on an aerodrome used for the take-off and landing of aircraft.

Runway guard lights
A light system which alerts pilots or vehicle drivers that they are about to enter an active runway.

Runway visual range (RVR)
The distance along which the pilot of an aircraft on the centre-line of a runway can see the runway surface markings or lights.

Safety recommendation
A proposal made by the accident investigation authority of the State conducting an investigation, based on information derived from the investigation, with the intention of preventing accidents or incidents.

Search and rescue aircraft
An aircraft equipped to conduct search and rescue missions.

Search and rescue region
An area of defined dimensions within which search and rescue service is provided.

Search and rescue services unit
A generic term meaning either rescue coordination centre, rescue subcentre or alerting post.

Secondary radar
Radar system where an 'interrogating' radio signal transmitted from the radar station prompts a 'reply' signal to be sent from an aircraft transponder.

Secondary surveillance radar (SSR)
Radar system that uses transmitters/receivers (interrogators) and transponders.

Serious incident
An event that almost resulted in an accident.

Note: The only difference between an accident and an incident is the result: damage and/or injury = accident; could have been damage and/or injury = incident.

Serious injury
An injury sustained by a person in an accident which:

* requires hospitalisation for more than 48 hours (from within 7 days of the accident);
* results in a bone fracture (apart from simple fractures of fingers, toes or nose);
* involves lacerations which cause severe haemorrhage, nerve, muscle or tendon damage;
* involves injury to any internal organ;
* involves second or third degree burns, or any burns that affect more than 5% of body surface;
* involves verified exposure to infectious substances or harmful radiation.

SIGMET information
Information issued by a met office concerning weather conditions or expected weather conditions that may affect the safety of flights.

Signal area
An area on an aerodrome used for the display of ground signals.

ICAO ANNEX TERMINOLOGY

Slush
Water-saturated snow which, with a heel-and-toe slap-down motion against the ground, will be displaced with a splatter.

Snow (on the ground)

- **Dry snow.** Snow which can be blown if loose or, if compacted by hand, will fall apart again on release.

- **Wet snow.** Snow which, if compacted by hand, will stick together and tend to form a snowball.

- **Compacted snow.** Snow which has been compressed into a solid mass that resists further compression and will hold together or break into lumps if picked up.

Special VFR flight
A VFR flight cleared by air traffic control to operate within a control zone in meteorological conditions below VMC.

State of Design
The State that has jurisdiction over the organisation responsible for the design of a particular aircraft type.

State of Manufacture
The State that has jurisdiction over the organisation responsible for final assembly of an aircraft.

State of Occurrence
The State in which an aircraft accident or incident occurs.

State of the Operator
The State in which the operator's principal place of business is located, or if there is no such place, the operator's permanent residence.

State of Registry
The State (nation) in which an aircraft is registered.

Stopway
A defined rectangular area on the ground at the end of the take-off end of a runway, prepared as a suitable area in which an aeroplane can stop in the case of an abandoned take-off.

Surveillance radar
Radar equipment used to determine the range and position of aircraft in azimuth.

Take-off runway
A runway intended for take-off only.

Taxi-holding position
A designated position at an aerodrome where taxiing aircraft may be required to hold before entering or crossing a runway.

Taxiing
Movement on the surface of an aerodrome of an aircraft under its own power, excluding take-off and landing.

Taxiway
A defined path on an aerodrome for the taxiing of aircraft.

Terminal control area
A control area normally established around a major aerodrome.

Threshold
The beginning of the usable portion of a runway (normally indicated by 'piano key' markings).

ICAO ANNEX TERMINOLOGY

Touchdown zone
The portion of a runway, beyond the threshold, where it is intended that landing aeroplanes first contact the runway.

Track
The path of an aircraft in flight over the earth's surface.

Traffic avoidance advice
Advice given by air traffic control to pilots to assist in collision avoidance.

Traffic information
Information given by air traffic control to pilots regarding other known traffic near or on the flight-planned route.

Transition altitude
The altitude at or below which the vertical position of aircraft is controlled by reference to altitudes (i.e. with Regional QNH set). Transition altitudes vary considerably between countries: 3,000 ft in the UK, 18,000 ft in the USA.

Transition layer
Airspace between the transition altitude and transition level.

Transition level
The lowest flight level available for use above the transition altitude.

Uncertainty phase
When the safety of an aircraft and its occupants is uncertain.

VFR flight
Flight conducted under the Visual Flight Rules.

Visibility
The distance over which prominent unlighted objects by day and prominent lighted objects by night can be seen.

Visual approach
An approach to land by an IFR flight where part or all of an instrument approach procedure is not completed and the approach is conducted by visual reference to terrain.

Visual meteorological conditions
Meteorological conditions expressed in terms of visibility, distance from cloud, and ceiling, equal or better than specified minima.

VMC
Visual meteorological conditions.

Waypoint
A specific geographical location used by an area navigation system.

Regulations Structure

Each Part to each implementing regulation has its own **Acceptable Means of Compliance and Guidance Material (AMC/GM)**. These AMC and GM are amended along with the amendments of the regulations. These AMC/GM are so-called 'soft law' (non-binding rules), and put down in form of EASA Decisions. A comprehensive explanation on AMC in form of questions and answers can be found on the FAQ section of the EASA website.

Furthermore, **Certification Specifications** are also related to the implementing regulations, respectively their parts. Like AMC/GM they are put down as Decisions and are non-binding.

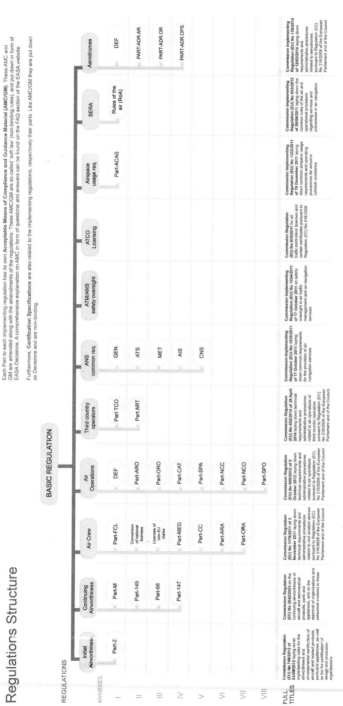

Section **Two**

Meteorology

Aviation Meteorology

Aviation meteorology concerns itself with the daily variation of the atmosphere that is significant for aviation operations. Weather affects the planning and decision-making associated with any given flight and it is vital that a pilot understands how to interpret operational aviation meteorological products. Terrain, airspace and weather can sometimes conspire together to threaten the safety of an aircraft or lead to unmanageable workload for a pilot that can have adverse effects on flight safety and efficiency.

The Atmosphere

The solid earth is surrounded by a mixture of gases which are held to it by the force of gravity forming an ovoid shaped atmosphere in which aeroplanes fly. The atmosphere extends further into space above the equator than at the poles because of the earth's rotation and greater heating at the equator. Spinning about the earth's axis tends to 'throw' air outward and the thickness of the atmosphere is proportional to its temperature. This thermal equator is a belt encircling the earth that has the highest mean annual temperature and so the thickest part of the atmosphere; it moves north of the geographical equator during the northern hemisphere summer (June-September), and south during the southern hemisphere summer (December to March).

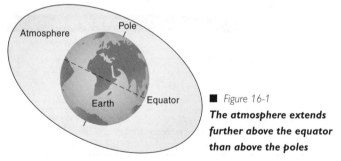

■ *Figure 16-1*
The atmosphere extends further above the equator than above the poles

Subdivision of the Atmosphere

The atmosphere is divided vertically into four regions:
(A) Troposphere
(B) Stratosphere *(some jets operate here)*
(C) Mesosphere
(D) Thermosphere

Most significant aviation weather takes place in the troposphere –the layer of the atmosphere that ranges from the Earth's surface up to the stratosphere. The boundary between the troposphere and stratosphere is called the tropopause and its altitude varies with latitude, and in some cases, weather system (see fig. 16-2). The majority of light aircraft operate within the lowest 10,000ft of the troposphere and the majority of jet transport aircraft operate in the highest part, between 30,000 and 50,000ft.

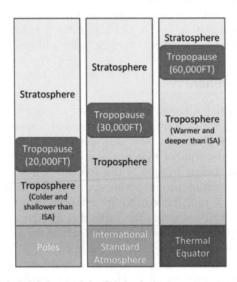

■ *Figure 16-2* **Subdivision of the Atmosphere**

PROPERTY	TROPOSPHERE	STRATOSPHERE
Temperature	*Falls with altitude gained*	*Constant (approx. -57°C)*
Dynamics (air movement)	*• Marked vertical movement and mixing.* *• Warm air rising, cold air descending.*	*Generally limited vertical movement and mixing.*
Water Vapour	*Contains most atmospheric water leading to cloud formation and weather systems.*	*Very limited water vapour and generally clear of cloud.*

Composition of Air

Air is a mixture of gases shown in the table below. While nitrogen is the main constituent of air, the other constituents vital to aviation are: oxygen (for life support and combustion) and water vapour (a significant factor in weather).

COMPOSITION OF AIR	
Gas	*Volume (%)*
Nitrogen	78%
Oxygen	21%
Other gases (argon, carbon dioxide, neon, helium, etc.)	1%
Total	*100%*

Water Vapour

Air always contains some water vapour and even though it is in relative small amounts in the atmosphere it is the critical factor for cloud formation from which precipitation forms (rain, snow, hail, etc.) - essential for life on earth. The ability of air to carry water vapour is proportional to its temperature - the warmer the air the greater its potential is to carry water vapour. The amount of water vapour actually within a given volume of air depends on the surface moisture source it has either originated from or travelled over. A cold polar maritime airmass has a lower potential to carry water vapour than a tropical airmass originating over a dry continental landmass. However, as the cold polar air passes over an ocean region it is likely to contain more water vapour than the tropical continental air mass.

The International Standard Atmosphere (ISA)

The variation of pressure, temperature and density have an important effect on the performance of an aircraft, especially during critical phases of flight; take off and landing, and on the way instrumentation operate, for example the pitot-static system. These parameters in the 'real' atmosphere can vary considerably on a daily basis and the International Standard Atmosphere (ISA) is used as a 'measuring stick' to compare just how much this variation is at a given time and location. You will see the ISA referenced in many Pilot's Operating Handbooks (POH) and so it is very useful to know its characteristics (*figure 16-3*).

The ISA atmosphere is completely dry and pressure, temperature and density all decrease as altitude is gained. Temperature decreases at 2°C per 1000 feet gained in the Troposphere until the tropopause (36,000ft above mean sea level

- amsl) above which it becomes a constant -57°C in the Stratosphere.

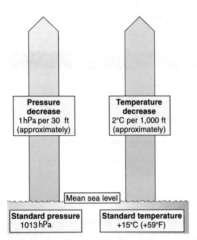

■ *Figure 16-3* ***The International Standard Atmosphere (ISA) (NB: in precise terms, the temperature lapse rate is 1.98°C per 1000ft and remains a constant -56.5°C at 36,090ft)***

The international standard for the unit of pressure used is the hectopascal, abbreviated hPa. As height above sea level is gained in the lower levels of the atmosphere, the pressure drops by approximately 1 hPa per 30 ft up to about 5000 feet amsl.

Mean sea level values in the ISA are:
- Sea Level Pressure 1013.2 hPa (Standard Pressure Setting)
- Temperature +15°C;
- Density 1,225 gm/cubic metre.The difference between ISA and a parameter value inthe 'real'atmosphere is called the ISA deviation.

POH Performance Charts, such as that in *figure 16-4,* enable a pilot to compare the relative impact of actual atmospheric parameters on performance to that if there were ISA conditions.

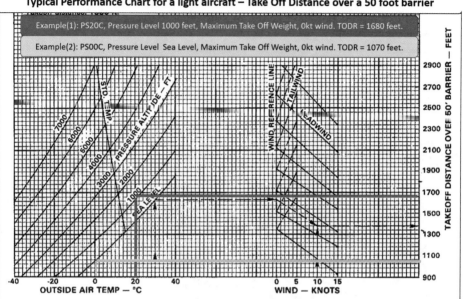

Typical Performance Chart for a light aircraft – Take Off Distance over a 50 foot barrier

Example(1): PS20C, Pressure Level 1000 feet, Maximum Take Off Weight, 0kt wind. TODR = 1680 feet.

Example(2): PS00C, Pressure Level Sea Level, Maximum Take Off Weight, 0kt wind. TODR = 1070 feet.

Figure 16-4 **Typical Performance Chart for Light Aircraft**

ATMOSPHERIC PRESSURE: ITS VERTICAL VARIATION The molecules that make up the air move at high speed in random directions and bounce off any surface that they encounter. The force which they exert on a unit area of that surface is called the **atmospheric pressure**. Atmospheric pressure decreases with height because there are fewer air molecules at the higher altitudes and the lower weight of molecules pressing down from above. An aircraft flying at altitude, or a town located in a mountainous area, will therefore experience a lower pressure than at sea level.

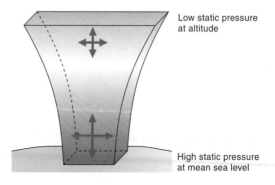

Low static pressure at altitude

High static pressure at mean sea level

■ *Figure 16-5* **Atmospheric pressure decreases with height**

ATMOSPHERIC PRESSURE: ITS HORIZONTAL VARIATION AND THE PRESSURE GRADIENT. Measurements of atmospheric pressure are taken at many locations on a regular basis and, because these locations are at various altitudes, the readings are reduced to a sea level value so that they may be compared. Places that are experiencing the same calculated sea level pressures are then joined with lines on maps known as isobars which may be depicted on meteorological charts. The isobars often form patterns on the weather map that represent what is known as the synoptic situation – the large-scale weather situation of the day. High and low pressure regions with frontal zones can be very helpful for pilots in understanding the big picture for the day and with interpretation of more detailed aviation weather products.

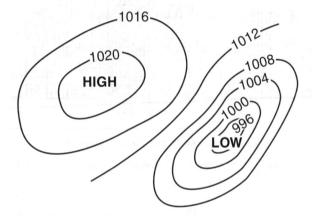

■ Figure 16-6 **Isobars join places of equal sea level pressure**

The variation of pressure with horizontal distance is called the pressure gradient, which is at right-angles to the isobars. If the isobars are very close together rapid changes in pressure occur and the pressure gradient is said to be 'steep' or 'strong'; if they are widely spaced, the pressure changes are more gradual and so the pressure gradient is 'flat' or 'weak'. There is a natural tendency for air to flow from areas of high pressure to areas of low pressure.

This increases with the steepness of the pressure gradient. As we shall see in the chapter on 'Wind'.

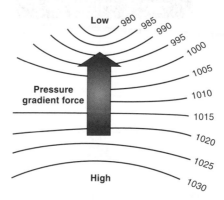

■ *Figure 16-7* **Pressure gradient**

Air Density

Air density decreases with altitude and air density affects aircraft performance.

Density is the mass per unit volume. The force of gravity between each individual air molecule and earth results in a layer of air held around the earth's surface. More air per unit volume is held closer to the surface – therefore air density is greatest at the earth's surface. Air density is important for aviation because:

LIFT FORCE: Supports the aircraft's weight and is generated by the flow of air around the wings. The greater the air density the lower the indicated air speed required to generate a particular lift force.

THRUST FORCE/ENGINE POWER: Is generated by burning fuel and air. Greater air density enables greater engine power. However, greater air density usually results in lower fuel efficiency.

DRAG: A resistive force created by the air as the aircraft moves through it. Greater air density increases air resistance.

HUMAN FACTOR: Flight crew and passengers need air to live and operate effectively. They uptake more oxygen per breath when the air density is higher. At medium to high altitudes the air density falls below the value required to support life.

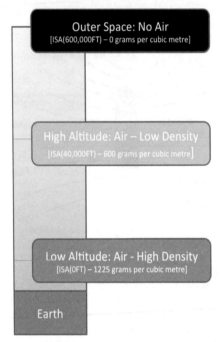

Figure 16-8 **Air density decreases with increasing altitude**

■ *Figure 16-9* **Flying a normally aspirated multi-engine piston aircraft in the mountains is demanding, especially because of the effects of density altitude on performance. Here, the aircraft is at a pressure altitude of 12,800 feet above mean sea level (AMSL) and heading towards an airfield at 10,000 feet (AMSL). Yet daytime surface heating will locally reduce air density at the airfield and reduce aircraft performance to appear as if it were operating at 12,000 feet during take-off and landing**

The water molecule (H_2O) is relatively light and its presence in large numbers in an air mass lowers the overall air density, which affects both the aerodynamic performance of an aeroplane and the power production from engines, making performance slightly poorer on a damp day compared with a dry day. This is an important consideration when operating in conditions of high relative humidity.

Altimetry and Variation in Atmospheric Pressure

Altimetry is covered in more detail in other parts of this series – *Altimeter Setting Procedures* in this volume, *Vertical Navigation* in Volume 3, and *Pressure Instruments* in Volume 4.

The atmospheric pressure at a particular place is continually varying. These variations may be:

- irregular, because of pressure systems which are passing, intensifying or weakening; and
- regular, because of the daily heating and cooling effects of the sun – known as the semi-diurnal variation of pressure, since it has a 12 hour (½ day) cycle, with maximum pressures occurring at about 1000L and 2200L, and pressures some 2 or 3 hPa less occurring in between.

Atmospheric pressure can be measured with either:

- A **mercury barometer**, where atmospheric pressure at sea level can support a column of approximately 30 inches of mercury by pushing it into a partial vacuum.
- An **aneroid barometer**, where a flexible metal chamber that is partially evacuated is compressed by the atmospheric pressure. The aneroid is used in aircraft altimeters to measure the atmospheric pressure and equate variations in air pressure to changes in altitude.

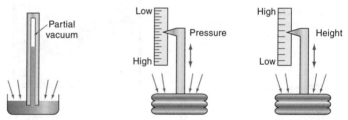

■ *Figure 16-10* **The mercury barometer, aneroid barometer & altimeter**

An altimeter that reads 0 ft at sea level is calibrated to read 30ft when the pressure has dropped by 1 hPa, 300 ft when it has dropped 10 hPa, and 1,000ft when it has dropped 33 hPa, and so on.

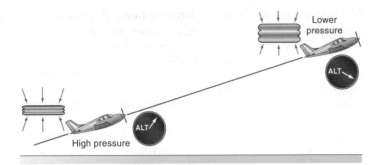

■ *Figure 16-11* **The Altimeter equates a pressure drop with an increase in height.**

ATMOSPHERIC PRESSURE AND DENSITY VARIATION: PRACTICAL CONSIDERATIONS IN ALTIMETRY. Flights cruising with QNH set in the altimeter subscale should reset the QNH to the **Regional Pressure Setting** (RPS) when away from the terminal area and also when entering a new Altimeter Setting Region (ASR). If the QNH is not revised whilst flying towards an area of low pressure the altimeter will read the same altitude in straight and level flight but the aeroplane would actually be descending.

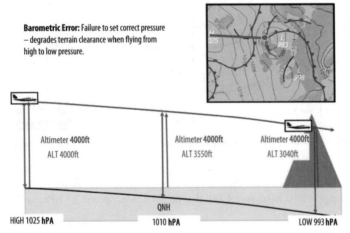

■ *Figure 16-12* **When cruising, reset the altimeter to the correct regional pressure setting**

This situation could be dangerous, since the altimeter will be indicating the altitude above the pressure level in the subscale, and this will be higher than the aeroplane's actual altitude above sea level, i.e. the altimeter will over-read unless the subscale is reset to the lower QNH. Conversely, flying towards an area of high pressure the situation is reversed. The altimeter will under-read, the aeroplane being at a higher altitude than that indicated, unless the subscale is periodically reset to the higher QNH.

In certain circumstances it is considered to be good airmanship to use alternatives to the Regional Pressure Setting. For instance, pilots flying beneath a Terminal Control Area (TMA) may set the QNH pertaining to that TMA, e.g. the London Pressure Setting when under the London TMA. Alternatively, pilots flying within 25 nm of an aerodrome may set the QNH pertaining to that aerodrome.

Now complete: **Practice Questions - The Atmosphere**

1. In what part of the atmosphere do normally aspirated Single Engine Piston (SEP) aircraft fly:

    (a) *Troposphere*
    (b) *Mesosphere*
    (c) *Stratosphere*
    (d) *Thermosphere*

2. The atmospheric boundary between the troposphere and stratosphere is called the:

    (a) *Stratopause*
    (b) *Exosphere*
    (c) *Tropopause*
    (d) *Mesolayer*

3. The main gases that form the atmosphere are:

    (a) *Oxygen, Hydrogen.*
    (b) *Nitrogen, Oxygen.*
    (c) *Water Vapour, Oxygen.*
    (d) *Nitrogen, Carbon Dioxide.*

4. Most of the water vapour in the atmosphere is contained in the:

    (a) *Troposphere*
    (b) *Mesosphere*
    (c) *Stratosphere*
    (d) *Thermosphere*

---

5. Aircraft take off and landing performance reduces at lower air density. Which airfield would you expect the lowest air density to be found:

    (a) *An airfield at 10,000 feet above mean sea level with an air temperature of 30° Celsius.*
    (b) *An airfield at 10,000 feet above mean sea level with an air temperature of 0° Celsius.*
    (c) *An airfield at 1,000 feet above mean sea level with an air temperature of 30° Celsius.*
    (d) *An airfield at mean sea level with an air temperature of 15° Celsius.*

6. What is the International Standard Atmosphere (ISA):

    (a) *A theoretical atmosphere used to calculate performance above the transition altitude.*
    (b) *The actual atmospheric conditions on a given day.*
    (c) *A theoretical reference atmosphere with which actual atmospheric conditions can be compared.*
    (d) *The atmosphere used to calculate actual performance of an aircraft.*

7. In the ISA what happens to temperature as altitude is gained in the troposphere:

    (a) *Increases.*
    (b) *Constant.*
    (c) *Decreases.*
    (d) *Stays constant then decreases.*

8. In the ISA and for unsaturated air, the temperature changes as follows:

    (a) *Decreases by 2°C for each 1000 ft gained.*
    (b) *Decreases by 1.5°C for each 1000 ft gained.*
    (c) *Decreases by 3°C for each 1000 ft gained.*
    (d) *Increases by 2°C for each 1000 ft gained.*

9. Above approximately 36,000 ft in the theoretical ISA:

    (a) *Is the troposphere where temperature continues to decrease with altitude gained.*
    (b) *Is the mesosphere where temperature remains a constant with altitude gained.*
    (c) *Is the stratosphere where temperature continues to decrease with altitude gained.*
    (d) *Is the stratosphere where temperature remains a constant with altitude gained.*

10. On a given day, the sea level pressure is 1013.2 hPA. The temperature at 3,000 ft AMSL is given as minus 4°C. The temperature difference compared with the ISA is:

    (a) ISA -13°C
    (b) ISA -4°C
    (c) ISA -10°C
    (d) ISA +10°C

11. As altitude increases, atmospheric pressure:

    (a) Increases.
    (b) Remains constant.
    (c) Decreases.
    (d) Decreases then increases.

12. Aircraft measure static atmospheric pressure using:

    (a) Thermocouple.
    (b) Aneroid barometer.
    (c) Pitot tube.
    (d) Radio altimeter.

13. A line on a map joining places of equal sea level pressure is called:

    (a) An isobar.
    (b) An isopress.
    (c) A pressure gradient.
    (d) An equi-pressure line.

14. The variation of pressure with horizontal distance is called:

    (a) An isobar.
    (b) An isopress.
    (c) A pressure gradient.
    (d) An equi-pressure line.

15. An aircraft is flying from point A where there is high pressure to point B where there is low pressure. The Minimum Safe Altitude (MSA) along the route is 2500ft and the aircraft is flying at an indicated altitude of 2500ft at point A. Unless the pilot periodically resets the lower regional pressure setting as an aeroplane flies towards point B:

(a) *The altitude will continue to read 2500ft on the altimeter but terrain clearance will reduce.*

(b) *The altitude will reduce on the altimeter but the terrain clearance will remain constant.*

(c) *The altitude will continue to read 2500ft on the altimeter and terrain clearance will remain constant.*

(d) *Altitude as read on the altimeter will increase and terrain clearance will increase.*

Answers: 1a, 2c, 3b, 4a, 5a, 6c, 7c, 8a, 9d, 10a, 11c, 12b, 13a, 14c, 15a.

Heating Effects in the Atmosphere

Heating effects in the atmosphere

The sun radiates energy and heats the earth.

The source of energy on earth is electromagnetic radiation emitted from the sun – we experience some of this energy as light and heat. A lot of the visible solar radiation incident to the atmosphere passes through it and is absorbed by the earth's surface causing it to heat up and re-emit infra-red radiation (longer wavelength) which is absorbed more readily by the atmosphere. The earth's curved surface presents itself at different angles from incident radiation; ranging from oblique at the poles to perpendicular at the equator. Therefore, radiation incident on the surface is spread over a greater area at the poles than at the equator and heating of the surface is less.

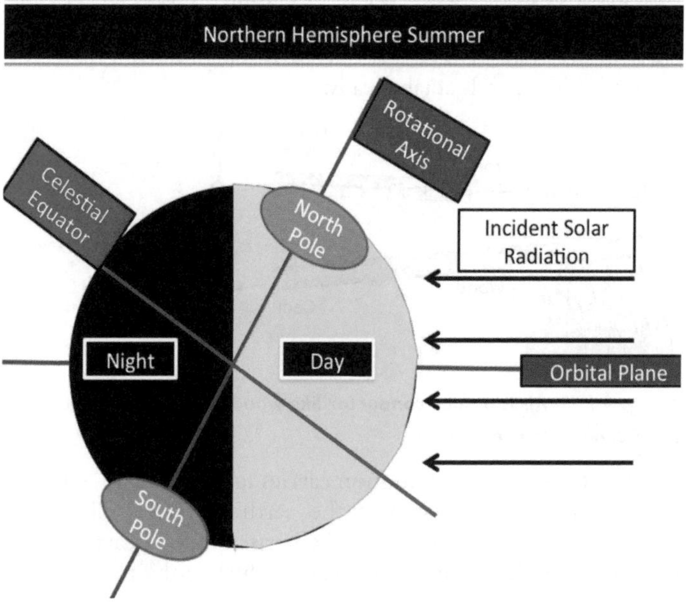

■ Figure 17-1 **The earth's rotation causes day and night**

Solar Heating

Heating from solar radiation is greatest in the tropics.

Solar radiation is like a torch beam that produces more intense light on a perpendicular surface than on an oblique surface. Since solar radiation strikes tropical regions from approximately directly overhead throughout the year, the heating is intense.

In contrast, the sun's rays strike polar regions of the earth at an oblique angle and, during the winter these regions may not receive any solar heating at all.

The Transfer of Heat Energy

A diabatic process is one in which heat energy is transferred from one body to another, or redistributed in the one body by a number of means, including:

RADIATION All bodies transmit energy in the form of electromagnetic radiation: the higher the temperature of the body, the shorter the wavelength of the radiation. Radiation from the sun is therefore of shorter wavelength than the re-radiation from the earth, which is much cooler.

ABSORPTION Any body in the path of radiation will absorb some of its energy. How much it absorbs depends upon both the nature of the body and of the radiation. A densely-forested area will absorb more solar radiation than snow-covered mountains.

CONDUCTION .Is the process of heat transfer within a body or between bodies in contact with one another. Iron is a good conductor of heat – wood is a poor conductor, as is air. A parcel of air in contact with the earth's surface is heated by conduction, but will not transfer this heat energy to neighbouring parcels of air instead it expands adiabatically.

Adiabatic Processes
Heat is neither added to nor removed from the system. The expansion and compression of gases are adiabatic processes where, although heat is neither added nor removed, the temperature of the system may change, eg. placing a finger over the outlet of a bicycle pump will illustrate that compressing air increases its temperature. Conversely, air that is compressed and stored at room temperature will feel cool if released to the atmosphere and allowed to expand. Reducing pressure will lower the temperature.

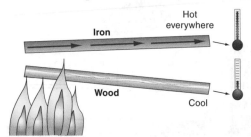

■ *Figure 17-2* **Air is a poor conductor like wood. A metal airframe is a good conductor like iron**

CONVECTION A body in motion carries its heat energy with it. A mass of air that is heated at the earth's surface will expand, becoming less dense, and rise. As it rises, it will carry its heat energy higher into the atmosphere – which is the process called convection.

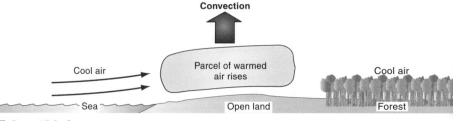

■ *Figure 17-3* **Convection**

ADVECTION When air moves in to replace air that has risen by convection, this horizontal motion of air is known as advection. The air mass, moving horizontally by advection, will of course bring its heat energy (and moisture content) with it.

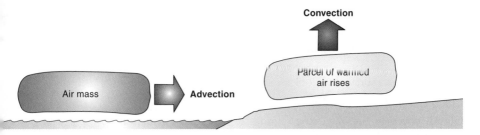

■ *Figure 17-4* **Advection is the horizontal transfer of air and heat energy**

The general vertical circulation pattern of airflow that occurs on a large scale around the earth also happens on a smaller scale in localised areas.

Surface Heating

Different surfaces heat differently.

The heating of various surfaces and the temperatures which they reach depends upon a number of factors:

THE SPECIFIC HEAT CAPACITY OF THE SURFACE Because of the molecular structure of any given material, a certain amount of energy is required to increase its temperature. The specific heat capacity is a measure of the amount of energy required to raise the temperature of one kilogram of a material by one degree Celsius. Water has a higher heat capacity than most land surfaces and requires more heat energy to raise its temperature. Land will therefore heat and cool more quickly than water bodies.

REFLECTIVITY AND EMISSIVITY OF A SURFACE Different materials interact differently with incoming solar radiation. Surfaces with high reflectivity absorb less solar radiation and therefore heat up less quickly, examples: include snow and water.

Any particular surface will have a temperature and so also emit radiation as well as absorb it. The amount of radiation emitted is proportional to surface emissivity. Land surfaces typically have a lower emissivity than water.

CONVECTION ABOVE A SURFACE As a surface is heated by solar radiation, a temperature difference develops between the surface and the air. The greater the difference (i.e rising current of warm air) the greater the thermal, generated and there is therefore a cooling effect as heat is transported away from the surface by convection. If a wind is blowing at the same time, the rate of cooling increases.

CONDUCTIVITY OF SURFACE As the surface is heated it becomes warmer than the layers below. Heat is conducted away from the surface and it cools during the day. Overnight the surface cools by emitting radiation into space, the temperature gradient reverses and it is typically warmed by the underlying layers.

EVAPORATION ABOVE A SURFACE Most surfaces contain water either within them or above them. Heat transfers to the water causing it to evaporate and cool the surface.

Cloud Cover

Cloud coverage by day stops some of the solar radiation penetrating to the earth's surface, resulting in reduced heating of the earth and lower temperatures. The air in contact with the surface will therefore be subject to less heating by day.

Cloud cover affects surface heating and cooling.

By night, however, cloud coverage causes the opposite effect and prevents some of the heat energy escaping from the earth's surface. The atmosphere beneath the cloud will experience less cooling and higher temperatures will result.

Terrestrial Re-radiation

Solar radiation penetrates the atmosphere and heats the earth. Heat energy in the earth's surface is re-radiated into the atmosphere. However, it is different from incident solar radiation in that is has a longer wavelength which means it is more readily absorbed by the atmosphere, especially by water vapour and carbon dioxide.

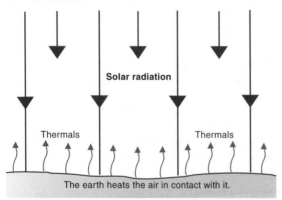

■ *Figure 17-5* **Indirect heating of the atmosphere by the sun**

Vertical Temperature Structure and Stability

The net result of heat transfer in the atmosphere is described by the ISA (Chapter 16) in which temperature decreases at 2°C for each 1,000 ft climbed. However, this is not the real atmosphere which contains water vapour and is influenced by many different heating process – it cools at what is known as the **Environmental Lapse Rate (ELR)** that is specific to weather conditions on any particular day.

A discrete "parcel" of air behaves adiabatically. If a dry, unsaturated "parcel" of air rises it will cool at 3°C for each 1,000ft climbed – the **Dry Adiabatic Lapse Rate (DALR)**.

Any water vapour in this parcel of air that cools to its dewpoint will condense and release latent heat energy. The parcel of air will then cool at a lower rate – the Saturated Adiabatic Lapse Rate (SALR). Its value varies considerably, but at low levels, it is approximately 1.5°C per 1,000 ft climbed.

Lapse rates are important because they impact the performance of an aircraft in the real atmosphere, atmospheric stability and the type of weather that may develop. The stability of the atmosphere can be determined as follows:

- **ELR less than SALR and DALR. Stable:** air has a tendency to return back to its original position if displaced. Likely weather includes clear skies, fog, stratus and mountain waves.

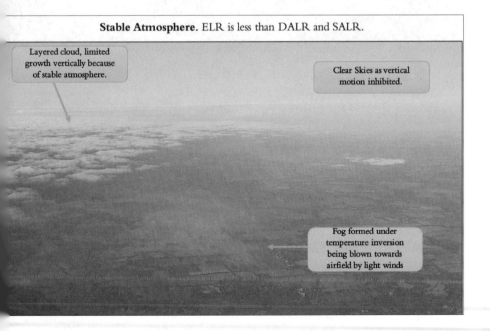

Stable Atmosphere. ELR is less than DALR and SALR.

Layered cloud, limited growth vertically because of stable atmosphere.

Clear Skies as vertical motion inhibited.

Fog formed under temperature inversion being blown towards airfield by light winds

- **ELR greater than SALR and DALR. Unstable:** air has a tendency to rise if displaced. Likely weather includes cumulus and cumulonimbus cloud

Unstable Atmosphere. ELR is greater than DALR and SALR.

Thunderstorms; *cloud tops reaching the Tropopause*

Cumulus Cloud; *indicating air continuing to rise after initial displacement*

- **ELR less than DALR but greater than SALR. Conditional Instability:** dry, unsaturated air is stable. Moist, saturated air is unstable.

Conditional Instability: ELR is less than DALR but greater than SALR.

Cloud growth as moist, saturated air becomes unstable

Haze associated with stab dry layer

Temperature Inversions

Under low wind conditions and on clear nights the earth cools down by losing a great deal of heat through terrestrial radiation and the air in contact with the surface also cools by conduction. The cooler air tends to sink and does not mix with air at the higher levels. This will lead to the air at ground level being cooler than the air at altitude, a phenomenon known as a **temperature inversion which can range from twenty feet to hundreds of feet above the ground**. It is an important consideration for pilots as an inversion can result in meteorological threats such as poor visibility including ground fog, low cloud (stratus) or windshear. Inversions can also be elevated (detached from the surface) usually because of high pressure weather systems.

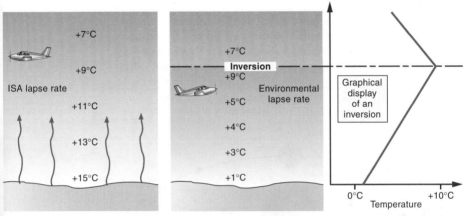

■ *Figure 17-6* **The normal temperature situation and the temperature inversion**

Local Heating and Cooling

The earth rotates on its axis once every 24 hours resulting in day and night on the earth and the apparent motion of the sun across the earth.

Solar heating of the earth's surface occurs only by day, but terrestrial re-radiation of heat energy occurs continually through both the day and the night. The net result is that the earth's surface heats up by day, reaches its maximum temperature about mid-afternoon, and cools by night, reaching its minimum temperature around sunrise.

This continual heating and cooling on a daily basis is called the **diurnal variation of temperature** – a typical daily pattern of heating and cooling that is most extreme in desert areas and more moderate over the oceans.

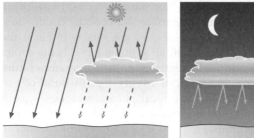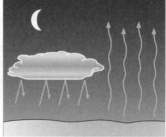

■ Figure 17-7 **Cloud reduces surface heating by day and cooling by night**

Seasonal Variations

The earth's axis is tilted (approximately 23 degrees from the vertical). This means that radiation incident on the hemisphere tilted away from the sun arrives at a more oblique angle with less heat transferred - placing that hemisphere in winter and the other tilted towards the sun in summer. Seasons result from the earth orbiting the sun once every year producing a shift in which hemisphere is tilted towards the sun and which is away.

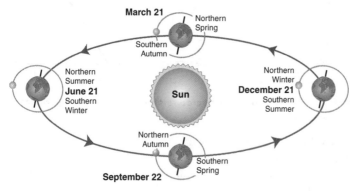

■ Figure 17-8 **Solar radiation received at the earth's surface is more intense in summer**

General Circulation

The greater heating of the earth's surface in the tropics causes the air above it to become relatively warm, expand, become less dense and rise. At the top of the troposphere this rising air cannot continue vertically (because of the stratospheric isotherm/ inversion) and so moves outwards towards higher latitudes. As a result, new air moves in across the earth's surface to replace the air which has risen.

In contrast, the cooler air over the polar regions sinks down, creating a large-scale vertical circulation pattern in the

troposphere. This process is known as the **general circulation** pattern and consists of three main 'cells':
* the polar cell;
* the mid-latitude cell (or Ferrel cell); and
* the tropical cell (or Hadley cell).

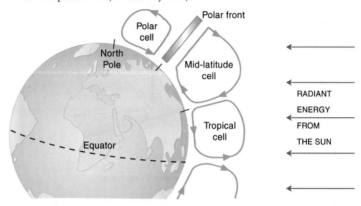

■ Figure 17-9 **The general circulation pattern**

The hot and less dense air rising over the tropics creates a band of low pressure at the earth's surface known as the **equatorial trough**, into which other surface air will move (known as *convergence*).

The cool and dense air subsiding in the polar regions creates a high-pressure area at the earth's surface in the very high latitudes and the surface air will spread outwards (known as *divergence*).

Temperature Measurement

Heat Energy

As a body of matter absorbs heat energy, its molecules become more agitated. This agitation and motion is measured as temperature, which can be used as a measure of heat energy. The temperature at which molecular agitation would theoretically be zero is known as absolute zero, i.e. zero on the scientific absolute scale of temperature, and this occurs at −273°C.

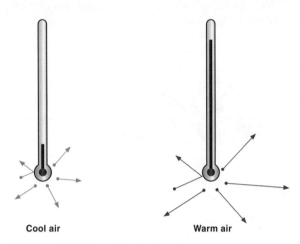

Cool air   Warm air

■ *Figure 17-10* **Air molecules 'move' more in warm air**

Temperature Scales

Various scales are used to measure temperature, but the one used in most countries for aviation and meteorology is the **Celsius** scale (previously called *centigrade*). The Celsius scale divides the temperature difference between the boiling and freezing points of water into 100 degrees. On the Celsius scale, water boils at 100°C and freezes at 0°C, at the standard pressure setting, but different temperatures will apply at different pressure settings.

In the United States, the Fahrenheit temperature scale is predominantly used, though the Celsius scale is being introduced. The Fahrenheit scale is based on water boiling at 212°F and freezing at 32°F.

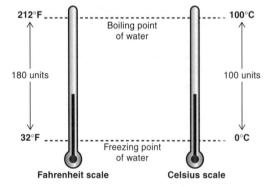

■ *Figure 17-11* **Different temperature scales measure the same thing**

There is a requirement for pilots (who may fly in different countries) to be able to convert from °F to °C and vice versa. Flight navigation computers have conversion scales marked on them to make these conversions easy, but you should still know the mathematical relationship that exists between °C and °F.

- Temperature in °F = $9/5 \times$ °C + 32.
- Temperature in °C = $5/9 \times$ (°F − 32).

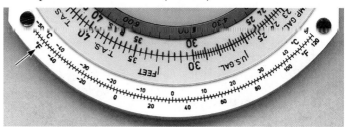

■ *Figure 17-12* **Temperature conversion scale on a navigation computer**

Now complete: **Practice Questions - Heating Effects**

---

1. The transfer of heat as electromagnetic waves is called the process of:

(a) Convection
(b) Conduction
(c) Radiation
(d) Advection

2. The transfer of heat from body to body is called the process of:

(a) Convection
(b) Conduction
(c) Radiation
(d) Advection

3. The transfer of heat by the horizontal motion of an air mass is called:

(a) Convection
(b) Conduction
(c) Radiation
(d) Advection

4. The transfer of heat by the vertical motion of an air mass is called:

(a) *Convection*
(b) *Conduction*
(c) *Radiation*
(d) *Advection*

5. The troposphere is mostly heated:

(a) *Directly by the solar radiation.*
(b) *By the Earth's surface via convection and re-radiation.*
(c) *By Earth's surface re-radiation into space.*
(d) *By Earth's surface by conduction.*

6. Solar heating of the earth's surface is:

(a) *The same across the globe.*
(b) *Greatest at polar regions.*
(c) *Greatest at mid-latitude, temperate zones.*
(d) *Greatest at the tropics.*

7. Differences in solar radiation heating of the earth's surface results in:

(a) *No effect on the atmosphere in contact with the earth's surface.*
(b) *Heating of the stratosphere.*
(c) *Differences in heating of the atmosphere close to the earth's surface and convection.*
(d) *Differences in heating of the atmosphere close to the earth's surface but no changes in its buoyancy.*

8. At night, air at the top of a mountain range cools more quickly than the ambient environmental air. What will happen to the air at the top of the mountain range throughout the night:

(a) *It will stay where it is.*
(b) *It will become less dense and ascend.*
(c) *It will become denser than ambient, environmental air and descend into the valleys.*
(d) *It will become denser than surrounding air and ascend.*

9. Terrestrial radiation is:

(a) *The direct heating of the earth by solar radiation.*
(b) *Thermal radiation emitted into the atmosphere as a result of the earth's temperature.*
(c) *Conduction of solar radiation heating of the earth.*
(d) *Thermal radiation emitted into the earth.*

10. At a given latitude and longitude, solar heating of the sea:

    (a) Is less rapid than land because water has a greater heat capacity.
    (b) The same as land because water has the same heat capacity.
    (c) More rapid than land because water has a greater heat capacity.
    (d) More rapid than the land in the morning and less rapid in the afternoon as its heat capacity changes throughout the day.

11. A day with clear skies compared to one with overcast cloud will result in (assuming the same air mass):

    (a) A warmer day and colder night.
    (b) A colder day and colder night.
    (c) Warmer day and warmer night.
    (d) A colder day and warmer night.

12. If the air at the earth's surface is cooler than that above there is a:

    (a) Hydrolapse.
    (b) Temperature reversion.
    (c) Temperature inversion.
    (d) Convective situation.

13. Convert 10° Celsius to degrees Fahrenheit:

    (a) 32°F
    (b) 50°F
    (c) 60°F
    (d) 15°F

14. Convert 41° Fahrenheit to degrees Celsius:

    (a) 5°C
    (b) 10°C
    (c) 0°C
    (d) 41°C

Wind

What is Wind?

Wind refers to the horizontal flow of air across the Earth. Wind can enhance, degrade or pose a hazard to an aircraft's performance enroute and during critical flight phases (takeoff/landing). Vertical airflow only accounts for 0.1% of wind but it results in cloud formation and is associated with severe hazards such as thunderstorms or wind shear. It is important for pilots to understand how wind and vertical airflow interact as this will help with the interpretation of weather reports and forecasts and a proper assessment of impact on flight operations.

How Wind is Described

* **wind direction** is the direction from which the wind is blowing and is expressed in degrees measured clockwise from north;
* **wind strength** is expressed in knots (abbreviated kt).
* **wind velocity:** direction and strength together, usually written in the form 270/35, or 270/35kt (to specify the unit), i.e. a wind blowing from due west (270°) at a strength of 35 knots.

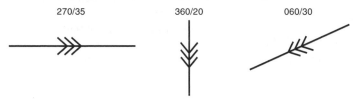

| 270/35 | 360/20 | 060/30 |

■ *Figure 18-1* **Examples of wind velocity**

Meteorologists reports and forecasts relate wind direction to true north, expressed in degrees true (°T). For example **34012KT** means a wind strength of 12 knots from a direction of 340°T. **23020G35KT** indicates a wind from 230°T at 20 knots, with **gusts** to 35 knots.

Runways, however, are described in terms of their **magnetic direction,** which would align to the direction indicated by a magnetic compass of an aeroplane lined up on that runway.

The wind direction relative to the runway direction is critical for takeoff and landing. For this reason, winds passed to the pilot by the tower have direction expressed in **degrees magnetic.** This is also the case for the recorded messages on the Automatic Terminal Information Service (ATIS) that pilots can listen to on the radio at some airfields.

Veering and Backing

A wind whose direction is changing in a clockwise direction is called a **veering** wind. For example, following a change from 150/25 to 220/30, the wind is said to have veered.

A wind whose direction is changing in an anticlockwise direction is called a **backing** wind. A change from 100/15 to 030/12 is an example of a wind that has backed.

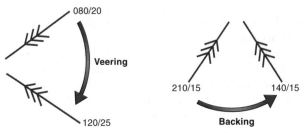

■ *Figure 18-2* **A veering wind and a backing wind**

What Causes a Wind to Blow?

A change in velocity (speed and/or direction) is called acceleration. Acceleration is caused by a force (or forces) being exerted on an object, be it an aeroplane, a car or a parcel of air.

The combined effect of all the forces acting on a body is known as the net (or resultant) force, and determines the acceleration of the body. If all of the forces acting on a parcel of air balance each other so that the resultant force is zero, then the parcel of air will not accelerate, but will continue to move in a straight line at a constant speed (or stay still). A steady wind velocity is known as **balanced flow** (also known as the geostrophic wind).

The Pressure Gradient Force

In the atmosphere, the force that is usually responsible for starting a parcel of air moving is the **pressure gradient force**. This acts to move air from areas of **high** pressure to areas of **low** pressure.

Places on the earth where air pressure is the same are joined on meteorological maps with lines which are called **isobars**, so the pressure gradient force will act at right angles to these and in the direction from the high to the low pressure. The stronger the pressure gradient (i.e. the greater the pressure difference over a given distance), the greater this force will be and, consequently, the stronger the wind will blow.

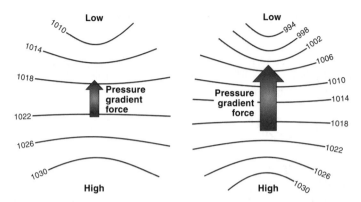

■ *Figure 18-3* **The pressure gradient force will start a parcel of air moving**

If the pressure gradient force were the only force acting on a parcel of air, it would continue to accelerate towards the low pressure, getting faster and faster, and eventually the high- and low-pressure areas would disappear because of this transfer of air.

We know that this, in fact, does not occur, so there must be some other force that acts on the parcel of air to prevent it rushing from the high-pressure area into the low-pressure area. This other force occurs because of the rotation of the earth and is known as the **Coriolis** force.

The Coriolis Force

The Coriolis force acts on a **moving** parcel of air. It is not a 'real' force, but an apparent force resulting from the passage of the air over the rotating earth. The Coriolis force may also cause gyroscopic wander - see Instrumentation, in Volume 4 of the *Air Pilots Manual*.

Imagine a parcel of air that is stationary over Point A on the equator. It is in fact moving with Point A as the earth rotates on its axis from west to east. Now, suppose that a pressure gradient exists with a high pressure at A and a low pressure at Point B, directly north of A. The parcel of air at A starts moving towards B, but still with its motion towards the east because of the earth's rotation.

The further north one goes from the equator, the less is this easterly motion of the earth and so the earth will lag behind the easterly motion of the parcel of air. Point B will only have moved to B', but the parcel of air will have moved to A". In other words, to an observer standing on the earth's surface the parcel of air will **appear** to turn to the right. This effect is because of the Coriolis force.

If the parcel of air were being accelerated in a southerly direction from a high-pressure area in the northern hemisphere towards a low near the equator, the earth's rotation towards the east would 'get away from it' and so the airflow would appear to turn right also – A having moved to A', but the airflow having only reached B" to the west.

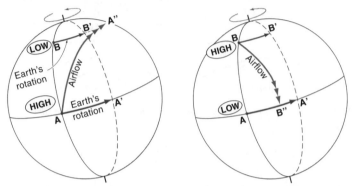

■ *Figure 18-4* **The Coriolis force acts towards the right in the northern hemisphere**

The faster the airflow, the greater the Coriolis effect – if there is no air flow, then there is no Coriolis effect. The Coriolis effect is also greater in regions away from the equator and towards the poles, where changes in latitude cause more significant changes in the speed at which each point is moving towards the east.

In the northern hemisphere, the Coriolis force deflects the wind to the **right**; in the southern hemisphere, the situation is reversed and it deflects the wind to the left.

The Geostrophic Wind

The two forces acting on a moving airstream are:
• the pressure gradient force; and
• the Coriolis force.

The pressure gradient force gets the air moving and the Coriolis effect turns it to the right. This curving of the airflow over the earth's surface will continue until the pressure gradient force is balanced by the Coriolis force, resulting in a wind flow that is steady and blowing in a direction **parallel to the isobars**. This **balanced flow** is called the **geostrophic wind**.

The **geostrophic wind** is important to a weather forecaster because it flows in a **direction** parallel to the isobars with the low pressure to its left, and at a strength directly proportional to the spacing of the isobars (i.e. proportional to the pressure gradient). The closeness of the isobars on a chart enables a reasonable forecast of the wind strength to be made.

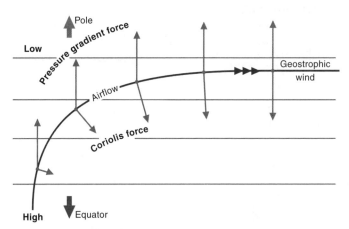

■ *Figure 18-5* **Balanced flow will occur parallel to the isobars – the geostrophic wind**

Buys Ballot's Law

Buys Ballot was a Dutchman who noticed that:

"If you stand with your back to the wind in the northern hemisphere, the low pressure will be on your left."

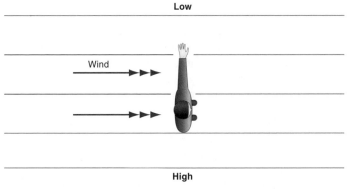

■ *Figure 18-6* **Buys Ballot's law – with your back to the wind, the low pressure is on your left (northern hemisphere)**

Flying from high to low (Flying from high to low, beware below)

Flying from high to low, beware below.

If an aeroplane in the northern hemisphere is experiencing right (starboard) drift, the wind is from the left and therefore, according to Buys Ballot's law, the aeroplane is flying towards an area of lower pressure. Low pressure often has poor weather associated with it, such as low cloud, rain and poor visibility. Also, unless the pilot periodically resets the lower Regional Pressure Settings (RPS), the altimeter will over-read, which is not a healthy situation, so beware below.

Flying from low to high

If an aeroplane in the northern hemisphere is experiencing left (port) drift, the wind is from the right and therefore, according to Buys Ballot's law, the aeroplane is flying towards an area of higher pressure. High pressure often indicates a more stable atmosphere and generally better weather (although fog may occur).

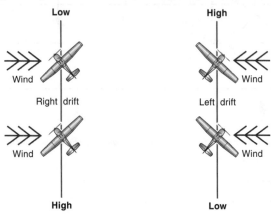

■ *Figure 18-7* **Right (starboard) drift – low pressure area ahead**

■ *Figure 18-8* **Left (port) drift – high pressure area ahead**

The Gradient Wind

Isobars (the lines joining places of equal pressure) are usually curved. For the wind to flow parallel to these isobars, it must be accelerated, in the sense that its direction is changing. In the same manner as a stone when being swung on a string is pulled into the turn by a force, a curving air flow must have a resultant (or net) force acting on it to pull it into the turn.

For a wind that is blowing (anticlockwise) around a **low** in the northern hemisphere, the net force results from the pressure gradient force being greater than the Coriolis force, thereby pulling the air flow in towards the **low.**

For a wind that is blowing (clockwise) around a **high,** the net force results from the Coriolis force being greater than the pressure gradient force. Since the Coriolis force increases with wind speed, it follows that wind speed around a **high** will be greater than wind speed around a **low** with similarly spaced isobars.

In the northern hemisphere, the result is a wind flowing parallel to the isobars, clockwise around a **high** (known as anticyclonic motion) and anticlockwise around a **low** (known as cyclonic motion). Balanced wind flow around curved isobars is called the **gradient wind.**

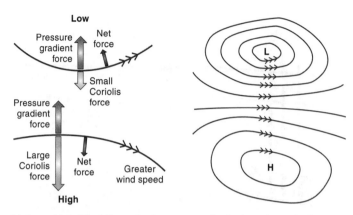

■ *Figure 18-9* **Wind flows clockwise around a high and anticlockwise around a low in the northern hemisphere**

The Surface Wind

The surface wind is very important to pilots because of the effect it has on take-offs and landings. Surface wind is measured at 10 metres (30 ft) above level and open ground, i.e. where windsocks and other wind indicators are generally placed. Wind is usually less strong near the surface than at higher levels because of the friction exerted by the Earth's surface - the rougher the surface, the greater the slowing down. Friction forces will be least over oceans and flat desert areas, and greatest over hilly or city areas with many obstructions.

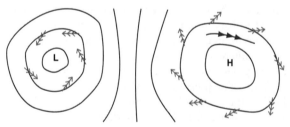

■ *Figure 18-10* **Friction causes the surface wind to weaken in strength and back in direction**

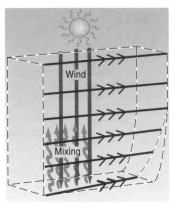 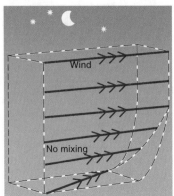

Wind stronger and does not back as much   Wind weaker and backs more

■ *Figure 18-11* **The diurnal variation of wind**

Frictional forces caused by the earth's surface decrease rapidly with height throughout what is known as the atmospheric boundary layer – a larger version of that which forms over the surface of a wing. The top of the boundary layer is defined as the height at which frictional and thermodynamic effects of the earth on the atmosphere become negligible. The height of the top varies with stability of the air and roughness of the surface. However, a good rule of thumb is that frictional effects generally become negligible at between 2000 and 3000 feet above ground level.

At the top of the boundary layer, the gradient wind flows parallel to curved isobars unimpeded by surface frictional forces. The surface wind is influenced significantly by friction, it is much slower than the gradient wind and so the Coriolis effect reduces and the resultant surface wind direction will back compared to that of the gradient. The pressure gradient force will have a more pronounced effect in the lower levels, causing the wind to flow in towards the low-pressure area and out from the high-pressure area.

Different surface friction effects have an impact on the degree of backing of the surface wind and its speed compared to that at 2000FT AGL. The atmospheric stability also has an impact on how well mixed the different layers are and the amount of energy transferred to the lower levels of the boundary layer. The table below provides an approximate guide.

Terrain	Atmospheric Stability	Degrees of Backing	% of 2000ft AGL Wind
Land	Stable	Backs 40-50°	25%
Land	Average	Backs 30°	35%
Land	Unstable	Backs 10-20°	50%
Sea	Stable	Backs 15-20°	80%
Sea	Unstable	Backs 5-10°	90%

Diurnal (Daily) Variation in the Surface Wind

During the day, solar radiation heats the earth's surface heating which in turn heats the air in contact with it. This air becomes buoyant and convection then mixes air at different levels in the boundary layer. Faster air at the top of the boundary layer is 'brought' down to lower levels in this way which means that daytime surface winds are usually stronger and veered compared to night time surface winds.

Day – veer and increase.
Night – slack and back.

During the night, mixing of the layers will decrease. The gradient wind will continue to blow at altitude, but its effects will not be mixed with the airflow at the surface to such an extent as during the day. The night wind at surface level will drop in strength and the Coriolis effect will weaken, i.e. compared to the day wind, the night wind will drop in strength and back in direction. Wind shear may be greatest at night. Turbulence may be greater during the day. Both are threats to aircraft operation.

Localised Friction Effects

The surface wind may bear no resemblance to the gradient wind at 2,000 ft agl and above if it has to blow over and around obstacles such as hills, trees, buildings, etc. The wind will form turbulent eddies, the size of which will depend on both the size of the obstructions and the wind strength. Most aerodrome plates in the AIP (Aeronautical Information Publication) will warn when localised friction/turbulent effects may occur in the vicinity of aerodromes in strong winds. However, expect localised effects to occur at any airport with significant hangarage or urban areas nearby, or with aerodromes in the vicinity of steep gradient hills or cliffs.

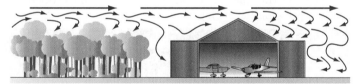

■ *Figure 18-12* **Friction and obstacles affect the surface wind**

Local Air Movements

The Sea Breeze by Day

The process known as a sea breeze occurs on sunny days, when the land heats more quickly than the sea. The combination of light winds and convection together produce sea breezes. The air above the land becomes warmer and rises (usually by mid- to late afternoon). This sets up the situation for a vertical circulation pattern with the cooler air from offshore moving in to replace the air from over the land which has risen as a result of surface heating.

The vertical extent of a sea breeze is usually only 1,000 to 2,000 ft.

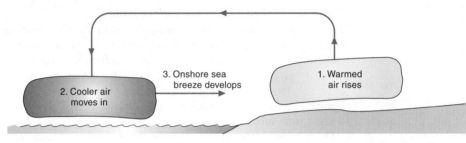

■ *Figure 18-13* ***The sea breeze – a small circulation cell***

Sea breezes may have a significant, localised effect on aerodromes near a coastline. If the sea breeze opposes the general wind pattern, it is quite possible that the wind velocity at circuit height will be quite different from that at ground level resulting in windshear and turbulence during takeoff and landing.

A sea breeze may cause visibility problems as it brings cool, moist sea air over the land - mist and fog may form especially in the evening and even in the summer. If there is already sea fog then an onshore sea breeze could bring it over coastal airfields.

Other associated weather include slow moving troughs (sea breeze fronts) that promote the formation of thunderstorms inland. This is especially so when there are near parallel coastlines with their own sea breeze developing and meeting over the land.

The Land Breeze by Night

By night, the land cools quicker than the sea, causing the air above it to cool and subside. The air over the sea is warmer and will rise.

A land breeze could hold a sea fog offshore early in the day but, as the land warms, the land breeze will diminish and a sea breeze develop, bringing the sea fog.

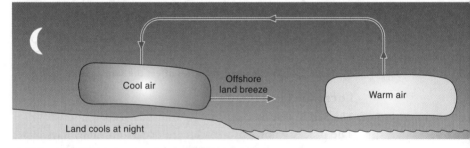

■ *Figure 18-14* ***The land breeze blows offshore at night***

Katabatic Winds

During night-time the earth's surface loses a lot of heat through terrestrial radiation and cools down. This is particularly the case on clear, cloudless nights. The air in contact with the ground loses heat to it by conduction, cools down, becomes denser and starts to sink.

In mountainous regions the cool air will flow down the sides of the mountain slopes and into the valleys, creating what is called a **katabatic wind**. In certain areas, katabatic winds can reach a strength of 30 knots in the valleys below by sunrise.

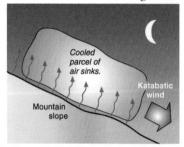

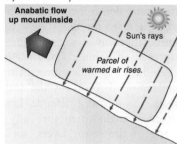

■ *Figure 18-15* **Katabatic winds blow down mountain slopes and valleys at night**

■ *Figure 18-16* **Anabatic winds drift up mountain slopes by day**

Anabatic Winds

Heating of a mountain slope by day causes the air mass in contact with it to warm, decreasing its density and causing it to flow up the slope. Since its flow uphill is opposed by gravity, the daytime anabatic wind is generally a weaker flow than katabatic wind.

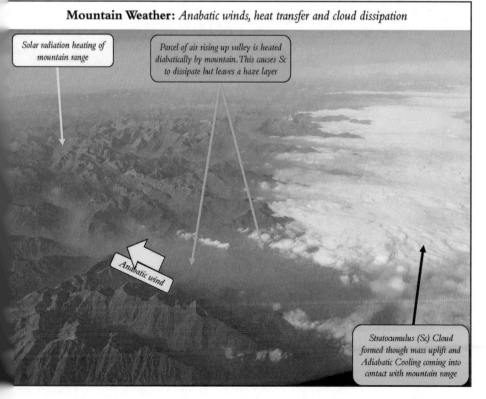

Mountain Weather: *Anabatic winds, heat transfer and cloud dissipation*

Solar radiation heating of mountain range

Parcel of air rising up valley is heated diabatically by mountain. This causes Sc to dissipate but leaves a haze layer

Anabatic wind

Stratocumulus (Sc) Cloud formed though mass uplift and Adiabatic Cooling coming into contact with mountain range

Windshear

Windshear is the variation of wind speed and/or direction from place to place. It affects the flightpath and airspeed of an aeroplane and can be a hazard to aviation. Generally, vertical windshear is difficult to detect by standard meteorological instrumentation making it hard for flight crew to anticipate this hazard. Flight considerations involving windshear are covered in the *Windshear* chapter 36 of Volume 4 of *The Air Pilot's Manual*.

Windshear is usually present to some extent during take-off and landing, because of the shift in surface wind speed and direction from that at altitude. Low-level windshear can be quite marked at night or in the early morning when there is little mixing of the lower layers, for instance when a temperature inversion exists.

Windshear can also be expected when a sea breeze or a land breeze, in the vicinity of mountain waves or thunderstorms. Cumulonimbus clouds have severe updraughts and downdraughts with them, and up to 20 nautical miles in the clear air around them – they can cause serious damage to an aircraft.

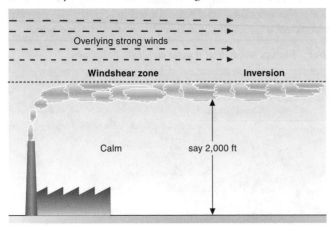

■ *Figure 18-17* **Windshear caused by a temperature inversion**

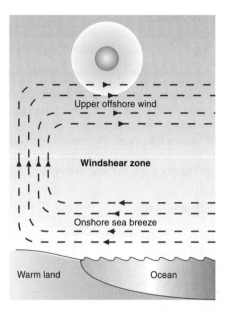

■ *Figure 18-18* **Windshear caused by a sea breeze**

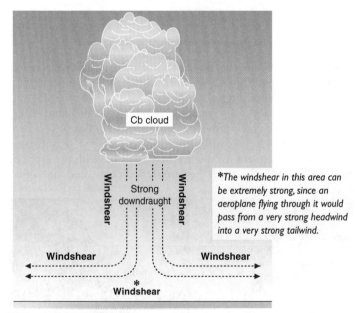

■ *Figure 18-19* **Windshear near a dissipating thunderstorm can be extremely hazardous**

Wind Associated with Mountains

Moderate to severe turbulence is likely over a mountain and on the lee side under strong wind conditions. Mountain waves are likely when strong winds perpendicular to mountain ridges are accompanied by a temperature inversion close to the mountain tops (such as under a high pressure synoptic system) then an effect called **mountain waves** is possible. In some cases, the up-currents and down-currents can exceed the maximum climb and maximum descent rates of an aircraft; typically with a Vertical Speed (VSP) of 500 to 1000 feet per minute up to the height of the inversion and extending between 50NM and 100NM to the lee of the mountain range.

> These winds may be forecasted, abbreviated code MTW on most area forecasts with maximum vertical speed given in feet per minute and its level eg. MTM MAX VSP 500 FPM 070.

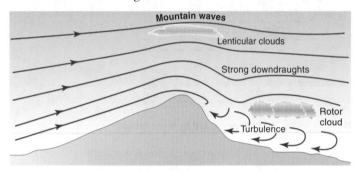

■ Figure 18-20 **Avoid flying near mountains in strong winds**

An aircraft should, for this reason, maintain a sufficient vertical separation (about 2000-3000 feet) with mountainous terrain under these meteorological conditions.

Mountain waves can create their own type of cloud called lenticular cloud which provides a useful visual indicator of where some of the most severe turbulence can be expected. Rotor areas with severe to violent turbulence may form beneath the crests of the lee waves closest to the mountain range and are often characterised by a roll cloud.

■ *Figure 18-21* **Left: A view looking away from the leeward side of mountains – a wave pattern can be seen in the medium level clouds which is indicative of mountain waves. Right: A visible satellite image showing a wave pattern in cloud over both the UK and Ireland in the vicinity of respective mountain ranges.**

Wind in the Tropics

In tropical areas, pressure gradients are generally fairly weak and so will not cause the air to flow at high speeds. Local effects, such as land and sea breezes, may have a stronger influence than the pressure gradient.

The Coriolis force that causes the air to flow parallel to the isobars is very weak in the tropics since the distance from the earth's axis remains fairly constant. The pressure gradient force, even though relatively weak, will dominate and the air will tend to flow more from the high-pressure areas to the low-pressure areas than parallel to the isobars.

Instead of using isobars (which join places of equal pressure) on tropical weather charts, it is more common to use:

- **streamlines** to indicate wind direction, which will be *outdraughts* from high-pressure areas and *indraughts* to low-pressure areas; in combination with
- **isotachs,** which are dotted lines joining places of equal wind strength.

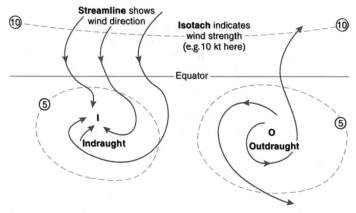

■ *Figure 18-22* **Streamline/isotach analysis chart**

Flight in Turbulence

Some degree of turbulence is almost always present in the atmosphere and pilots quickly become accustomed to its minor forms. Moderate or severe turbulence, however, is uncomfortable and can even overstress the aeroplane. Gusts will increase the angle of attack, causing an increase in the lift generated at that particular airspeed and therefore an increased load factor. Of course, if the angle of attack is increased beyond the critical angle, the wing will stall and this can occur at a speed well above the published 1g stalling speed.

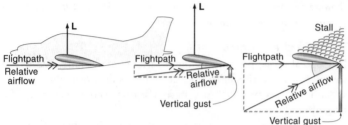

■ *Figure 18-23* **Vertical gusts increase angle of attack and will increase the load factor and/or stall the wing**

Load factor (or g-force) is a measure of the stress on the aeroplane and each category of aeroplane is built to take only certain load factors which should not be exceeded. The Pilot's Operating Handbook should be consulted and aircraft specific training on managing turbulence is important. There are some general points to consider:

– Flying at turbulence penetration speed, which is usually 10–20% slower than normal cruise speed, but not so slowly as to allow the aeroplane to stall - remembering that in turbulence the aeroplane may stall at a speed higher than that published.
– Secure crew and passengers by fastening seatbelts.
– In order not to overstress the aircraft it may be important to hold the attitude and not the altitude for the desired flight phase, using whatever aileron movements are needed to retain lateral control, but being fairly gentle on the elevator to avoid over-stressing the airframe structurally through large changes in angle of attack and lift produced.
– The airspeed indicator will probably be fluctuating, so aim to have the airspeed fluctuate around the selected turbulence penetration speed, which may require reduced power. Use power to maintain speed.
– Know the operating procedure for use of the autopilot. In some cases or on some aircraft types it may need to be disengaged.

It is of course better to avoid turbulence, and to some extent this is possible:

• Avoid flying under large cumulus clouds because of the large updraughts that cause them.
• Avoid flying in or around cumulonimbus cloud where there can be severe turbulence even in the clear air well away from the actual cloud (10-20nm).

- Avoid flying in the lee of hills when strong winds are blowing, since they will tumble over the ridges and be quite turbulent, as well as flowing down into valleys at a rate which an aeroplane may not be able to out-climb.
- High pressure weather systems with strong winds over mountains/hills can result in mountain waves with severe turbulence up to 100nm leewards.

Now complete: **Practice Questions - Wind**

1. Meteorological reports on wind direction are relative to:

   (a) True north.
   (b) Isobars.
   (c) Magnetic north.
   (d) The pressure gradient.

2. Reports of wind at an airfield passed to a pilot from its Air Traffic Control (tower frequency) are relative to:

   (a) True north.
   (b) Isobars at the airfield.
   (c) Magnetic north at the airfield.
   (d) The pressure gradient at the airfield.

3. 280/34kt on a meteorological forecast or observation means:

   (a) Wind strength of 34 miles per hour blowing from a direction of 280° true.
   (b) Wind strength of 34 knots blowing from a direction of 280° true.
   (c) Wind strength of 34 knots blowing from a direction of 280° magnetic.
   (d) Wind strength of 34 knots blowing from a direction of 100° true.

4. A wind of 270/25G45kt at an airfield is passed to the pilot of an aeroplane on approach to land by the tower. This means:

   (a) Wind strength of 25 miles per hour, gusting 45 miles per hour, blowing from a direction of 270° true.
   (b) Wind strength of 25 knots, gusting 45 knots, blowing from a direction of 270° true.
   (c) Wind strength of 25 knots, gusting 45 knots, blowing from a direction of 270° magnetic.
   (d) Wind strength of 25 knots, gusting 45 knots, blowing from a direction of 90° magnetic.

5. A wind whose direction has changed in a clockwise direction (from $280°$ magnetic to $340°$ magnetic) has:

    (a) Retrograded
    (b) Veered
    (c) Backed
    (d) Tracked

6. A wind whose direction has changed in an anti-clockwise (from $100°$ true to $50°$ true) direction has:

    (a) Retrograded
    (b) Veered
    (c) Backed
    (d) Tracked

7. A still 'parcel' of air that is situated between an area of high and an area of low pressure will experience:

    (a) A force acting in the direction from high to low pressure called the pressure gradient force.
    (b) A force acting in the direction from low to high pressure called the pressure force.
    (c) A friction force acting between it and the surface of the earth.
    (d) A coriolis force.

8. When a 'parcel' of air begins to move from high to low pressure, an 'apparent' or 'inertial' force begins to act on it which is:

    (a) The coriolis force, which acts parallel to the direction of motion.
    (b) The pressure gradient force, which acts to slow the parcel of air down.
    (c) The coriolis force, which acts perpendicular to the direction of motion.
    (d) The friction force, which acts perpendicular to the direction of motion.

9. The coriolis force is caused by and is proportional to the:

    (a) Pressure gradient between high and low pressure regions.
    (b) Rotation of the earth, it is greatest at the equator.
    (c) Friction between the air and surface of the earth.
    (d) Rotation of the earth and latitude, it is greater at the poles.

10. The coriolis force is proportional to:

    (a) Wind speed.
    (b) Pressure gradient.
    (c) Friction.
    (d) Gradient wind.

11. The geostrophic wind is formed by the:

(a) *Pressure gradient force being balanced by the coriolis force, and flows parallel to the isobars.*

(b) *Pressure gradient being balanced by the frictional force, and flows parallel to the isobars.*

(c) *Coriolis force being balanced by the frictional force, and flows perpendicular to the isobars.*

(d) *Pressure gradient force being balanced by the coriolis force, and flows perpendicular to the isobars.*

12. In the northern hemisphere, in a particular point of a weather system where there is a geostrophic wind direction of $020°$ true, the centre of low pressure is:

(a) *In the direction of $020°$ true from that point.*

(b) *In the direction of $290°$ true from that point.*

(c) *In the direction of $110°$ true from that point.*

(d) *In the direction of $200°$ true from that point.*

13. An aircraft is flying in the northern hemisphere and its track is $180°$ true. Its onboard flight computer is indicating that there is a wind blowing from $90°$ true. The aircraft is:

(a) *Experiencing right drift and flying from a region of high pressure to a region of low pressure.*

(b) *Experiencing left drift and flying from a region of high pressure to a region of low pressure.*

(c) *Experiencing right drift and flying in a col.*

(d) *Experiencing right drift and flying parallel to the isobars.*

14. For the wind to blow anti-clockwise around a low-pressure system in the Northern Hemisphere, the pressure gradient force will:

(a) *Be less than the coriolis force.*

(b) *Be equal to the coriolis force.*

(c) *Be greater than the coriolis force.*

(d) *Be equal to the coriolis force and frictional force.*

15. For the wind to blow clockwise around a high-pressure system in the northern hemisphere, the pressure gradient force will:

(a) *Be less than the coriolis force.*

(b) *Be equal to the coriolis force.*

(c) *Be greater than the coriolis force.*

(d) *Be equal to the coriolis force and frictional force.*

16. The wind that flows around curved isobars is called the:

 (a) *Curved wind.*
 (b) *Geostrophic wind.*
 (c) *Gradient wind.*
 (d) *Isobaric wind.*

17. At an airfield the surface wind is measured at:

 (a) *10 metres above ground level.*
 (b) *30 feet above ground level.*
 (c) *30 metres above ground level.*
 (d) *10 feet above ground level.*

18. Compared to the wind at medium (>5,000ft) and high altitudes (>20,000ft), the surface wind direction and speed are substantially altered by:

 (a) *The frictional force exerted by the earth's surface as well as heating and cooling of the lower (<5,000ft) atmosphere by the earth's surface.*
 (b) *Coriolis force as well as cooling of the lower (<5,000ft) atmosphere by the earth's surface.*
 (c) *Pressure gradient force as well as heating of the lower (<5,000ft) atmosphere by the earth's surface.*
 (d) *Isallobaric effects.*

19. In the northern hemisphere, the mean surface wind direction compared to the gradient wind direction will:

 (a) *Back.*
 (b) *Remain the same.*
 (c) *Veer.*
 (d) *Back during the day and veer during the night.*

20. The backing of the surface wind is more pronounced over:

 (a) *Land because of an increased friction force compared to the sea.*
 (b) *Sea because of an increased friction force compared to the sea.*
 (c) *Land because of a reduced friction force compared to the sea.*
 (d) *Sea because of a reduced friction force compared to the sea.*

21. In a low pressure synoptic weather system, compared to a high pressure system, there is:

(a) *More upward vertical motion throughout the troposphere because the atmosphere is unstable.*

(b) *Less upward vertical motion throughout the troposphere because the atmosphere is stable.*

(c) *More upward vertical motion throughout the troposphere because the atmosphere is stable.*

(d) *Less upward vertical motion throughout the troposphere because the atmosphere is unstable.*

22. Over land, under a constant pressure gradient and clear skies; the surface wind speed by day is generally:

(a) *The same as gradient wind speed throughout.*

(b) *Less than at night.*

(c) *The same as at night.*

(d) *Greater than at night.*

23. Under calm conditions, with clear skies and strong daytime heating of the land. A sea breeze:

(a) *Blows onshore during the morning.*

(b) *Does not develop.*

(c) *Blows offshore during the afternoon.*

(d) *Blows onshore during the afternoon.*

24. The wind that flows down mountain slopes at night as a result of cooling is called:

(a) *Geostrophic wind.*

(b) *Katabatic wind.*

(c) *Anabatic wind.*

(d) *Gradient wind.*

25. The wind that flows up mountain slopes by day caused by heating is called:

(a) *Geostrophic wind.*

(b) *Katabatic wind.*

(c) *Anabatic wind.*

(d) *Gradient wind.*

26. A flight at low level (below 3,000ft above ground level) in strong winds is likely to:

(a) *Experience no turbulence.*

(b) *Experience more frequent and severe turbulence over the land than over the sea.*

(c) *Experience more frequent and severe turbulence over the sea than over the land.*

(d) *Experience the same turbulence over the land and sea.*

27. In the northern hemisphere, at an inland airfield the wind at altitude is 240/35kt. There is unstable atmosphere and so the most likely wind on the ground is in an:

(a) *Mean wind direction 270° true, mean speed 15 knots, gusts up to 30 knots.*

(b) *Mean wind direction 220° true, mean speed 15 knots, gusts up to 30 knots.*

(c) *Mean wind direction 150° true, mean speed 20 knots, gusts up to 30 knots.*

(d) *Mean wind direction 270° true, mean speed 10 knots with no gusts.*

28. In the northern hemisphere and over the sea, the surface wind is 330/20kt in a stable atmosphere. The wind at 2,000ft is likely to be:

(a) *350/25kt.*

(b) *310/30kt.*

(c) *350/15kt.*

(d) *350/80kt.*

29. When wind speed reduces or increases and/or wind direction varies with height it is called:

(a) *Wind variance.*

(b) *Wind shear.*

(c) *Turbulence.*

(d) *Clear air turbulence.*

30. Associated with a region of high pressure, there is a strong gradient wind and a sharp temperature inversion between 2300 and 2700 feet (ft) above ground level. Where would you expect the greatest wind shear to be:

(a) *3500 to 4000ft above ground level.*
(b) *Surface to 1000ft above ground level.*
(c) *2300 to 2700ft above ground level.*
(d) *1500 to 2000ft above ground level.*

31. A region of high pressure extends over a mountain range resulting in a sharp temperature inversion over the mountain peaks. A strong wind blows perpendicular to the mountain range and will cause:

(a) *Cumulonimbus cloud on the leeward side of the mountain range.*
(b) *Mountain waves on the leeward side of the mountains whose vertical speed could exceed the climb performance of most aircraft.*
(c) *Performance enhancing updraughts on the leeward side of the mountain range.*
(d) *Drizzle on the leeward side of the mountain range.*

32. Lenticular clouds form above mountains and can extend throughout the troposphere. They are:

(a) *Stratiform cloud that pose no hazard to aircraft.*
(b) *Associated with mountain waves and are indicative of severe turbulence whose vertical speed could exceed the climb performance of most aircraft.*
(c) *Associated with cumulonimbus and are indicative of hail.*
(d) *Associated with nimbus cloud and indicative of the onset of heavy rain.*

33. A good indication that mountain waves are present is the formation of:

(a) *Stratus clouds on the windward side of mountains.*
(b) *Hill fog.*
(c) *Lenticular cloud and stationary stratus clouds to the lee of mountains.*
(d) *Cumulus cloud on top of a mountain range.*

34. Mountain waves can produce strong vertical motion:

   (a) Up to 50nm to the lee of the mountains.

   (b) Never more than 5nm to the lee of the mountains.

   (c) Only over the mountain range.

   (d) Only on the windward side of the mountain range.

Cloud and Precipitation

A cloud is a visible aggregate of minute particles of water and/or ice in the free air. The effect of cloud on aviation, particularly visual flight, makes it an important topic in pilot training. The presence of low *stratus* cloud, for example, can cause a flight to divert or even turn back without reaching the destination. In 'unstable' atmospheric conditions, large build-ups of cloud can develop into cumulonimbus clouds that produce severely hazardous thunderstorms.

The classification of cloud types and of individual cloud is not straightforward because it may take on numerous different forms that continually change or evolve into other types of clouds. It is important to have an understanding of cloud classification because meteorological forecasts and reports use these terms to give a picture of the weather for the pilot.

The Naming of Clouds

The four main groups of clouds are:
- **cirriform** (or fibrous);
- **cumuliform** (or heaped);
- **stratiform** (or layered); and
- **nimbus** (or rain-bearing).

Clouds are further divided according to the level of their bases above mean sea level, resulting in ten basic types.

High-Level Cloud

High-level cloud has a base above 20,000 ft and looks quite fine and spidery because it is usually formed in the coldest region of the troposphere and composed of ice crystals rather than water particles.

1. CIRRUS (Ci). Detached clouds in the form of white delicate filaments, white patches or narrow bands. These clouds have a fibrous or silky appearance.

2. CIRROCUMULUS (Cc). A thin, white patch, sheet or layer of cloud without shading, composed of very small elements in the form of grain or ripples, joined together or separate, and more or less regularly arranged. Most of the elements have an apparent width of less than $1°$ of arc (approximately the width of the little finger at arm's length). *Cirrus* indicates high and *cumulus* indicates lumpy or heaped.

3. CIRROSTRATUS (Cs). A transparent whitish veil of fibrous or smooth appearance, totally or partly covering the sky and generally producing a halo phenomenon (a luminous white ring around the sun or moon with a faint red fringe on the inside). *Cirrus* indicates high and *stratus* indicates layer.

Middle-Level Cloud

Middle-level cloud has a base above about 6,500 ft but below 20,000ft amsl.

4. ALTOCUMULUS (Ac). A layer of patches of cloud composed of laminae or rather flattened globular masses, rolls, etc., the smallest elements having a width of between 1° and 5° of arc (the width of three fingers at arm's length). They are arranged in groups or lines or waves which may be joined to form a continuous layer or appear in broken patches and shaded either white or grey. **Coronae** (one or more coloured rings around the sun or moon) are characteristic of this cloud. In an unstable atmosphere, the vertical development of *Ac* may be sufficient to produce precipitation in the form of **virga** (rain that does not reach the ground) or slight showers. *Alto* means middle-level and *cumulus* means heaped.

5. ALTOSTRATUS (As). A greyish or bluish cloud sheet of fibrous or uniform appearance totally or partly covering the sky and having parts thin enough to reveal the sun at least vaguely as though through ground glass. Precipitation in the form of rain or snow can occur with *As*. *Stratus* means layer, so *Altostratus* is middle-level layer cloud.

Low-Level Cloud

Low cloud has a base below about 6,500 ft amsl.

6. NIMBOSTRATUS (Ns). A dark grey cloud layer generally covering the whole sky and thick enough throughout to hide the sun or moon. *Nimbus* means rain-bearing and *stratus* means layer. It typically extends throughout the troposphere and is associated with continuous heavy precipitation, severe turbulence and icing. At times *Ns* may be confused with *As* since it is like thick altostratus, but its darker grey colour and lack of a distinct cloud base distinguish it as *Ns*.

7. STRATOCUMULUS (Sc). A grey or whitish patch or sheet of cloud which has dark parts composed of rounded masses or rolls which may be joined or show breaks between the thicker areas. Most of the rounded masses have an apparent width of more than 5° of arc (the width of three fingers at arm's length). The associated weather, if any, is very slight rain, drizzle or snow. *Stratus* means layer and *cumulus* means heaped.

8. STRATUS (St). A generally grey cloud layer with a fairly uniform base, which may give precipitation in the form of drizzle. When the sun is visible through the cloud, its outline is clearly discernible. *Stratus* means layer.

9. CUMULUS (Cu). Detached clouds, generally dense and with sharp outlines, developing vertically in the form of rising mounds, domes or towers, of which the upper part often resembles a cauliflower. The sunlit parts of these clouds are mostly brilliant white. Their base is relatively dark, since sunlight may not reach it, and nearly horizontal. Precipitation in the form of rain or snow showers may occur with large cumulus. *Cumulus* means heaped.

10. CUMULONIMBUS (Cb). *Cumulo* means heaped and *nimbus* means rain-bearing. A heavy and dense cloud with considerable vertical extent in the form of a mountain or huge tower. At least part of its upper portion is usually fibrous or striated, often appearing as an anvil or vast plume. The base of the cloud appears dark and stormy. Low ragged clouds are frequently observed below the base and generally other varieties of low cloud, such as *Cu* and *Sc,* are joined to or in close proximity to the *Cb*. Lightning, thunder, heavy to violent precipitation (including hail, rain or snow) and severe turbulence and associated weather are characteristic of this type of cloud.

The above are the ten main cloud classifications, but there are certain variations that you may see mentioned, such as:

- **Stratus fractus** and **cumulus fractus** – stratus or cumulus, as appropriate, observed as shreds or fragments below the base of nimbostratus or altostratus. Stratus fractus and cumulus fractus can also be observed in the vicinity of cumulonimbus.
- **Castellanus** – a number of small, cumuliform clouds that appear to be turret shaped (ie. taller than they are wide) sharing a common base and indicating the growth of middle-level clouds in an unstable atmosphere.
- **Lenticularis** – lens-shaped clouds formed in standing waves over mountains caused by strong winds aloft and often associated with stable atmospheres. Indicative of mountain wave activity.

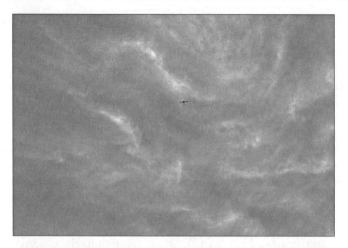

■ *Figure 19-1*
Filaments of cirrus (Ci)

■ *Figure 19-2*
Cirrostratus (Cs)

■ *Figure 19-3*
**Altostratus (As),
thickening towards
horizon; Cu fractus
below**

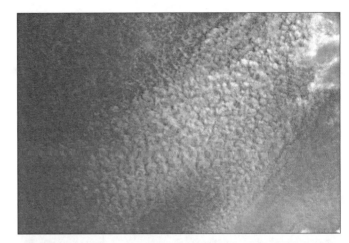

■ Figure 19-4
Altocumulus (Ac)

◀ Figure 19-5
Nimbostratus (Ns)

Figure 19-6
Stratocumulus (Sc)

■ *Figure 19-7*
**Stratus (St); terrain
(and TV mast!) in
cloud**

■ *Figure 19-8*
Cumulus (Cu)

■ *Figure 19-9*
**Large cumulus
build-up (showers and
poor visibility below)**

■ Figure 19-10
**Mature cumulo -
nimbus (Cb) (avoid Cb
clouds, with or without
anvil)**

◀ Figure 19-11
**Ac castellanus
formation**

◀ Figure 19-12
**lenticular
Altocumulus**

Moisture in the Atmosphere

Cloud is formed from water vapour that is contained in the atmosphere. It is taken up into the atmosphere by evaporation from the oceans and other bodies where water is present.

The Three States of Water

Water in its vapour state is not visible, but when the water vapour condenses to form water droplets we see it as cloud, fog, mist, rain or dew. Frozen water is also visible as cloud (high-level), snow, hail, ice or frost. Water therefore exists in three states – gas (vapour), liquid (water) and solid (ice).

Under certain conditions, water can change from one state to the other, absorbing heat energy if it moves to a higher-energy state (from ice to water to vapour) and giving off heat energy if it moves to a lower-energy state (vapour to water to ice). This heat energy is known as **latent heat** and is a vital part of any change of state.

The three states of water, the names of the various transfer processes and the absorption or giving off of latent heat are shown in Figure 19-13.

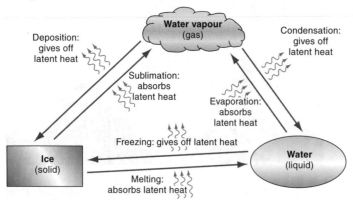

■ Figure 19-13 **The three states of water**

Humidity

The **amount of water vapour** present in the air is called **humidity**, but the actual amount is not as important as whether the air can support that water vapour or not.

Relative Humidity

When a parcel of air is supporting as much **water vapour** as it can, it is said to be **saturated** and have a **relative humidity of 100%**. If it is supporting less than its full capacity of water vapour, it is said to be unsaturated and its relative humidity will be less than 100%. Air supporting only a third of the water vapour that it could has a relative humidity of 33%. There are of course many degrees of saturation ranging from 0% to 100%. In cloud and fog it is 100%, whereas over a desert it may be 20%.

Relative humidity (RH) is defined as the ratio of water vapour actually in the parcel of air relative to what it can hold (i.e. when it is saturated) at a particular temperature and pressure.

$$RH = (Vapour\ Pressure / Saturation\ Vapour\ Pressure)\%$$

How much water a particular parcel of air can support is dependent on the air temperature – warm air being able to support more than cool air. Saturation vapour pressure is proportional to temperature. If the temperature falls, the amount of water vapour that the air can support decreases and so the relative humidity will increase. In other words, even though no moisture has been added, the relative humidity of a parcel of air will increase as its temperature drops.

Dewpoint Temperature

Dewpoint is the temperature at which a parcel of air becomes saturated if it cools (at constant pressure), i.e. the temperature at which it is no longer able to support all of the water vapour that it contains; the more moisture in the air, the higher its dewpoint temperature.

A parcel of air that has a temperature higher than its dewpoint will be unsaturated, i.e. its relative humidity is *less* than 100%. The closer the actual temperature is to the dewpoint, the closer the air is to being saturated.

At its dewpoint, the air will be fully saturated (RH = 100%) and if it becomes cooler than its dewpoint, then the excess water vapour will condense as visible water droplets (or, if it is cool enough, as ice). This process can be seen both when moist air cools at night to form fog, dew or frost, and as air rises and cools, the water vapour condensing into the small water droplets that form clouds. If the air is unable to support these water droplets (for example, if they become too large and heavy), then they fall as precipitation (rain, hail or snow).

Cloud Formation

Clouds form when the temperature within a 'parcel of air' falls below the dew point. There are five key ways in which this can happen:

A. *Mass/widespread uplift (adiabatic): large-scale forced uplift of air causes it to expand and cool adiabatically below its dew point. The air is either forced by the dynamics of a large-scale weather system or a mountain range.*

B. *Convection (adiabatic): initially heating of a 'parcel of air' close to the earth's surface results in a difference in density between that parcel and the surrounding atmosphere. The parcel rises and expands cooling adiabatically below its dew point.*

C. *Turbulence and mixing: eddies cause air to rise and fall. The rising air cools – sometimes sufficiently for its temperature to fall below the dew point.*

D. *Advection (diabatic): warm and moist air passes over a colder surface and heat transfers from the air to the surface causing it to cool below the dew point.*

E. *Radiation (diabatic): radiation energy (infra-red) leaving a 'parcel of air' becomes more than that entering it causing it to cool below the dew point.*

> Diabatic process is one in which heat is exchanged to and from the system.

Unsaturated air will cool adiabatically at about 3°C/1,000 ft as it rises. This is known as the dry adiabatic lapse rate (DALR).

Cooler air can support less water vapour, so, as the parcel of air rises and cools, its relative humidity will increase. At the height where its temperature is reduced to the dewpoint temperature (i.e. relative humidity reaches 100%), water will start to condense and form cloud.

Above this height the now saturated air will continue to cool as it rises but, because latent heat will be released as the water vapour condenses into the lower energy liquid state, the cooling will not be as great. The rate at which saturated air cools as it rises is known as the **saturated adiabatic lapse rate (SALR)** and may be assumed to have a value of approximately half the DALR, i.e. 1.5°C/1,000 ft.

Which Cloud Type Forms?

The nature and extent of any cloud that forms depends on the stability of the atmosphere. On any given day the actual rate at which temperature changes with altitude is referred to as the Environmental Lapse Rate (ELR). If we move a parcel of air within this environment that parcel will follow the adiabatic principle – its temperature will decrease at the dry adiabatic lapse rate or DALR (if water is in its vapour state) or the saturated adiabatic lapse rate - SALR (if water vapour is condensed). What happens to that parcel of air is then determined by the difference between the ELR and DALR or SALR and the associated stability state of which there are three:

UNSTABLE: (ELR > DALR or SALR) a parcel of air continues to move vertically after being displaced from its original position. This results in cumuliform clouds which may continue to develop up to high altitudes.

NEUTRAL: (ELR = DALR or SALR) a parcel of air remains in the position to which it was vertically displaced. This usually results in stratiform clouds.

STABLE: (ELR < DALR or SALR) a parcel of air returns back to the position from which it was displaced. This results in stratiform clouds or fog formation.

Cloud Formed by Convection as a result of Heating

Suppose that a parcel of air overlying a large ploughed field is heated to +17°C, whereas the air in the surrounding environment is only 12°C. The heated parcel of air will start to rise, because of its lower density, and cool at the dry adiabatic lapse rate of 3°C /1,000 ft.

If the environmental lapse rate happens to be 1°C/1,000 ft, then the environmental air through which the heated parcel is rising will cool at only 1°C/1,000 ft.

Suppose that the moisture content of the parcel of air is such that the dewpoint temperature is 11°C. By 2,000 ft agl the rising parcel of air will have cooled to this temperature and so water will start to condense and form cloud. At 2,000 ft agl, the environmental air will have cooled to 10°C, so the parcel of air will continue rising since it is still warmer (11°).

As the parcel of air continues to rise above the level at which cloud first forms, latent heat will be released as more and more vapour condenses into liquid water. This reduces the rate at which the rising air cools to the **saturated adiabatic lapse rate** of 1.5°C/1,000 ft.

In this example, at this new rate of cooling the parcel of air will have cooled to the same temperature as the surrounding environment (8°C) at a height of 4,000 ft agl, and so will cease rising. A cumulus cloud, base 2,000 ft and top 4,000 ft, has been formed.

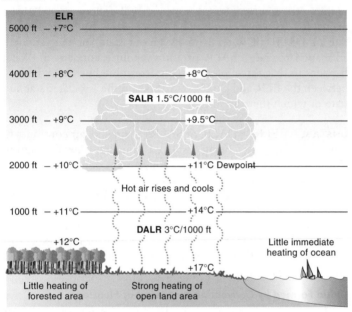

■ *Figure 19-14* **The formation of a cumulus cloud**

Cloud Formed by Orographic Uplift

Air flowing over mountains rises and cools adiabatically. If it cools to below its **dewpoint temperature**, then the water vapour will condense and cloud will form.

Descending on the other side of the mountains, however, the airflow will warm adiabatically and, once its temperature exceeds the dewpoint for that parcel of air, the water vapour will no longer condense. The liquid water drops will now start to vaporise, and the cloud will cease to exist below this level.

A cloud that forms as a 'cap' over the top of a mountain is known as **lenticular** cloud. It will remain more or less stationary whilst the air flows through it.

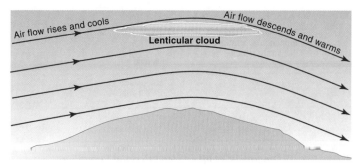

■ *Figure 19-15* **Lenticular cloud as a cap over a mountain**

Sometimes, when an air stream flows over a mountain range and there is a stable layer of air above, **standing waves** occur. This is a wavy pattern as the airflow settles back into a more steady flow and, if the air is moist, lenticular clouds may form in the crest of the lee waves, and a **rotor** or **roll cloud** may form at a low level.

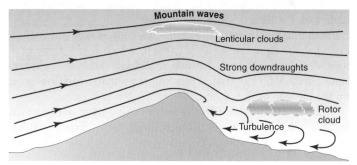

■ *Figure 19-16* **Mountain waves**

The level at which the cloud base forms depends on the moisture content of the parcel of air and its dewpoint temperature. The cloud base may be below the mountain tops or well above them, depending on the situation. Once having started to form, the cloud may sit low over the mountain as stratiform cloud (if the air is stable), or (if the air is unstable) the cloud will be cumuliform and may rise to high levels.

For interesting reading regarding '*Flight Over and in the Vicinity of High Ground*', refer to Aeronautical Information Circular (AIC) 82/2008 (Pink 148).

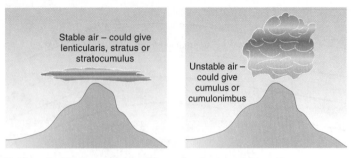

■ *Figure 19-17* **Orographic uplift can lead to cloud formation**

THE FÖHN WIND EFFECT. If the air rising up a mountain range is moist enough to have a high dewpoint temperature and is cooled down to it before reaching the top of the mountain, then cloud will form on the windward side. If any precipitation occurs, moisture will be removed from the airflow and, as it descends on the lee side of the mountain, it will therefore be drier. The dewpoint temperature will be less and so the cloud base will be higher on the lee side of the mountain.

As the dry air beneath the cloud descends, it will warm at the dry adiabatic lapse rate of 3°C/1,000 ft, which is at a greater rate than the rising air cooled inside the cloud (saturated adiabatic lapse rate: 1.5°C/1,000 ft). The result is a warmer and drier wind on the lee side of the mountains.

This very noticeable effect is seen in many parts of the world, for example the **föhn** (or *foehn,* pronounced "fern") wind in Switzerland and Southern Germany, from which this effect gets its name.

More locally for the UK, the föhn effect is commonly experienced in North Wales, due to the interaction of south-westerly winds with the mountains of Snowdonia.

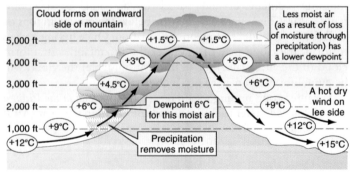

■ *Figure 19-18* **The föhn wind effect**

Cloud Formed by Turbulence and Mixing

As air flows over the surface of the earth, frictional effects cause variations in local wind strength and direction. Eddies are set up which cause the lower levels of air to mix – the stronger the wind and the rougher the earth's surface, the larger the eddies and the stronger the mixing.

The air in the rising currents will cool and, if the turbulence extends to a sufficient height, it may cool to the dewpoint temperature, water vapour will condense to form liquid water droplets and cloud will form.

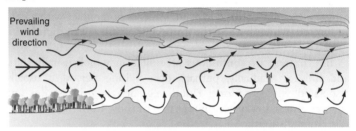

Prevailing wind direction

■ *Figure 19-19* **Formation of turbulence cloud**

The descending air currents in the turbulent layer will warm and, if the air's dewpoint temperature is exceeded, the liquid water droplets that make up the cloud will return to the water vapour state. The air will dry out and cloud will not exist below this level.

With turbulent mixing, stratiform cloud may form over quite a large area, possibly with an undulating base. It may be continuous stratus or broken stratocumulus.

Cloud formed by Widespread Ascent

When two large masses of air of differing temperatures meet, the warmer and less dense air will flow over (or be undercut by) the cooler air. As the warmer air mass is forced aloft it will cool and, if the dewpoint temperature is reached, cloud will form.

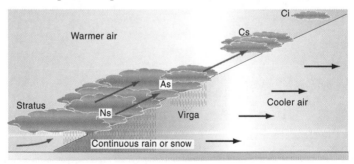

Warmer air — Ci — Cs — As — Ns — Virga — Stratus — Cooler air — Continuous rain or snow

■ *Figure 19-20* **Cloud formation due to widespread ascent**

The boundary layer between two air masses is called a **front**. Weather associated with frontal activity is covered in Chapter 21.

Precipitation Associated with Cloud

Precipitation refers to falling water that finally reaches the ground, including:

- **rain** consisting of liquid water drops (which could be sub–zero degrees Celsius);
- **drizzle** consisting of fine water droplets;
- **snow** consisting of branched and star-shaped ice crystals;
- **hail** consisting of small balls of ice;
- **freezing rain or drizzle** which freezes on contact with a cold surface (which may be the ground or an aircraft in flight).

Intermittent or continuous precipitation which usually starts and finishes gradually, perhaps over a long period is usually associated with stratiform cloud, e.g. drizzle from stratus and stratocumulus, heavy continuous rain or snow from nimbostratus, rain from altostratus.

Showers are a form of precipitation that starts and stops suddenly and may be followed by a clear sky. They only fall from convective, cumuliform clouds such as cumulus and cumulonimbus.

It is possible to use precipitation as a means of identifying cloud type. Continuous and widespread rain or snow is often associated with stratiform cloud such as altostratus clouds and becomes heavy when nimbostratus is present. Drizzle is usually associated with thick, overcast stratus cloud.

Rain or snow showers are associated with cumuliform clouds such cumulus and altocumulus. Heavy precipitation, including hail, is usually associated with cumulonimbus.

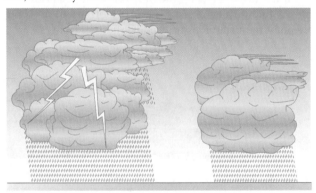

■ *Figure 19-21* **Showers fall from cumuliform clouds**

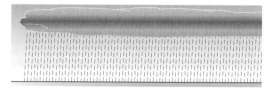

■ *Figure 19-22* **Non-showery precipitation from stratiform clouds**

Rain that falls from the base of clouds but evaporates before reaching the ground (hence is not really precipitation) is called **virga**. It can, of course, affect aircraft which fly through it.

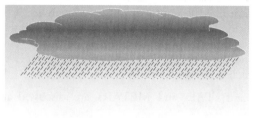

■ *Figure 19-23* **Virga**

Cloud Description in Forecasts and Reports

Aerodromes

Cloud observations may be reported in a Meteorological Terminal Air Report (METAR) or forecasted in a Terminal Aerodrome Forecast (TAF) using the following convention:

CLOUD AMOUNT ABBREVIATIONS (EXCEPT CB)	
SKC	*Sky clear*
FEW	*Few (1–2 oktas, or eighths of sky covered)*
SCT	*Scattered (3–4 oktas)*
BKN	*Broken (5–7 oktas)*
OVC	*Overcast (8 oktas), sky is completely covered with the cloud layer*

The base of the layers or masses of cloud is given in feet above aerodrome level (aal), in ascending order of height. For example, **FEW005 SCT012 BKN050** indicates 1-2 oktas of cloud, base 500 ft aal; a layer of cloud covering 3-4 oktas at 1,200 ft aal; and a layer of cloud covering 5 7 oktas at 5,000 ft aal. The cloud type is not given in TAFs and METARs; however, significant convective clouds (Cumulonimbus, CB and Towering Cumulus, TCU) are appended after the cloud statement, e.g. **SCT008CB**. A CB is not necessarily forecasted in a TAF unless it causes a change group in cloud base.

NOTE The military and civil authorities in some countries (e.g. Australia), show cloud in TAFs and METARs using a slightly different system. For example, **3ST004 6SC035** indicates 3 oktas of stratus, base 400 ft aal; and 6 oktas of stratocumulus at base 3,500 ft aal.

Area Forecasts

NOTE Area forecasts differ between countries. The UK Met Office format on the UK Area Forecast Form F215 and European Area Forecast Form F415 represents cloud in the following format: **SCT/BKN CU SC 030-040 / 060-XXX**. In this example, there is a general condition (75-100%) in weather zone involving SCT to BKN (3/8-6/8) cloud cover with cloud type CU SC (Cumulus or Stratocumulus) that has a cloud base between 3000 and 4000 FT AMSL and cloud top between 6000 to beyond the upper level of the forecast (which is 10,000 feet).

NOTE Area Forecasts, TAFs and METARs are discussed in Chapter 23.

Now complete: **Practice Questions - Cloud & Precipitation**

1. Name the four main families of clouds:

   (a) *Cumuliform, Cumulonimbus, Stratiform, Cirriform.*
   (b) *Cumuliform, Nimbus, Stratiform, Altocirrus.*
   (c) *Cumuliform, Nimbus, Stratiform, Cirriform.*
   (d) *Cumulus, Cumulonimbus, Stratus, Cirrus.*

2. Clouds formed by convection that have a 'lumpy' or 'heaped' appearance belong to:

   (a) *Cumuliform.*
   (b) *Stratiform.*
   (c) *Altoform.*
   (d) *Cirrus.*

3. Extensive, layered cloud formed by mass uplift of air that has a featureless appearance belong to:

   (a) *Cumuliform.*
   (b) *Stratiform.*
   (c) *Altoform.*
   (d) *Cirrus.*

4. A cloud that extends through most of the troposphere, produces heavy rain showers and thunder/lightning is called:

   (a) *Stratus (ST).*
   (b) *Cumulus (CU).*
   (c) *Altocumulus (AC).*
   (d) *Cumulonimbus (CB).*

5. Cloud is formed when water vapour condenses to form liquid water which:

   (a) *Gives off latent heat energy and the cloud becomes warmer than the ambient, environmental air.*
   (b) *Absorbs latent heat energy and the cloud becomes colder than the ambient, environmental air.*
   (c) *Absorbs latent heat energy and the cloud becomes warmer than the ambient, environmental air.*
   (d) *Absorbs latent heat energy and the cloud becomes colder than the ambient, environmental air.*

6. Compared to cold air, warm air has the potential to:

   (a) *Carry less water vapour before saturation.*
   (b) *Carry the same amount of water vapour before saturation.*
   (c) *Carry more water vapour before saturation.*
   (d) *Saturate earlier.*

7. Dewpoint temperature of a 'parcel' of air is:

   (a) *Proportional to the number of cloud condensation nuclei.*
   (b) *Inversely proportional to the amount of water vapour within it.*
   (c) *Proportional to its temperature.*
   (d) *Proportional to the amount of water vapour within it.*

8. The percentage of water vapour in the air compared to what it is capable of carrying at that temperature is called its:

   (a) *Emissivity.*
   (b) *Heat capacity.*
   (c) *Triple point.*
   (d) *Relative humidity.*

9. A a 'parcel' of air's total water content (vapour+liquid+ice) is important for airframe and engine icing potential. When it cools this potential:

   (a) *Increases.*
   (b) *Decreases.*
   (c) *Remains the same.*
   (d) *Evaporates.*

10. If a 'parcel' of air cools to the particular temperature where it is carrying the maximum amount of water vapour that it can, then:

   (a) It is in equilibrium and its relative humidity remains at 50%.
   (b) Its relative humidity increases to 100% and it is saturated.
   (c) Its relative humidity decreases to 0% and it is unsaturated.
   (d) Its relative humidity increases to 50% and it is saturated.

11. The temperature at which a cooling 'parcel' of air reaches saturation is called its:

   (a) Saturation temperature.
   (b) Dewpoint temperature.
   (c) Moisture temperature.
   (d) Cooling temperature.

12. When the temperature of a 'parcel' of air is cooled to its dewpoint:

   (a) Relative humidity reaches 100%, saturation occurs and water vapour condenses into liquid.
   (b) Relative humidity becomes 0%, the 'parcel' becomes unsaturated and liquid water becomes water vapour.
   (c) Relative humidity reaches 100%, the 'parcel' becomes unsaturated and water vapour condenses into liquid.
   (d) Relative humidity becomes 50%, saturation occurs and water condenses into liquid.

13. A 'parcel' of air in contact with the earth's surface is heated more than the surrounding environmental air.

   (a) It will ascend and cool adiabatically – heat is neither added to nor subtracted from the 'parcel'.
   (b) It will ascend and cool katabatically – heat is taken away from the 'parcel'.
   (c) It will ascend and cool anabatically – heat is added to the 'parcel'.
   (d) It will remain at the earth's surface at constant temperature.

14. As 'parcel' of air ascends, its relative humidity will:

   (a) Decrease.
   (b) Remain constant.
   (c) Increase.
   (d) Increase then decrease once water vapour condenses.

15. A 'parcel' of air with a relative humidity less than 100% ascends and:

(a) Cools at the Dry Adiabatic Lapse Rate (DALR) which is about -3°C/1000ft.

(b) Cools at the Saturated Adiabatic Lapse Rate (SALR) which is about -1.5°C/1000ft.

(c) Cools at the specific dewpoint temperature it is at.

(d) Heats up at the Dry Adiabatic Lapse Rate (DALR) which is about -3°C/1000ft.

16. A 'parcel' of air with a relative humidity equal to 100% ascends and:

(a) Cools at the Dry Adiabatic Lapse Rate (DALR) which is about -3°C/1000ft.

(b) Cools at the Saturated Adiabatic Lapse Rate (SALR) which is about -1.5°C/1000ft.

(c) Cools at the specific dewpoint temperature it is at

(d) Heats up at the Dry Adiabatic Lapse Rate (DALR) which is about -3°C/1000ft.

17. The rate of change of temperature in the surrounding air that is not rising is called the:

(a) The Dry Adiabatic Lapse Rate (DALR) which is about -3°C /1000ft.

(b) The Saturated Adiabatic Lapse Rate (SALR) which is about -1.5°C/1000ft.

(c) The Environmental Lapse Rate (ELR) whose value is specific to the particular weather conditions of the day.

(d) The Environmental Lapse Rate (ELR) which is about -3°C /1000ft.

18. Just considering heat exchange, if the moisture content of a parcel of air is such that its dewpoint temperature is +7°C, at what height above the ground is the cloud base likely to form if the surface air temperature is +16°C?

(a) 3000ft.

(b) 6000ft.

(c) 1500ft.

(d) 9000ft.

19. Just considering heat exchange, if the moisture content of a parcel of air is such that its dewpoint temperature is +7°C, at what height above the ground is the cloud base likely to form if the surface air temperature is +19°C?

   (a) 3000ft.
   (b) 4000ft.
   (c) 8000ft.
   (d) 400ft.

20. Just considering heat exchange, if the moisture content of a parcel of air is such that its dewpoint temperature is +10°C, at what height above the ground is the cloud base likely to form if the surface air temperature is +22°C?

   (a) 3000ft.
   (b) 4000ft.
   (c) 8000ft.
   (d) 16000ft.

21. Cloud formed by a mountain range causing the uplift of air is called:

   (a) Cumuliform.
   (b) Stratiform.
   (c) Terrain cloud.
   (d) Orographic cloud.

22. Orographic uplift of unstable air is more likely to cause the formation of:

   (a) Cumuliform.
   (b) Stratiform.
   (c) Hill fog.
   (d) Cirriform.

23. Orographic uplift of stable air is more likely to cause the formation of:

   (a) Cumuliform.
   (b) Stratiform.
   (c) Hill fog.
   (d) Cirriform.

24. If moist air flows up a mountain causing rain on the windward side, the wind on the lee side of the mountain range will be:

(a) The same temperature with the same humidity.
(b) Warmer with a greater humidity.
(c) Colder and drier.
(d) Warmer and drier.

25. Moist air flows up the windward side of a mountain range forming cloud and producing rain. The same air then flows down the leeward side of the mountain range.

(a) The lapse rate on the windward side will be 1.5°C/1000ft. On the leeward side it will be 3°C/1000ft.
(b) The lapse rate on the windward side will be 3°C/1000ft. On the leeward side it will be 1.5°C/1000ft.
(c) The lapse rate on the windward side will be 3°C/1000ft. On the leeward side it will be 3°C/1000ft.
(d) The lapse rate on the windward side will be 1.5°C/1000ft. On the leeward side it will be 1.5°C/1000ft.

26. Mountain waves can be hazardous to aircraft. Mountain waves can sometimes produce two types of cloud which are indicative of their presence:

(a) Lenticular cloud and rotor cloud.
(b) Ventral cloud and lenticular cloud.
(c) Cumulo-nimbus and ventral cloud.
(d) Lenticular cloud and reversal cloud.

27. Precipitation consisting of water drops, which can wet a runway significantly, is called:

(a) Hail.
(b) Snow.
(c) Virga.
(d) Rain.

28. Precipitation consisting of small balls of ice, which can damage an aircraft skin, is called:

(a) Hail.
(b) Snow.
(c) Virga.
(d) Rain/Drizzle.

29. Precipitation consisting of branched and star-shaped ice crystals which can cause engine intake icing is called:

   (a) Hail.
   (b) Snow.
   (c) Virga.
   (d) Rain/Drizzle.

30. Showers generally fall from:

   (a) Cumuliform.
   (b) Stratiform.
   (c) Cirriform.
   (d) Fog.

31. Drizzle generally falls from:

   (a) Cumuliform.
   (b) Stratiform.
   (c) Cirriform.
   (d) Fog.

32. Rain which falls from the base of clouds but evaporates before reaching the ground is called:

   (a) Hail.
   (b) Snow.
   (c) Virga.
   (d) Rain/Drizzle.

33. The synoptic situation is high pressure. A sharp temperature inversion lies over a mountain range and a strong wind is blowing across it. To the lee of the mountain range is an airfield with stationary stratus cloud at 600ft above ground. There are three anemometers, spread across the airfield, and reporting: VRB/05KT, 350/30KT, 170/10KT. What are the most likely weather phenomena at the airfield:

   (a) Rotor activity (mountain waves) associated with severe turbulence.
   (b) Cumulonimbus.
   (c) Turbulence associated with thermals.
   (d) Sea breeze.

Answers: 1c, 2a, 3b, 4d, 5a, 6c, 7d, 8d, 9c, 10b, 11b, 12a, 13a, 14c, 15a, 16b, 17c, 18a, 19b, 20b, 21d, 22a, 23b, 24d, 25a, 26a, 27d, 28a, 29b, 30a, 31b, 32c, 33a.

Visibility

Flight visibility is one of the most important aspects of weather as it can have a critical impact on flight safety of both visual and instrument flights. In visual flying, a natural horizon is essential for attitude control of the aeroplane (pitch and bank) and sufficient slant visibility to be in sight of the ground is vital for visual navigation.

Meteorological visibility is defined as the greatest horizontal distance at which a specified object can be seen in daylight conditions. It is a measure of how transparent the atmosphere is to the human eye.

Visibility for a Pilot

The most important visibility for a pilot under visual flight rules is that from the aeroplane to the ground, i.e. **slant or oblique visibility.** This may be quite different from the horizontal visibility, for example, when a shallow fog forms at an airfield. To an observer on the ground, horizontal visibility might be reduced to just a few hundred metres, yet vertical visibility might be unlimited with a blue sky quite visible above. Similarly, for a pilot flying overhead the aerodrome, the runway might be clearly visible and the horizontal visibility ahead unlimited, yet, once the aircraft is positioned on final approach, the runway could be obscured. This is because the line of sight must now penetrate a much greater thickness of fog.

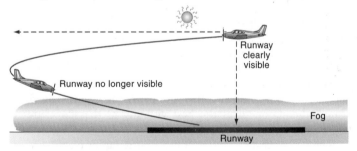

■ *Figure 20-1* **Slant visibility may be severely reduced by fog, smog or stratus**

Particles in the Air

On a perfectly clear day visibility can exceed 100 nm; however, this is rarely the case since there are always some particles suspended in the air to prevent all of the light from a distant object reaching the observer.

Visibility can be reduced by particles suspended in the air.

Particles that restrict visibility include:
* minute particles of smoke so small that even very light winds can support them;
* dust or oil causing haze;
* liquid water or ice producing mist, fog or cloud;
* larger particles of sand, dust or sea spray which require stronger winds and turbulence for the air to hold them in suspension;
* precipitation (rain, snow, hail), the worst visibility being associated with very heavy rain or with large numbers of small particles, e.g. thick drizzle or heavy, fine snow.

Rain or snow will reduce the distance that a pilot can see, as well as possibly obscuring the horizon. Poor visibility in the whole area may occur in mist, fog, smog, stratus, drizzle or rain. Unstable air may cause cumuliform clouds to form with poor visibility in the showers falling from them, but good visibility otherwise.

Heavy rain may collect on the windscreen, especially if the aeroplane is flying fast, and cause optical distortions. If freezing occurs on the windscreen, either as ice or frost, vision may also be impaired.

Strong winds can raise dust or sand from the surface and, in some parts of the world, visibility may be reduced to just a few metres in **dust** and **sand storms.**

Sea spray often evaporates after being blown into the atmosphere, leaving behind small salt particles that can act as condensation nuclei. The salt particles attract water and can cause condensation at relative humidities as low as 70%, restricting visibility much sooner than would otherwise be the case. Haze produced by sea salt often has a whitish appearance.

Position of the Sun or Moon

When flying *down-sun* where the pilot can see the sunlit side of objects, visibility may be much greater than when flying into the sun. As well as reducing the visibility, flying into the sun may cause glare. If landing into the sun is necessary, consideration should be given to altering the time of arrival. Conversely, flying *towards* the moon gives the best visibility as the silhouettes of objects can be seen better.

Remember that the onset of darkness is earlier on the ground than at altitude and, even though visibility up high might be good, flying low in the circuit area and approaching to land on a darkening airfield may cause visibility problems.

Inversions and Reduced Visibility

An inversion occurs when the air temperature increases with height (rather than the usual decrease), and this can stop vertical convection currents as any rising air will meet a layer of warmer air, lose its relative buoyancy and so will stop rising.

Particles suspended in these lower layers will be prevented from mixing throughout the atmosphere and usually form a brownish looking haze layer – especially in the vicinity of industrial areas. Furthermore, these small particles may act as **condensation particles** and encourage the formation of fog (N.B. the combination of smoke and fog being known as **smog).**

Similar effects can be seen in rural areas if there is a lot of pollen, dust or other matter in the air.

Temperature inversions that can lead to these types of visibilities can occur by localised cooling of the air in contact with the earth's surface overnight, or by large-scale subsidence (descending air) associated with a *high pressure weather system.*

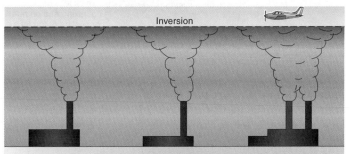

■ *Figure 20-2* **Inversions can lead to reduced visibility**

Mist and Fog

Mist and fog occur when small water droplets are suspended in the air and the relative humidity is above 95%. In both cases the visibility is reduced; **mist** 1 km or more, **fog** below 1 km.

The condensation process that causes mist/fog is usually associated with cooling of the air by an underlying cold surface (causing radiation fog or advection fog) or by the interaction of two air masses (frontal fog). It is usual for mist to precede fog and to follow fog as it disperses, unless an already formed fog is blown into an area (advected) – for example from the sea.

Radiation Fog

Conditions suitable for the formation of radiation fog are:
- **a cloudless night**, allowing the earth to lose heat by radiation to the atmosphere and thereby cool, also causing the air in contact with it to lose heat;
- **moist air** (i.e. a high relative humidity) that only requires a little cooling to reach the dewpoint temperature; and
- **light winds** (5–7 knots) to mix the lower levels of air with very light turbulence, thereby thickening the mist/fog layer.

These conditions are commonly found with an anticyclone (high-pressure system).

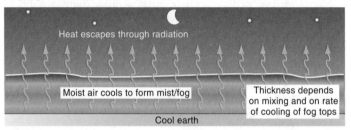

■ *Figure 20-3* **Radiation fog**

Air is a very poor conductor of heat and so, under calm wind conditions, only the very thin layer of air (an inch or two thick) in contact with the Earth's surface will lose heat to it. In this case, **Dew** will form at temperatures above zero and **frost** will form at sub-zero temperatures.

If the wind is stronger than about 7 knots, the extra turbulence may cause too much mixing and, instead of fog right down to the ground, a layer of stratus may form above the surface.

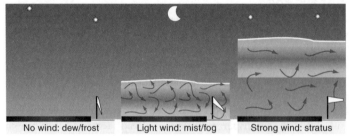

■ *Figure 20-4* **Wind strength will affect the formation of dew/frost, mist/fog or stratus cloud**

The temperature of the sea remains fairly constant throughout the year, unlike that of the land which warms and cools quite quickly on a diurnal (daily) basis. Radiation fog is therefore much more likely to form over land than over the sea.

Dispersal of Radiation Fog

As the earth's surface begins to warm up again some time after sunrise, the air in contact with it will also warm, causing the fog to dissipate gradually. In the UK spring it is common for this to occur by early or mid-morning. Possibly the fog may rise to form a low layer of stratus before the sky clears fully.

If the fog that has formed overnight is thick, however, it may act as a blanket, shutting out the sun and impeding the heating of the earth's surface after the sun has risen. As a consequence, the air in which the fog exists will not be warmed from below and the fog may last throughout the day. This is sometimes experienced in the UK during autumn. There are other mechanisms in addition to diurnal heating. Thick fog areas have edges around which drier air exists. During the day as the surface around the fog is heated it generates increased mixing and therefore entrainment of drier surrounding air within the fog bank, causing it to reduce in size or disperse. Increased wind speed may help, as would the advection of cloud over the fog layer.

Time: 0900Z Visibility: 200M FG   Time: 1100Z Visibility: 3000M BR   Time: 1300Z Visibility: 12KM NSW

■ Figure 20-5 **High Pressure with high moisture content as a result of a Tropical Maritime (Tm) airmass in the Northern Hemisphere Summer. Near an inland airfield radiation fog formed overnight and dispersed slowly as a result of insolation.**

Advection Fog

A warm, moist air mass blowing across (advecting) a significantly colder surface will be cooled from below and **advection fog will form** if its temperature is reduced to the dewpoint temperature.

The onset of advection fog can be quite sudden and be in the day or night, for example, a moist maritime airflow over a cold land surface can lead to advection fog over land during the afternoon.

Furthermore, advection fog can persist in much stronger winds than radiation fog.

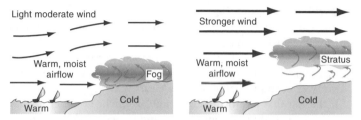

■ Figure 20-6 **Fog or stratus caused by advection**

Fog at Sea and Along Coastal Areas

Sea fog is advection fog, and it may be caused by:
- tropical maritime air moving towards the pole over a colder ocean or meeting a colder air mass; or
- an airflow from a warm land surface moving over a cooler sea, which can occur in the UK summer, affecting aerodromes in coastal areas.

■ Figure 20-7 **A flight to the Channel Islands from the UK; one taking place in the Autumn and the other in the Summer – both under high pressure synoptic conditions. Advection fog formed over the Channel Islands in the Summer as moist air from France advected over a relatively cold sea.**

Frontal Fog

This type of fog forms from the interaction of two air masses in one of two ways:

- as cloud that extends down to the surface during the passage of the front (forming mainly over hills and consequently called **hill fog**); or
- as air becomes saturated by the evaporation of rain that has fallen.

These conditions may develop in the cold air ahead of a warm front (or an occluded front), the pre-frontal fog possibly being very widespread.

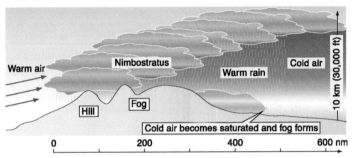

■ Figure 20-8 **Fog associated with a warm front**

Orographic Fog

As moist air is forced to rise over a hill, it may condense and form hill fog or stratus. The Channel Islands are a classic case where this happens.

Visibility in Forecasts and Reports

Prevailing visibility is reported in METARs or forecasted in TAFs, Special and Trend Reports. The prevailing visibility is defined as the visibility across a swathe of the sky at least half the horizon circle around an airfield or within at least half of the surface of the aerodrome. (METAR and TAF decodes are explained in chapter 23).

Visibility is given to the pilot in kilometres or, if it is very poor, in metres. An Aerodrome Forecast that contains the term **4000 –RADZ** can be interpreted, using a decode table, as "Visibility 4,000 metres in slight rain and drizzle".

If the visibility is 10 km or more (i.e. in excess of 9999 metres), it will be written as '9999'; a visibility of less than 50 metres will be written as '0000'. Under very poor visibility the **runway visual range** (RVR) may be reported in metres, for instance, **R25/0300** on a Meteorological Observation means "Runway visual range along Runway 25 is 300 metres". RVR provides added details important for operations under Instrument Flight Rules

(IFR) that otherwise might not be reported in the prevailing visibility. See UK AIP GEN 3-5.

Now complete: **Practice Questions - Visibility**

---

1. Small liquid droplets suspended in the air:

    (a) Increase visibility by lensing available light to the pilot.
    (b) Decrease visibility by scattering it away from the pilot.
    (c) Have no effect on visibility.
    (d) Increase visibility through refraction.

2. A slow moving high pressure weather system results in a clear night, light winds and high dewpoint at an airfield. What is the most likely weather at dawn:

    (a) Radiation fog.
    (b) Haze.
    (c) Cumulonimbus.
    (d) Frontal fog.

3. A warm, maritime airflow over a relatively colder land surface may give rise to:

    (a) Advection fog, mist and stratus.
    (b) Heavy precipitation and associated poor visibility.
    (c) Mountain waves.
    (d) Cumuliform cloud formation.

4. Fog formed by the interaction of two air masses is called:

    (a) Radiation fog.
    (b) Advection fog.
    (c) Frontal fog.
    (d) Hill fog.

5. A sharp temperature inversion over land with light winds is likely to cause:

    (a) Poor visibility, haze in the summer and fog/mist in the winter.
    (b) Instability and thunderstorm formation.
    (c) Mountain waves.
    (d) Rainfall in the summer, snowfall in the winter.

6. In winter, there is radiation fog over an airfield. In the morning the wind strength increases. What will be likely to happen to the fog in the morning:

(a) *The radiation fog will change to advection fog.*
(b) *The radiation fog will become mist.*
(c) *The radiation fog will become low cloud (stratus).*
(d) *There will be no effect.*

7. An airfield is 10 nautical miles north from the coast and has clear skies. Before dusk a weather satellite picture shows an extensive area of sea fog. The wind chart is showing a wind of 180/10kt at 2000ft above sea level. What risk is there for night flying:

(a) *The sea fog will advect over the airfield.*
(b) *The sea fog will become cumulus cloud over the airfield.*
(c) *There is no risk, the sea fog will remain over the sea.*
(d) *The sea fog will provide moisture for a cumulonimbus to form over the airfield.*

8. A pilot is flying through an extensive area of haze. Within an hour of sunset, the reported visibility at their destination airfield is 5km, however, the actual slant visibility when looking towards the runway on approach will appear:

(a) *Much less than reported especially flying away from the sun.*
(b) *Much more than reported especially flying away from the sun.*
(c) *Much more than reported especially flying into the sun.*
(d) *Much less than reported especially flying into the sun.*

9. Under a low pressure weather system, there is a cool and cloudless night with no wind, and the air in contact with the surface cooled to its dewpoint temperature of +5°C, which of the following is most likely to form?

(a) *Dew*
(b) *Frost.*
(c) *Mist.*
(d) *Fog.*

10. Under a low pressure system, there is a cool and cloudless night with no wind, and the air in contact with the surface cooled to its dewpoint temperature of –5°C, which of the following is most likely to form?

(a) Dew.
(b) Frost.
(c) Mist.
(d) Fog.

11. Under a high pressure system, there is a cool and cloudless night with a light wind. The very moist air in contact with the surface cooled to its dewpoint temperature (say +7°C), which of the following is most likely to form?

(a) Dew.
(b) Frost.
(c) Mist.
(d) Fog.

12. In winter there is a high pressure weather system. At a coastal airfield there is a light, onshore wind bringing a mild maritime air flow over a cold land surface, it may form:

(a) Radiation.
(b) Frontal.
(c) Advection fog.
(d) Clear skies.

13. A high pressure ridge extends over your route resulting in a sharp temperature inversion at 3000ft above mean sea level. Flying beneath the inversion:

(a) Will result in an improvement in visibility compared to flying on top of it.
(b) Will result in considerably reduced visibility compared to flying on top of it.
(c) There will be the same visibility as if flying on top of the inversion.
(d) Greater visibility whilst flying into sun.

14. Area Report (METAR) and Terminal Aerodrome Forecast (TAF) both incorporate '6000 HZ' which means:

(a) 6000 metres horizontal visibility in hazardous conditions.
(b) 6000 feet horizontal visibility in haze.
(c) 6000 feet cloud base in haze.
(d) 6000 metres horizontal visibility in haze.

15. The visibility group 'R35/0400' in a Meteorological Area Report (METAR) means:

(a) *A runway visual range of 400 metres for runway 35.*
(b) *Reduced visibility to 35 metres at 0400 zulu.*
(c) *Visibility of 35metres for the right runway at 0400 zulu.*
(d) *A general, horizontal visibility of 400 metres.*

Answers: 1b, 2a, 3a, 4c, 5a, 6c, 7a, 8d, 9a, 10b, 11d, 12c, 13b, 14d, 15a.

Air Masses, Pressure Systems and Frontal Weather

Air Masses

The term 'air mass' is used to describe a large region of the atmosphere (continental scale) that has similar thermal and humidity properties throughout. It is usual to classify an air mass according to:

- its **origin**;
- its **path** over the earth's surface; and
- whether the air is **diverging** or **converging**.

The Origin of an Air Mass

Maritime air flowing over an ocean will absorb moisture and tend to become saturated in its lower levels. **Continental air** flowing over a land mass will remain reasonably dry since little water is available for evaporation.

The Path of an Air Mass

Polar air flowing towards the lower latitudes will be warmed from below and so become unstable. Conversely, **tropical air** flowing to higher latitudes will be cooled from below and so become more stable.

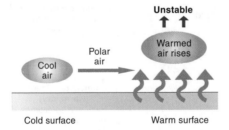

■ *Figure 21-1* **Polar air warms and becomes unstable**

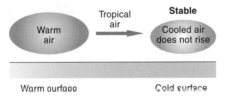

■ *Figure 21-2* **Tropical air cools and becomes stable**

Divergence or Convergence

An air mass influenced by the divergence of air flowing out of a *high*-pressure system at the earth's surface will slowly sink (known as *subsidence*) and become warmer, drier and more stable. An air mass influenced by convergence as air flows into a *low*-pressure system at the surface will be forced to rise slowly, becoming cooler, more moist and less stable.

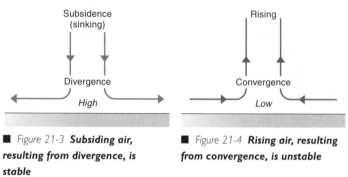

■ *Figure 21-3* **Subsiding air, resulting from divergence, is stable**

■ *Figure 21-4* **Rising air, resulting from convergence, is unstable**

The sources of most air masses that affect the United Kingdom are shown below, classified by temperature and moisture level.

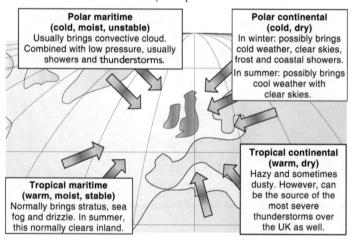

Polar maritime (cold, moist, unstable)
Usually brings convective cloud. Combined with low pressure, usually showers and thunderstorms.

Polar continental (cold, dry)
In winter: possibly brings cold weather, clear skies, frost and coastal showers.
In summer: possibly brings cool weather with clear skies.

Tropical maritime (warm, moist, stable)
Normally brings stratus, sea fog and drizzle. In summer, this normally clears inland.

Tropical continental (warm, dry)
Hazy and sometimes dusty. However, can be the source of the most severe thunderstorms over the UK as well.

■ *Figure 21-5* **Air masses that affect the United Kingdom**

Frontal Weather

Air masses have different characteristics, depending on their origin and the type of surface over which they have been passing. Because of these differences there is usually a distinct division between adjacent air masses. These divisions are known as **fronts,** and there are two basic types – cold fronts and warm fronts. *Frontal activity* describes the interaction between the air masses, as one mass replaces the other. In this APM frontal systems are introduced through what is known as the Norwegian Cyclone Model, in reality, they can behave and look very differently compared with what is described by this model. There are many other models to describe such weather systems but these are too advanced for the scope of this manual.

The Warm Front

If two air masses meet so that the warmer air replaces the cooler air at the surface, a **warm front** is said to exist. The boundary at the earth's surface between the two air masses is represented on a weather chart as a line with semicircles pointing in the direction of movement.

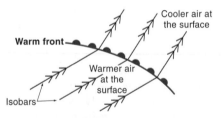

■ *Figure 21-6* **Depiction of a warm front on a weather chart**

The slope formed in a warm front as the warm air slides up over the cold air is fairly shallow and so the cloud that forms in the (usually quite stable) rising warm air is likely to be stratiform. In a warm front the frontal air at altitude is actually well ahead of the line as depicted on the weather chart. The cirrus could be some 600 nm ahead of the surface front, and rain could be falling up to approximately 200 nm ahead of it. The slope of the warm front is typically 1 in 150, much flatter than a cold front, and has been exaggerated in the diagram.

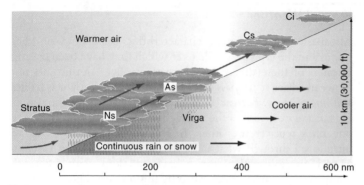

■ *Figure 21-7* **Cross-section of a warm front**

Observation from the Ground

As a warm front gradually passes, an observer on the ground may first see high cirrus cloud, which will slowly be followed by a lowering base of cirrostratus, altostratus and nimbostratus. Figure 21-7 shows an example.

Rain may be falling from the altostratus and possibly evaporating before it reaches the ground – this is called *virga*. Rain may fall continuously from the nimbostratus until the warm front passes and may, as a result of its evaporation, cause fog. Also, the visibility may be quite poor.

The atmospheric pressure will usually fall continuously as the warm front approaches and, as it passes, either stop falling or fall at a lower rate. The air temperature will rise as the warm air moves in over the surface. The warm air will hold more moisture than the cold air, and the dewpoint temperature in the warmer air will be higher.

In the northern hemisphere, the wind direction will veer as the warm front passes (and back in the southern hemisphere). Behind the warm front, and after it passes, there is likely to be stratus. Visibility may still be poor. Weather associated with a warm front may extend over several hundred miles.

The general characteristics of a warm front are:
- lowering stratiform cloud;
- increasing rain, with the possibility of poor visibility and fog;
- a falling pressure that slows down or stops;
- a wind that veers; and
- a temperature that rises.

Observation from the Air

Warm fronts, in reality, can vary considerably from that discussed and what a pilot observes depends on the direction of flight

relative to the warm front. However, the following are good indicators of a warm front if flying towards it from the cold sector:
- Widespread cloud with gradually lowering bases, increasing amounts of stratus and hill fog.
- Occasional becoming widespread precipitation, with risk of freezing rain if in sub-zero air underneath the cloud.
- Possible wind shear and un-trapped mountain waves
- Wind is likely to veer whilst passing through the front and a change of heading may be required to maintain track.

The Cold Front

If a cooler air mass undercuts a mass of warm air and displaces it at the surface, a cold front is said to occur. The slope between the two air masses in a cold front is generally quite steep (typically 1 in 50) and the frontal weather may occupy a band of only 30 to 50 nautical miles.

The boundary between the two air masses at the surface is shown on weather charts as a line with barbs pointing in the direction of travel of the front. The cold front moves quite rapidly, with the cooler frontal air at altitude lagging behind that at the surface.

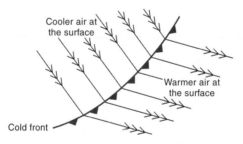

■ *Figure 21-8* **Depiction of a cold front on a weather chart**

The air that is forced to rise with the passage of a cold front is unstable and so the cloud that is formed is cumuliform in nature, e.g. cumulus and cumulonimbus. Severe weather hazardous to aviation, such as thunderstorm activity, squall lines, severe turbulence and windshear, may accompany the passage of a cold front.

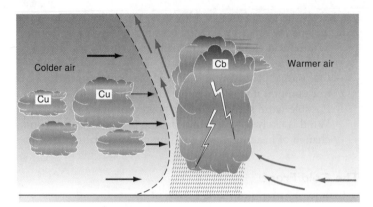

■ *Figure 21-9* **Cross-section of a cold front**

Observation from the Ground

The atmospheric pressure will fall as a cold front approaches and the change in weather with its passage may be quite pronounced. There may be cumulus and possibly cumulonimbus cloud with heavy rain showers, thunderstorm activity and squalls, with a sudden drop in temperature and change in wind direction as the front passes (veering in the northern hemisphere, backing in the southern hemisphere).

The cooler air mass will contain less moisture than the warm air, and so the dewpoint temperature after the cold front has passed will be lower. Once the cold front has passed, the pressure may rise rapidly.

The general characteristics of a cold front are:
- cumuliform cloud – cumulus, cumulonimbus;
- a sudden drop in temperature, and a lower dewpoint temperature;
- a veering of the wind direction; and
- a falling pressure that rises once the front is past.

Observation from the Air

There may be thunderstorm activity, violent winds (horizontal and vertical) from cumulonimbus clouds which are usually embedded within the front and difficult to visually distinguish. Weather threats include squall lines, windshear, heavy showers of rain or hail, and severe turbulence. Icing could be a problem. Passing through the cold front into the Polar Maritime air behind, visibility away from the showers and the cloud may be quite good, but it is still prudent to consider avoiding the severe weather activity that accompanies many cold fronts.Flying through a cold front may require diversions to avoid weather.

The Warm Sector

With classic frontal theory the warm sector exists between the warm and cold fronts, typically associated with tropical maritime air and strong southwest winds (for the UK). This is a stable area of a frontal system that can result in low stratus cloud and mountain wave activity or wind shear.

The Wave or Frontal Depression

The boundary between two air masses moving (relative to one another) side by side is often distorted by the warmer air bulging into the cold air mass, with the bulge moving along like a wave. This is known as a **frontal wave**. The leading edge of the bulge of warm air is a warm front and its rear edge is a cold front.

The pressure near the tip of the wave falls sharply and so a depression forms, together with a warm front, a cold front, and possibly an occlusion. It is usual for the cold front to move faster across the surface than the warm front.

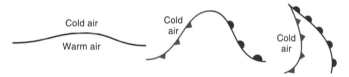

■ *Figure 21-10* **The frontal depression**

The Occluded Front

Because cold fronts usually travel much faster than warm fronts, it often happens that a cold front overtakes a warm front, creating an **occlusion** or **occluded front**. This may happen in the final stages of a frontal depression (which is discussed shortly). Three air masses are involved and their vertical passage, one to the other, will depend on their relative temperatures. The occluded front is depicted by a line with alternating barbs and semicircles pointing in the direction of motion of the front.

The two types of occluded fronts are illustrated in Figure 21-12. A cold front occlusion will occur when the original cold front remains at the surface. A warm front occlusion will occur when the original warm front remains at the surface. Which of the original fronts remains at the surface of the occlusion will depend on the relative temperatures of the three air masses involved.

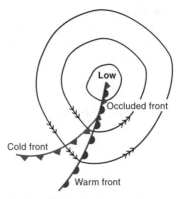

■ *Figure 21-11* **Depiction of an occluded front on a weather map**

In general the cold front occlusion is a summer phenomenon and the warm front occlusion is more likely to occur in winter.

The cloud that is associated with an occluded front will depend on what cloud is associated with the individual cold and warm fronts. It is not unusual to have cumuliform cloud (Cu, Cb) from the cold front as well as stratiform cloud from the warm front. Sometimes the stratiform cloud can conceal thunderstorm activity. Severe weather can occur in the early stages of an occlusion as unstable air is forced upwards, but this period is often short.

Flight through an occluded front may involve encountering intense weather, as both a cold front and a warm front are involved with a warm air mass being squeezed up between them. The wind direction will be different either side of the front.

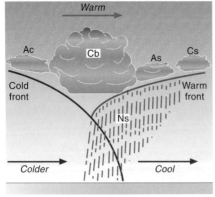

Cold front occlusion

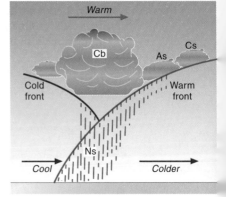

Warm front occlusion

■ *Figure 21-12* **Cross-sections of occluded fronts**

In this section we have described the classic Norwegian theory of frontal systems. Since this model was created the advent of satellite observations enabled meteorologists to recognise that the Norwegian theory did not describe all frontal behaviour and they developed what is known as conveyor belt theory which better characterises a whole host of frontal behaviour. Pilots should recognise that when they see frontal systems, observed or forecast, prior or during a flight that their characteristics may not always be as expected when considering the classic theory – therefore, fronts should be treated on a case by case basis utilising both valid forecasts and observations to identify associated hazards and their progression through time or over a route to be flown.

ATLANTIC WEATHER – February 16

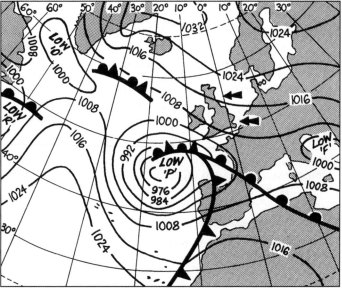

Lows 'P' and 'F' will move east and slowly fill as low 'R' tracks northeast and deepens. Low 'O' will lose its identity.

■ Figure 21-13 **A weather map showing cold, warm and occluded fronts**

Depressions – Areas of Low Pressure

A **depression** or **low** is a region of low pressure at the surface, the pressure gradually rising as you move away from its centre. A *low* is depicted on a weather chart by a series of concentric isobars joining places of equal sea level pressure, with the lowest pressure in the centre.

In the northern hemisphere, winds circulate anticlockwise around a *low.* Flying towards a *low,* an aeroplane will experience right (starboard) drift.

Depressions generally are more intense than *highs,* being spread over a smaller area and with a stronger pressure gradient (change of pressure with distance). The more intense the depression, the 'deeper' it is said to be. *Lows* move faster across the face of the earth than *highs* and do not last as long.

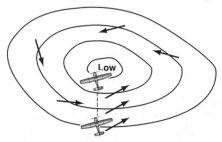

■ *Figure 21-14* **A depression or low pressure system**

Because the pressure at the surface in the centre of a depression is lower than in the surrounding areas, there will be an inflow of air, known as **convergence.** The air above the depression will rise and flow outwards.

The three-dimensional pattern of airflow near a depression is:
• convergence (inflow) in the lower layers;
• rising air above; and
• divergence (outflow) in the upper layers.

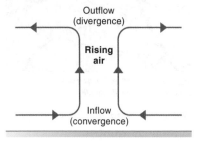

■ *Figure 21-15* **The three-dimensional flow of air near a low**

The depression at the surface may in fact be caused by the divergence aloft removing air faster than it can be replaced by convergence at the surface.

Weather Associated with a Depression

In a depression, the rising air will be cooling and so cloud will tend to form. Instability in the rising air may lead to quite large vertical development of cumuliform cloud accompanied by rain showers. Visibility may be good (except in the showers), since the vertical motion will tend to carry away all the particles suspended in the air.

Troughs of Low Pressure

A V-shaped extension of isobars from a region of low pressure is called a **trough**. Troughs are usually associated with unstable air and they increase low level convergence which forces air to rise; these are two key factors for the development of cumulonimbus cloud and associated thunderstorms.

Troughs act to organise convection in a long band generating hazardous weather that is difficult to avoid if routing through the trough - especially as cumulonimbus can be embedded within other cloud.

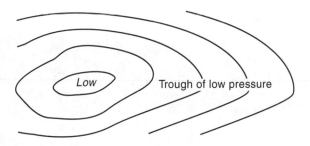

■ *Figure 21-16* **A trough**

Troughs increase low level convergence and usually act as a significant trigger action for the development of cumulonimbus cloud and associated thunderstorms.

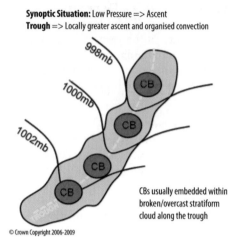

Synoptic Situation: Low Pressure => Ascent
Trough => Locally greater ascent and organised convection

998mb
1000mb
1002mb

CB
CB
CB
CB

CBs usually embedded within
broken/overcast stratiform
cloud along the trough

© Crown Copyright 2006-2009

■ Figure 21-17 **Synoptic situation**

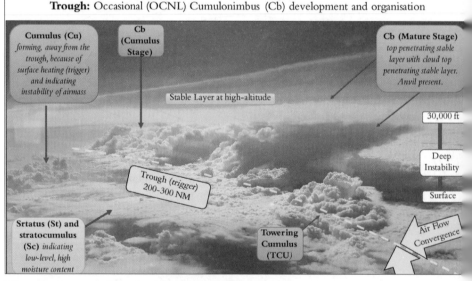

Trough: Occasional (OCNL) Cumulonimbus (Cb) development and organisation

Cumulus (Cu) *forming, away from the trough, because of surface heating (trigger) and indicating instability of airmass*

Cb (Cumulus Stage)

Stable Layer at high-altitude

Cb (Mature Stage) *top penetrating stable layer with cloud top penetrating stable layer. Anvil present.*

30,000 ft

Deep Instability

Surface

Trough (trigger) 200-300 NM

Srtatus (St) and stratocumulus (Sc) *indicating low-level, high moisture content*

Towering Cumulus (TCU)

Air Flow Convergence

The Cyclone or Tropical Revolving Storm

The tropical revolving storm can be violent and destructive. Fortunately they do not occur in the UK, but normally over warm tropical oceans at about 10–20° latitude during certain periods of the year.

Occasionally, weak troughs in these areas develop into intense depressions. Air converges in the lower levels and flows into the depression and then rises, the warm, moist air forming large cumulus and cumulonimbus clouds. The very deep depression may be only quite small (200–300 nm in diameter) compared to the typical depression in temperate latitudes, but its central pressure can be extremely low.

Winds can exceed 100 kt, with heavy showers and thunderstorm activity becoming increasingly frequent as the centre of the storm approaches.

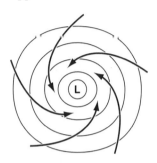

■ *Figure 21-18* **A tropical revolving storm or cyclone**

The **eye** of a tropical revolving storm is often only some 10 nm in diameter, with light winds and few clouds. It is occupied by very warm subsiding air, one reason for the extremely low pressure. Once the eye has passed, a very strong wind from the opposite direction will occur.

In the northern hemisphere, pronounced starboard (right) drift resulting from a strong wind from the left will mean that the eye of the storm is ahead (and vice versa in the southern hemisphere).

Tropical revolving storms are known as *cyclones* in the Indian and Pacific Ocean areas, as *hurricanes* in the Caribbean, and *typhoons* in the China Sea area.

These intense weather systems are best avoided by all aircraft.

Anticyclones – Areas of High Pressure

An **anticyclone,** or **high,** is an area of high pressure at the surface surrounded by roughly concentric isobars. *Highs* are generally greater in extent than *lows*, but with a weaker pressure gradient and slower moving, although they are more persistent and last longer.

In the northern hemisphere, the wind circulates clockwise around the centre of a *high*. Flying towards a *high* an aircraft will experience left (port) drift.

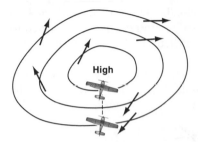

■ Figure 21-19 **The anticyclone or high**

The **three-dimensional flow** of air associated with an anticyclone is:
- an outflow of air from the high-pressure area in the lower layers (divergence);
- the slow subsidence of air over a wide area from above; and
- an inflow of air in the upper layers (convergence).

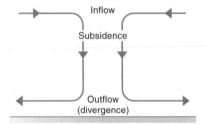

■ Figure 21-20 **The three-dimensional flow of air near a high**

The high-pressure area at the surface originates when the convergence in the upper layers adds air faster than the divergence in the lower layers removes it.

Weather Associated with a High

The subsiding air in a high-pressure system will be warming as it descends and so cloud will tend to disperse as the dewpoint temperature is exceeded and the relative humidity decreases. Subsiding air is very stable.

It is possible that the subsiding air may warm sufficiently to create an inversion, with the upper air warming to a temperature higher than that of the lower air, and possibly causing stratiform cloud to form (stratocumulus, stratus) and/or trapping smoke, haze and dust beneath it. This can happen in the UK winter, leading to rather gloomy days with poor flight visibility. In summer, heating by the sun may disperse the cloud, leading to a fine but hazy day.

If the sky remains clear at night, greater cooling of the earth's surface by radiation heat loss may lead to the formation of fog. If the high pressure is situated entirely over land, the weather may be dry and cloudless, but with any air flowing in from the sea, extensive stratiform cloud in the lower levels can occur. Mountain waves and wind shear can exist around the outskirts of the high as a result of the temperature inversion and stronger winds.

A Ridge of High Pressure

Isobars which extend out from a *high* in a U-shape indicate a ridge of high pressure (like a ridge extending from a mountain). Weather conditions associated with a ridge are, in general, similar to the weather found with anticyclones. The extent of cloud cover may change across a ridge, e.g. open cell shallow SCT CU to closed cell BKN SC, which may be significant for some aviation.

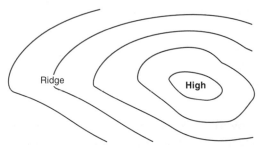

■ *Figure 21-21* **A ridge**

A Col

The area of almost constant pressure (and therefore indicated by a few very widely-spaced isobars) that exists between two *highs* and two *lows* is called a **col**. It is like a 'saddle' on a mountain ridge.

Light winds are often associated with cols, with fog a possibility in winter and high temperatures in summer possibly leading to showers or thunderstorms.

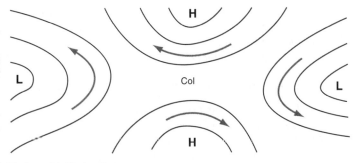

■ *Figure 21-22* **A col**

Now complete: **Practice Questions - Air Masses & Frontal Weather**

NOTE Some questions in this section will ask you what will happen in theory. Here we refer to the Norwegian theory of fronts as outlined in the main text. Yet real world frontal systems do not always follow the Norwegian theory, indeed the theory of fronts and airmasses itself has moved on considerably since the Norwegian model was developed. As a pilot do not always assume the weather will follow theory, practically, this is why weather forecasts and observations are so important for any given flight on any given day.

1. A tropical air mass that has originated over the ocean is referred to as:

    (a) *Polar Maritime (Pm).*
    (b) *Tropical Returning (Tr).*
    (c) *Tropical Maritime (Tm).*
    (d) *Tropical Continental (Tc).*

2. An air mass originating in the tropics and that has passed over a large land mass (e.g. Europe or Africa) is referred to as:

    (a) *Polar Continental (Pc).*
    (b) *Tropical Returning (Tr).*
    (c) *Tropical Maritime (Tm).*
    (d) *Tropical Continental (Tc).*

3. A cool, polar air mass moves across warmer land surface:

    (a) *Heat transfers to the air mass from the surface and it becomes more unstable.*
    (b) *Heat transfers to the air mass from the surface and it becomes more stable.*
    (c) *No heat transfers.*
    (d) *Heat transfers and it becomes neutral.*

4. A warm, tropical air mass moves across a cooler surface will:

    (a) *Lose heat to the surface and become more stable.*
    (b) *Lose heat to the surface and become more unstable.*
    (c) *Not transfer any heat and achieve neutral stability.*
    (d) *Not transfer any heat and become unstable.*

5. In the Northern Hemisphere winter, a tropical maritime air mass forms part of the warm sector in a frontal depression which:

(a) *Forces the air mass southwards, it heats up and becomes unstable. Cumuloform cloud forms with occasional rain showers developing.*

(b) *Forces the airmass from west to east and it remains at the same temperature with neutral stability. Cloud only forms when uplifted over mountains.*

(c) *Forces the airmass from east to west and it remains at the same temperature with neutral stability. Cloud only forms when uplifted over mountains.*

(d) *Forces the air mass northwards, it cools and becomes more stable. Extensive low stratus cloud forms as the moisture carried by the airmass condenses.*

6. A high pressure weather system is associated with:

(a) *Descending (subsiding), heating and drying air resulting in a temperature inversion and a stable atmosphere.*

(b) *An unstable atmosphere which results in ascending, cooling and saturated air.*

(c) *Descending, cooling and saturated air.*

(d) *No vertical motion of air and a neutral atmosphere.*

7. A low pressure weather system is associated with.

(a) *Descending (subsiding), heating and less saturated air resulting in a stable atmosphere.*

(b) *An unstable atmosphere which results in ascending, cooling and saturated air.*

(c) *Descending, cooling and saturated air.*

(d) *No vertical motion of air and a neutral atmosphere.*

8. A warm air mass replacing a cold air mass is called a:

(a) *Occluded front.*

(b) *Cold front.*

(c) *Warm front.*

(d) *Trough.*

9. The general cloud associated with a warm front is:

(a) *Stratiform.*

(b) *Cumuliform.*

(c) *Cirriform.*

(d) *Altoform.*

10. An aircraft is in clear air in the cold air mass (sub-zero) ahead of a warm front and flies towards the warm front. In theory, what conditions can be expected:

   (a) *Lowering cloud base. Widespread overcast low cloud (stratus). Freezing rain. Wind veering and turbulence as it passes through the front.*
   (b) *Cloud base increasing. Scattered altocumulus. Wind backing. Rain only at surface front.*
   (c) *Hail. Lightning. Microbursts.*
   (d) *Virga.*

11. It is winter and an aircraft flying is in the warm sector of a depression. There are mountains upwind. In theory, what conditions can be expected:

   (a) *Frequent cumulonimbus. Hail. Lightning. Microbursts.*
   (b) *Virga.*
   (c) *Widespread low cloud (stratus). Strong winds. Mountain waves. Extensive hill fog on the windward side of mountains. Poor low level visibility.*
   (d) *Calm winds. Widespread hill fog.*

12. An aircraft is in the cold polar maritime airmass behind a cold front. In theory, what conditions can be expected:

   (a) *Virga.*
   (b) *Occasional rain showers with possibility of cumulonimbus /thunderstorms. Strong, gusty winds. Excellent visibility outside the showers.*
   (c) *Mountain Waves.*
   (d) *Calm winds. Widespread hill fog.*

13. As a warm front approaches, in theory the first signs should be:

   (a) *Stratus up to 600 nautical miles (nm) ahead of the surface front.*
   (b) *No significant cloud.*
   (c) *Cumulus cloud up to 100nm ahead.*
   (d) *High level cirrus cloud up to 600nm ahead of the surface front.*

14. In theory, rain associated with a standard warm front may fall:

   (a) *Only after the surface front has passed.*
   (b) *Only in a narrow band some 10nm wide near the surface front.*
   (c) *Up to several hundred miles ahead of the surface front.*
   (d) *Will only occur on upslopes.*

15. In summer, a warm front that forms nimbostratus will result in:

   (a) *No significant weather.*
   (b) *Only extensive drizzle and widespread low cloud.*
   (c) *Veering of winds as the warm front passes a given location.*
   (d) *Widespread heavy rain along and ahead of the warm front. Widespread low cloud (stratus). A severe turbulence and severe icing risk.*

16. A cold air mass replacing a warm air mass at the surface is called a:

   (a) *Cold front .*
   (b) *Occluded front.*
   (c) *Warm front.*
   (d) *Trough.*

17. What type of clouds are generally associated with a cold front:

   (a) *Stratiform.*
   (b) *Cumuliform.*
   (c) *Cirriform.*
   (d) *Cumuliform, Stratiform and Cirriform.*

18. In theory, as a cold front passes:

   (a) *The air temperature and dewpoint will rise. Wind direction will veer.*
   (b) *The air temperature will fall and the dewpoint will rise. Wind direction will back.*
   (c) *The air temperature will rise and the dewpoint will fall. Wind direction will back.*
   (d) *The air temperature and dewpoint will fall. Wind direction will veer.*

19.   A cold front overtakes a warm front, it is called:

   (a) Uplifted front.
   (b) Rising front.
   (c) Occluded front.
   (d) Warm sector.

20.   A depression passing through your area and the airfield you are at lies within the warm sector. There is a southwest wind of 25 knots which, for runway 31, exceeds the cross wind limit of your aircraft. In theory, after the cold front has cleared the airfield:

   (a) Mean wind direction will veer and the cross wind will be within limits for runway 31.
   (b) Mean wind direction will back and the cross wind will be within limits for runway 13.
   (c) Mean wind direction will remain the same and continue to exceed cross wind limits.
   (d) Mean wind direction will veer and speed will increase exceeding cross wind limits.

21.   You are in Northern Europe and flying from east to west. Your aircraft has no de-icing or anti-icing capability. Widespread overcast cloud changes from cirriform to stratiform and the base lowers to 1000 feet above terrain. The outside air temperature is minus 2° Celsius, you enter a band of rain and ice forms on the airframe. What is the best course of action:

   (a) Climb to Minimum Safe Altitude (MSA), even though it means entering cloud as this will be temporary.
   (b) Descend into warmer air and continue. Reassess the icing situation in another 5 minutes.
   (c) Maintain track and level and reassess the icing situation in another 5 minutes.
   (d) Conduct a 180° turn and return to departure airfield or enroute diversion. Consider descending into warmer air if terrain clearance allows.

22. A low pressure weather system has polar maritime air embedded within it and a sharp trough which is likely to produce:

   (a) *Only extensive stratus cloud*
   (b) *Occasional cumulonimbus cloud along the trough.*
   (c) *Clear skies and scattered cumulus cloud.*
   (d) *Only stratocumulus and drizzle.*

23. It is summer and a col lies over the land area where you are about to fly. Embedded within it is a moist air mass.

   (a) *In the afternoon, daytime surface heating makes thunderstorms a possibility.*
   (b) *In the afternoon, cloud is unlikely to form.*
   (c) *Mountain waves are likely.*
   (d) *Strong, gusty winds will affect the area.*

Hazardous Conditions

Thunderstorms

Thunderstorms (TS) are associated with cumulonimbus cloud (CB) and present a very significant aviation hazard; lightning, heavy rain showers, hail, squalls and tornadoes are likely.

Lightning is a discharge of static electricity that has been built up in the cloud and the air along the path that the lightning follows experiences intense heating. This causes it to expand violently, and it is this expansion which produces the familiar clap of thunder.

The Three Necessary Conditions

For a thunderstorm to develop there must be deep instability, high moisture content and a trigger action.

Three conditions are necessary for a thunderstorm to develop:

- **deep instability** in the atmosphere, so that once the air starts to rise it will continue rising (for example, a steep lapse rate with warm air in the lower levels and cold air in the upper levels);
- a **high moisture** content;
- a **trigger action** (or catalyst) to start the air rising, from:
  - a front forcing the air aloft;
  - a mountain forcing the air aloft;
  - strong heating of the air in contact with the earth's surface;
  - heating of the lower layers of a polar air mass as it moves to lower latitudes (i.e. towards the equator); or
  - convergence of air flow, eg. a pressure trough or a sea breeze, which forces air to rise.

The Life Cycle of a Thunderstorm

1. The Cumulus Stage

As the moist air rises, it is cooled until its dewpoint temperature is reached. Then the water vapour starts to condense as liquid droplets and cloud forms. Latent heat is given off in the condensation process and so the rising air cools at a lesser rate. At this early cumulus stage in the formation of a thunderstorm, there are strong, warm updraughts over a diameter of one or two miles, with no significant downdraughts.

Air is drawn horizontally into the cell at all levels and causes the updraught to become stronger with height. The temperature inside the cloud is higher than the outside environment and the cloud continues to build to greater and greater heights. This often occurs at such a rate that an aeroplane cannot outclimb the growing cloud.

The strong, warm updraughts carry the water droplets higher and higher, to levels often well above the freezing level, where they may freeze or continue to exist as liquid water in a supercooled state. The liquid droplets will coalesce to form larger and larger drops.

The cumulus stage typically lasts 10 to 20 minutes. The cumulus stage involves small cumulus cloud developing and growing rapidly into towering cumulus cloud which may rise to over 20,000ft above ground level.

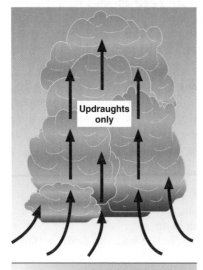

■ Figure 22-1 **The cumulus stage in the development of a thunderstorm**

2. The Mature Stage

The water drops eventually become too large and heavy to be supported by the updraughts (even though the updraughts may be in excess of 5,000 ft/min) and so start to fall. As they fall in great numbers inside the cloud, they drag air along with them causing **downdraughts**. Often the first lightning flashes and the first rain from the cloud base will occur at this stage.

The descending air warms adiabatically, but the very cold drops of water slow down the rate at which this occurs, resulting in very cool downdraughts in contrast to the warm updraughts. Heavy rain or hail may fall from the base of the cloud, generally being heaviest for the first 5 minutes.

The top of the cloud in this mature stage may reach as far as the tropopause, being some 20,000 ft in temperate latitudes and 50,000 ft in the tropics. The cloud may have the typical shape of a cumulonimbus, with the top spreading out in an *anvil* shape in the direction of the upper winds. The passage of an aeroplane through the windshear of these violent updraughts and downdraughts (which are very close to each other) can result in structural failure.

The rapidly changing direction from which the airflow strikes the wings could also result in a stall, so intentionally flying into a mature cumulonimbus cloud would be extremely foolhardy.

As the cold downdraughts flow out of the base of the cloud (at a great rate), they change direction and begin to flow horizontally as the ground is approached. Strong windshear will occur. This has caused the demise of many aeroplanes. The outflowing cold air will undercut the inflowing warmer air and, like a mini cold front, a gusty wind and a sudden drop in temperature may precede the actual storm.

A **roll cloud** may also develop at the base of the main cloud where the cold downdraughts and warm updraughts pass.

The mature stage may last from as little as one hour to as long as a few hours for larger more organised thunderstorms.

Beware of strong windshear near mature Cb clouds.

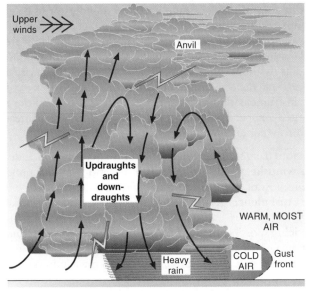

■ *Figure 22-2* **The mature stage**

3. The Dissipating Stage

The cold downdraughts gradually cause the warm updraughts to weaken and so reduce the supply of warm, moist air to the upper levels of the cloud. The cold downdraughts continue (since they are colder than the environment surrounding the cloud) and spread out over the whole cloud, which starts to collapse from above.

Eventually the temperature inside the cloud warms to reach that of the environment and what was once a towering cumulonimbus may collapse into a stratiform cloud.

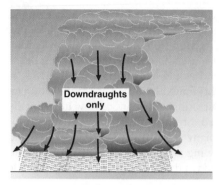

■ *Figure 22-3* **The dissipating stage**

The Danger of Thunderstorms

Thunderstorms are hazardous to aviation. The dangers to aviation from a thunderstorm do not just exist inside or under the cloud, but for quite some distance around it. Avoid thunderstorms by at least 10 nm and, in severe situations and higher altitudes, by 20 nm or more. Most jet transports and advanced aeroplanes are equipped with weather radar to enable their pilots to do this. Visual pilots without weather radar have to use their visual observations of the environment from the flight deck and whatever instrumentation on board (e.g. vertical speed indicator and indicated air speed to infer turbulence) to assess what threat thunderstorms/cumulo-nimbus present to the flight.

Avoid thunderstorms by at least 10 nautical miles.

Some obvious dangers to aeroplanes from thunderstorms include:
- **severe windshear** (causing flight path deviations and handling problems, loss of airspeed and possibly structural damage);
- **severe turbulence** (causing loss of control and structural damage);
- **severe icing** (possibly the very dangerous clear ice formed from large supercooled water drops striking a sub-zero surface);
- **damage from hail** (to the airframe and cockpit windows);
- **reduced visibility;**
- **low cloud base;**
- **may sometimes be embedded within other cloud;**
- **damage from lightning strikes,** including electrical damage;
- **interference to radio communications** and radio navigation instruments.

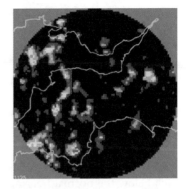

■ Figure 22-4 **Visually identifying cumulonimbus cloud, when possible, is essential for flight safety. Left: A mature stage cumulonimbus cloud over destination airfield; reported visibility 3000 metres in heavy rain with wind gusts up to 30knots. Right: the weather radar picture representative of the day, showing heavy rain showers (orange/red) associated with cumulonimbus.**

For further reading see AIC P056/2010.

Icing

Dangers of Icing

Icing can be hazardous to aviation.

Ice accretion on an aeroplane or within the engine induction system can significantly reduce flight safety by causing:

- **Adverse aerodynamic effects** – ice accretion on the *airframe* can modify the airflow pattern around aerofoils (wings, propeller blades, etc.), leading to a serious loss of lift and an increase in drag.
- **A loss of engine power**, or even complete stoppage, if ice blocks the air intake (in sub-zero temperatures) or carburettor ice forms (in moist air up to +25°C).
- **A weight increase** and a **change in the CG position** of the aeroplane, as well as unbalancing of the various control surfaces and the propeller, perhaps causing severe vibration and/or control difficulties.
- **Blockage of the pitot tube and/or static vent**, producing errors in the pressure instruments (airspeed indicator, altimeter, vertical speed indicator).
- **Degradation in radio communications** (if ice forms on the aerials).
- **Tailplane icing.** Latest research (NASA) has shown that almost twice as much ice accumulates on tailplanes when compared to main planes. This increases the likelihood of a tailplane stall and loss of control, with heavy pitch forward. The recovery is

opposite to a standard stall, pulling back on the control column and retracting flap.

- Visibility deterioration – through ice accretion on windscreens.

The Formation of Ice

If the temperature is less than 0°C, which is the freezing point of water, then ice may form, either:

- directly from water vapour (sublimation, causing hoar frost); or
- from water droplets freezing, causing rime ice and/or clear ice.

Supercooled water drops

Liquid water drops can exist in the atmosphere at temperatures well below the normal freezing point of water (0°C), possibly at –20°C or even lower. This is known as being *supercooled,* and such drops will freeze on contact with a surface – the skin of an aeroplane, or the propeller blades, for example.

Clear Ice

Once the freezing process actually begins, a large water drop with a temperature between 0°C and –20°C will not freeze instantaneously. The freezing process could be triggered by the drop striking a cold aircraft surface, where it will start to freeze. Because latent heat is released in this process, the rate of freezing will decrease, and the remaining liquid water will spread back and coalesce with water from other partially frozen water drops, before freezing on the cold airframe or propeller surfaces. The result is a sheet of solid, clear, glazed ice with very little air enclosed.

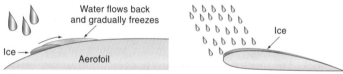

■ *Figure 22-5* **Clear ice formed from large, supercooled water drops**

The surface of clear ice is smooth, usually with undulations and lumps. Clear ice can alter the aerodynamic shape of aerofoils quite dramatically and reduce or destroy their effectiveness. Together with the increased weight, this creates a hazard to safety. Clear ice is very tenacious but, if it does break off, it could be in large chunks capable of doing damage.

Clear ice is a major hazard to flight safety.

Rime Ice

Rime ice is the most common form of icing.

Rime ice occurs when small, supercooled liquid water droplets freeze on contact with a surface whose temperature is sub-zero. Because the drops are small, the amount of water remaining after the initial freezing is insufficient to coalesce into a continuous sheet before freezing. The result is a mixture of tiny ice particles and trapped air, giving a rough, opaque, crystalline deposit that is fairly brittle.

Rime ice often forms on leading edges and can affect the aerodynamic qualities of an aerofoil or the airflow into the engine intake. It does not usually cause a significant increase in weight.

Cloudy or Mixed Ice

It is common for the drops of water in falling rain to be of many sizes and often, if ice forms, it will be a mixture of clear ice (from large drops) and rime ice (from small drops), resulting in cloudy or mixed ice.

Hoar Frost

Check static vent and pitot tube for ice contamination in these conditions.

Frost remaining on the wings is dangerous, especially during take-off.

Hoar frost occurs when moist air comes in contact with a sub-zero surface, the water vapour, rather than condensing to form liquid water, sublimating directly to ice in the form of hoar frost. This is a white crystalline coating that can usually be brushed off.

Hoar frost will form in clear air when the aeroplane is parked in sub-zero temperatures or when the aeroplane flies from sub-zero temperatures into warmer moist air – for example, on descent, or when climbing in an inversion. Although hoar frost is not as dangerous as clear ice, it can obscure vision through a cockpit window, and possibly affect the lifting characteristics of the wings.

Structural Icing and Cloud Type

If taking the option to descend to lower, warmer level, cross check level with MSA when IFR.

Ice adhering to the airframe is a very important consideration for instrument-rated pilots who may be flying in cloud; it is also an important consideration for visual pilots who may be flying in rain or drizzle which freezes on a cold aeroplane. Carburettor ice, which is discussed shortly, can of course occur without the presence of cloud or precipitation.

Cumulus-type cloud nearly always consists predominantly of liquid water droplets down to about −20°C, below which either liquid drops or ice crystals may predominate. Newly formed parts of the cloud will tend to contain more liquid drops than mature parts. The risk of airframe icing is severe in cumuliform cloud in the range 0 to −20°C, moderate to severe in the range −20° to −40°C, with the chance of airframe icing below −40°C being only small. Since there is a lot of vertical motion in convective clouds, the composition of the clouds may vary considerably at the one level, and the risk of icing may exist throughout a wide altitude band in (and under) the cloud. If significant icing does occur, it may be necessary to descend into warmer air.

Stratiform cloud usually consists entirely or predominantly of liquid water drops down to about −15°C, with the risk of airframe icing. If significant icing is a possibility, it may be advisable to fly at a lower level where the temperature is above 0°C, or at a higher level where the temperature is less than −15°C. In certain conditions, such as stratiform cloud associated with an active front or with orographic uplift, the risk of icing is increased at temperatures lower than usual; continuous upward motion of air generally means a greater retention of liquid water in the cloud.

Raindrops and drizzle from any sort of cloud will freeze if they meet an aeroplane whose surface is below 0°C, with a severe risk of clear ice forming, the bigger the water droplets are. You need to be cautious when flying in rain at freezing temperatures. This could occur, for instance, with an aeroplane flying in the cool sector underlying the warmer air of a warm front from which rain could be falling.

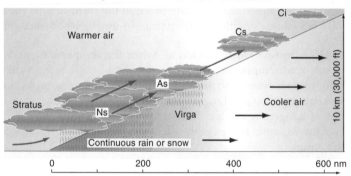

■ *Figure 22-6* **Danger area beneath a warm front**

Cirrus clouds are usually composed of ice crystals, and the risk of airframe icing is therefore only slight. However, turbine engine icing may be experienced, particularly in dense cirrus cloud associated with cumulonimbus.

Carburettor Icing

Ice can form in the carburettor and induction system in **moist air** with outside air temperatures as high as 30°C. It will disturb or prevent the flow of air and fuel into the engine, causing it to lose power, run roughly and perhaps even stop.

Cooling occurs when the induction air expands as it passes through the venturi in the carburettor (adiabatic cooling), and occurs also as the fuel vaporises (absorbing the latent heat of

When the air is moist, carburettor ice can form in temperatures as high as 30°C!

vaporisation). This can easily reduce what was initially quite warm air to a temperature well below zero and, if the air is **moist**, ice will form.

Throttle icing is more likely to occur at lower power settings when the partially closed butterfly creates a greater venturi cooling effect, compared with high power settings when the butterfly is more open and the venturi effect is less.

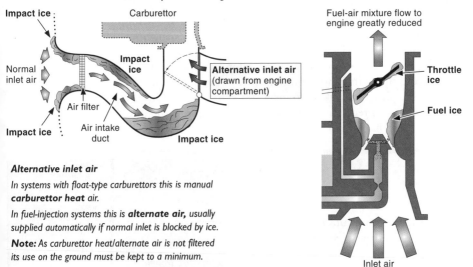

Alternative inlet air

In systems with float-type carburettors this is manual **carburettor heat** air.

In fuel-injection systems this is **alternate air,** usually supplied automatically if normal inlet is blocked by ice.

Note: As carburettor heat/alternate air is not filtered its use on the ground must be kept to a minimum.

■ *Figure 22-7* **Carburettor ice**

For more information on carburettor ice, see AIC P077/2009 and Vol. 4 of The Air Pilot's Manual.

All aeroplanes whose engines have carburettors are fitted with a carburettor heat control that can direct hot air from around the engine to be taken into the carburettor, instead of the ambient air. Being hot, it should be able to melt the ice and prevent further ice from forming. The correct method of using the carburettor heat control for your aeroplane will be found in the Pilot's Operating Handbook, and its use is also covered in Volume 1 of this series.

Remember that carburettor ice can form on a warm day in moist air!

Pitot-Static System Icing

This can adversely affect the readings of the pressure-operated flight instruments (i.e. the airspeed indicator, the altimeter, and the VSI). Refer to Vol. 4 of *The Air Pilot's Manual,* under *Pressure Instruments.*

Warning!

Ice of any type on the airframe or propeller, or in the carburettor and induction system, deserves the pilot's immediate attention and removal. Wings that are contaminated by ice prior to take-off will lengthen the take-off run because of the higher speed needed to fly – a dangerous situation!

An ice-laden aeroplane may even be incapable of flight. Ice or frost on the leading edge and upper forward area of the wings (where the majority of the lift is generated) is especially dangerous.

Most training aeroplanes are not fitted with airframe de-icers (removal) or anti-icers (preventative), so pilots of these aeroplanes should avoid flying in icing conditions (i.e. in rain or moist air at any time the airframe is likely to be at sub-zero temperatures). If a pitot heater is fitted, use it to avoid ice forming over the pitot tube and depriving you of airspeed information.

An ice-laden aeroplane may be completely incapable of flight.

Now complete: **Practice Questions - Thunderstorms**

1. List three conditions that enable a cumulonimbus /thunderstorm to develop:

    (a) *Unstable airmass, supply of moisture, low pressure trough.*
    (b) *Stable airmass, dry atmosphere, high pressure.*
    (c) *Unstable airmass, dry atmosphere, low pressure trough.*
    (d) *Stable airmass, supply of moisture, solar heating of the Earth's surface.*

2. The three stages of a thunderstorm's life cycle are (in sequential order):

    (a) *Dissipating stage, cumulus stage, mature stage.*
    (b) *Cumulus stage, dissipating stage, mature stage.*
    (c) *Cumulus stage, mature stage, dissipating stage.*
    (d) *Dissipating stage, mature stage, cumulus stage.*

3. There is an unstable atmosphere throughout the troposphere. What is likely to 'trigger' cumulonimbus cloud formation and thunderstorms:

    (a) *Maritime air mass. Low pressure with surface trough.*
    (b) *Maritime air mass. An upper high resulting in convergence of air flow at the top of the troposphere.*
    (c) *Continental air mass. An upper high resulting in convergence of air flow at the top of the troposphere.*
    (d) *Continental air mass. Divergence at low levels.*

4. At which stage of the lifecycle of a typical thunderstorm do strong updraughts over a diameter of 1 or 2nm first occur with no significant downdraughts?

(a) *Cumulus stage.*
(b) *Mature.*
(c) *Dissipating stage.*
(d) *Towering stage.*

5. At a given altitude, the temperature inside a cumulonimbus cloud compared to the ambient temperature of the environment is:

(a) *Higher.*
(b) *Lower.*
(c) *The same.*
(d) *Higher at high altitude, lower at low altitude.*

6. The beginning of what stage in the life of a typical thunderstorm is signalled by the first lightning flashes and the first rain from the cloud base?

(a) *Cumulus stage.*
(b) *Mature stage.*
(c) *Dissipating stage.*
(d) *Anvil stage.*

7. What is associated with the mature stage of a typical thunderstorm:

(a) *Lightning. Microbursts & severe turbulence. Hailstorm and/or heavy rain & poor visibility. Severe icing.*
(b) *Moderate rain showers. Moderate turbulence. Moderate icing.*
(c) *Slight rain showers. Turbulence reducing. Improving visibility.*
(d) *Anvil cloud. Virga. Moderate turbulence.*

8. If the top of a cumulonimbus cloud spreads out:

(a) *It is called an anvil and indicative of a well developed, mature cumulonimbus.*
(b) *The cloud is in the towering cumulus stage.*
(c) *There is embedded altocumulus castellanus.*
(d) *It is in the cirriform stage.*

9. A cumulonimbus cloud is a hazard to aviation:

(a) Only because of severe icing.

(b) Directly under the cloud because of downdraughts.

(c) Anywhere within 10nm of the visible cloud because of extensive updraughts and downdraughts.

(d) Only on top of the cloud because of sheet lightning.

Now complete: **Practice Questions - ICING**

1. Ice accretion on an airframe:

 (a) *Significantly reduces flight safety by adversely affecting flight dynamics.*

 (b) *Can sometimes improve flight dynamics and safety.*

 (c) *Adversely affects flight dynamics only when it exceeds 5mm in depth.*

 (d) *Adversely affects flight dynamics only when it exceeds 2mm in depth.*

2. Ice that forms on the wings, fuselage, propeller, is known as:

 (a) *Dynamic icing.*

 (b) *Static icing.*

 (c) *Airframe icing.*

 (d) *Generic icing.*

3. For piston engine aircraft with a carburettor, carburettor ice can form if:

 (a) *The atmospheric temperature is above 0°C and the humidity is minus 15°C.*

 (b) *The atmospheric temperature is above 20°C and the dewpoint is 18°C.*

 (c) *Only when the atmospheric temperature is below 0°C.*

 (d) *Only when the atmospheric temperature is below minus 5°C.*

4. A flight is taking place inside cloud and the Outside Air Temperature (OAT) reads minus 3°C. Compared to flight in cloud at minus 40°C:

 (a) *There is the same risk of airframe icing.*

 (b) *There is a greater risk of airframe icing.*

 (c) *There is a lesser risk of airframe icing.*

 (d) *There is no risk of airframe icing.*

5. Compared to ice crystals, liquid water droplets that are super-cooled below 0°C:

 (a) *There is the same risk of airframe icing*

 (b) *There is a greater risk of airframe icing*

 (c) *There is a lesser risk of airframe icing*

 (d) *There is no risk of airframe icing*

6. Large water droplets that are super-cooled below 0°C are likely to form on the airframe:

    (a) Clear ice.
    (b) Hoar frost.
    (c) Dry ice.
    (d) Rime ice.

7. Small water droplets that are super-cooled below 0°C are likely to form on the airframe:

    (a) Clear ice.
    (b) Hoar frost.
    (c) Dry ice.
    (d) Rime ice.

8. During the A-check of an aircraft, ice is observed on the wings and tail-plane:

    (a) Normal aircraft operation can be expected if the ice layer is less than 5mm thick.
    (b) It will reduce the performance of the aircraft and must be cleared before flight.
    (c) Normal aircraft operation can be expected if the ice layer is less than 1mm thick.
    (d) Does not need to be cleared if the air temperature is +1°C or above.

9. If ice forms over the static vent of an aeroplane and blocks it during the climb, the altimeter will read:

    (a) Zero.
    (b) A constant altitude.
    (c) Correctly.
    (d) A reducing altitude.

10. If ice forms over the static vent of an aeroplane and blocks it during the climb, the vertical speed indicator will read:

    (a) Zero.
    (b) Positive rate.
    (c) Correctly.
    (d) Negative rate.

11. If ice forms over the static vent of an aeroplane and blocks it during the climb, the airspeed indicator will read:

(a) *Zero.*
(b) *Too fast.*
(c) *Too slow.*
(d) *Correctly.*

12. For a normally aspirated, piston engine – throttle icing is more likely at:

(a) *High power setting.*
(b) *Low power setting.*
(c) *Mid-power setting.*
(d) *The same likelihood.*

13. The cold sector lies beneath the warmer air in a warm occlusion. When flying in the cold sector in Visual Meteorological Conditions (VMC) there is:

(a) *No possibility of airframe ice forming when the outside air temperature is 0°C.*
(b) *A possibility of clear ice forming on the airframe rain when the outside air temperature is 0°C.*
(c) *A possibility of clear ice forming on the airframe in rain when the outside air temperature is below 0°C.*
(d) *A possibility of airframe ice forming when the outside air temperature is 10°C.*

Weather Forecasts and Reports

Weather forecasts enable a pilot to anticipate hazards to flight safety and meteorological observations enable recognition of when these hazards will directly affect a flight. For many regions there is now an excess of aviation meteorology information available for pilots and so it is important to apply a structured approach to analysing this information and interpreting what it means for a particular flight.

Checking the weather can be done to a limited extent by making one's own observations around the airfield or from the flight deck. However, a Meteorological Office will supply a range of information that is necessary for the safe conduct of flight; air temperatures, winds, pressure patterns, the extent and base of any cloud, and the possibility of fog, icing, thunderstorms, turbulence and other weather phenomena.

Weather information available to pilots falls into two categories:
* **forecasts** of expected weather over an area or region, and at aerodromes with an issue time and validity period; and

observations, including reports of actual weather, satellite and radar images taken at a specific time.

Interpretation of this detailed information relative to aircraft type, qualifications and route to be flown will greatly facilitate safe and efficient planning and decision making. A top-down approach is recommended; first acquire the context from the synoptic situation in terms of pressure systems and large-scale weather (e.g. fronts) that will affect your flight. This then helps focus attention and prioritisation of the relevant information contained within the multitude of forecasts and observations available; area forecast and radar observations, terminal aerodrome forecasts and aerodrome reports. This approach also aids an understanding of why cloud base and type, visibility, wind and thunderstorms are evolving across the route and in time.

Weather and forecasts change and so it is good airmanship to keep updated during the course of a flight, particularly if it is a cross-country flight to another aerodrome so as to ensure that conditions are likely to remain suitable for the for the planned flight, and if not, to enable alternative plans to be made in time.

The National Meteorological Service (NMS) of any given country issues aviation meteorological information to the standards mandated by the International Civil Aviation Organisation (ICAO). However, the presentation and access to meteorological information can vary considerably.

In the United Kingdom the Meteorological Office issues much of its aviation meteorological forecasts and observations over the internet at **www.metoffice.gov.uk/aviation/ga-briefing-services**. Another good resource for worldwide aviation weather is provided by the US at **https://www.aviationweather.gov** Before proceeding in this section, it is suggested that the reader familiarise themselves with the products available from this website. Though used less frequently, telephone and facsimile services are sometimes also available.

Types of Weather Information

A **forecast** is a prediction (or prognosis) of what the weather is likely to be – the common aviation forecasts being:

* **Area Forecasts;**
* **Aerodrome Forecasts** (TAFs or TRENDs); and
* **Special Forecasts.**

A **report** is an observation of what the weather actually is (or was) at a specific time. The common aviation weather reports are:

* Aerodrome Weather Reports (**METARs** on a routine basis and **SPECIs** when special conditions exist);
* Automatic Terminal Information Service (**ATIS**);
* In-flight Weather Reports (obtainable in recorded form on a **VOLMET** VHF frequency, e.g. London VOLMET on 128.600 or 126.600 MHz, or from an ATIS, or by radio communication with an Air Traffic Service unit – although this is the least preferred method since it occupies a communications frequency).

Significant weather that may affect the safety of flight operations may be advised in the form of a **SIGMET**. The criteria for raising a SIGMET include frequent or embedded thunderstorms, tropical revolving storms, a severe line squall, heavy hail, severe turbulence, severe airframe icing, marked mountain waves, widespread dust or a sandstorm.

As a means of improving the meteorological information service to pilots, it is common to attach a forecast **TREND** to an Aerodrome Report (i.e. an observation of actual weather). The Trend Forecast indicates what the weather tendency over the following two hours is expected to be. It is valid only until 2 hours after the time of the observation – a much shorter period than the duration of a normal Aerodrome Forecast (9 hours) – and therefore should be more accurate.

A TREND is commonly referred to as a **landing forecast.**

Meteorological Forecasts

Area Forecasts

An Area Forecast provides information on expected weather for a certain area over a certain period. It may cover a large area such as the entire British Isles, or a more localised AIRMET region such as Northern England.

AIRMET Forecasts

AIRMETs are text-based and suitable for light aircraft operations as they cover from the surface (ground or sea level) up 24,000ft (6000ft for smaller regions), including winds and air temperatures. They are issued four times a day for each region and amended in case of significant weather changes. Each forecast will include a brief outlook to the end of the subsequent forecast period to give a preview of subsequent weather conditions. UK AIP GEN 3-5 and Met Office GetMet supply details of ways to acquire the AIRMET service.

```
AIRMET AREA FORECAST, NORTHERN REGION,
VALID DEC 24/1100Z TO 1900Z.

MET-SITUATION: AN UNSTABLE N TO NW AIRSTREAM, WILL COVER THE
               REGION.

               STRONG WIND WARNING: SFC WINDS WILL EXCEED 20KT, AT
               TIMES.

WINDS:
  1000FT:330/30KT PS01,  BEC 300/20KT PS01.
  3000FT:340/35KT MS03,  BEC 320/25KT MS02.
  6000FT:350/35KT MS09,  BEC 320/25KT MS09.
FREEZING LEVEL:2000FT.

WEATHER-CONDITIONS: 2 ZONES:

   ZONE 1: N OF A LINE, TEESSIDE, MANCHESTER, STRUMBLE, BELFAST.

           GEN 30KM, WITH 5/8CUSC 2500FT/6000.
           OCNL 6KM IN RA OR SLEET SH, WITH 6/8CU 1500FT/10000.
           ISOL 800M IN SN SH WITH TS, AND 6/8CB 500FT/20000.
     WRNG: CLD WILL COVER HILLS.
           MOD, ISOL SEV, TURB AND ICE IN CLD.
           MOD TURB BLW 6000FT.

   ZONE 2: ELSEWHERE.

           25KM, WITH 6/8CUSC 2000FT/6000.
           E OF 1 DEG W, 5/8AC 10000FT/18000, AND OCNL 6KM IN RA OR
           SLEET SH, WITH 6/8CU 1000FT/10000.
     WRNG: CLD WILL COVER HILLS.
           MOD TURB AND ICE IN CLD.
           IN E, MOD TURB BLW 6000FT.

OUTLOOK: UNTIL DEC 25/0100Z:

         SH BEC GEN ISOL, APART FROM NEAR IRISH SEA.
```

■ *Figure 23-8* **Example of a printed AIRMET Area Forecast (reduced) for the northern AIRMET region (obtained on internet or by facsimile)**

CIVIL AVIATION AUTHORITY
AIRMET COPY FORM
(for forecasts from 31 March 1995 onwards)

| Forecast Number | | Valid | 15 0500 | To | 15 1300Z |

All temperatures are in degrees Celsius. All heights are AMSL, and all times UTC(Z).

MET SITUATION

SAMPLE ONLY
Not to be used for flight
operations or flight planning

Strong unstable NW flow covers the region.

Strong wind warning; NW surface wind will gust to 35 kt in places.

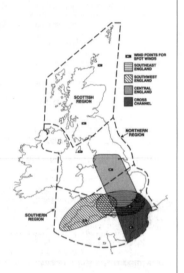

ALTITUDE	WINDS/TEMPERATURES	FORECAST AREA		
1000 Ft	320/30 kt +4°C	1. SOUTHERN REGION	40	X
3000 Ft	320/35 kt 0°C	2. NORTHERN REGION	41	
		3. SCOTTISH REGION	42	
6000 Ft	320/30 kt −4°C	4. UK SIG WEATHER	43	
		5. UK UPPER WINDS	44	
10000 Ft		6. UK UPDATE/OUTLOOK	45	
	FZ level 3000 ft	7. SOUTHWEST ENGLAND	46	
18000 Ft		8. SOUTHEAST ENGLAND	47	
		9. CROSS CHANNEL	48	
24000 Ft		10. CENTRAL ENGLAND	49	

■ Figure 23-9 **Example of an AIRMET regional forecast (reduced), taken down using the telephone service, onto the copy form**

WEATHER CONDITIONS

Vis gen 30 km, with nil to 3/8 Sc 2500 ft to 6000 ft.

Isol, mainly over sea, and coasts and hills exposed to NW, 10 km in rain showers, with 7/8 Cu 1500 ft to 10,000 ft.

Isol, in the far NE and NW, vis 3000 m in TS and hail, with 7/8 Cb 1000 ft to 20/24,000 ft, and in the NE 5/8 AC layered 10/16,000 ft.

Occ in extreme Sth at first, vis 8 km in rain, with 5 to 7/8 Sc and Ac layered to 1500 ft to 16,000 ft.

WARNING

Cloud covering hills. Mod turb and mod ice in cloud, but isol severe ice and severe turb in Cb in NE and NW.

Mod turb below 6000 ft over land due to strong surface winds.

OUTLOOK   UNTIL   15/1900Z

More showers developing over land as a trough moves south across region; to lie Cherbourg to Straits of Dover by 1800Z.

TELEPHONE NUMBERS

All forecasts between 0530 and 2300 on 0891 77 13 plus two digit code for selected forecasts.	All forecasts between 2300 and 0530 **PLUS** Consultation for amplification of all forecasts.
TAFs/METARs ALDERGROVE 018 494 23275 BIRMINGHAM 0121 717 0580 CARDIFF 01222 390 492 LEEDS 01132 457 687 BRACKNELL 01344 856 267 MANCHESTER 0161 429 0927 GLASGOW 0141 221 6116	BRACKNELL 01344 856 267 MANCHESTER 0161 429 0927 GLASGOW 0141 221 6116

Copies of this form, and of CAA document No 397 AIRMET FORECASTS; USERS NOTES-2nd ISSUE, may be obtained free of charge by writing to: The Technical Secretary, AOPA, 50a Cambridge Street, London SW1V 4QQ, provided a suitable A4 size stamped addressed envelope is enclosed with the request.

■ *Figure 23-10* **The forecast concluded on the rear side of the copy form**

Graphic Area Forecasts

Graphic Area Forecasts are distributed by forecast offices and cover a large area. The Met Office *Low-Level Weather Forecast chart* (Metform 215, Figure 23-11) covers the entire area of the UK and shows general weather below 10,000 ft amsl; it is valid for nine hours and is issued four times a day (every six hours). The Met Office also issues the *UK Spot Wind chart (Metform 214*, Figure 23-12)* which details spot winds and temperatures to 24,000 ft amsl, it is issued four times a day (every six hours) and covers a six hour forecast period. An amended Metform 215 is issued with the word AMENDED at the bottom of the form.

Explanatory notes for the Low-Level Weather Chart (METFORM 215T) are available from forecast offices and the dial-up METFAX service. AIP GEN 3-5 also contains information on Form 215T. To decode weather forecasts and reports it is necessary to know the meaning of various symbols and abbreviations. These are included later in this chapter. Symbols can also be found in the AIP GEN 3-5 section, and abbreviations are included in the general list of abbreviations in AIP GEN 3-5.

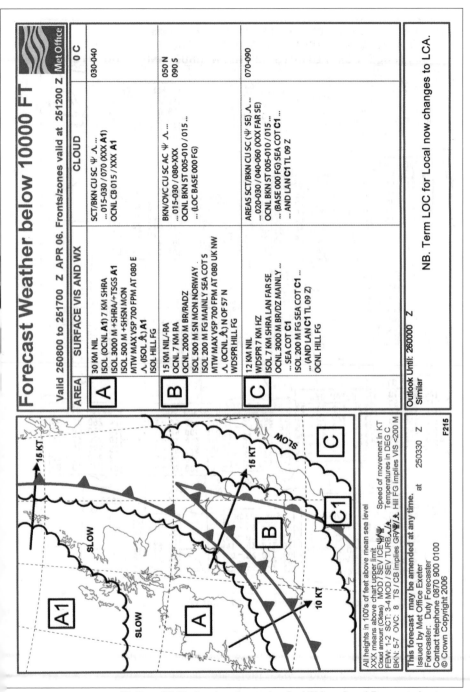

■ Figure 23-11 **A reduced sample of a UK Low-Level Forecast chart**

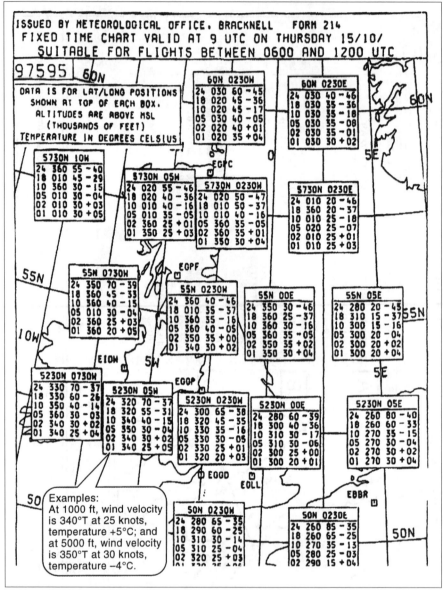

■ Figure 23-12 *A reduced sample excerpt of a UK Spot Winds chart*

To decode weather forecasts and reports it is necessary to know the meaning of various symbols and abbreviations. These are included later in this chapter. Symbols can also be found in the AIP GEN 3-5 section, and abbreviations are included in the general list of abbreviations in AIP GEN 3-5.

Special Forecasts

For departure from aerodromes where the weather information is inadequate or unavailable, the pilot can request a forecast office to prepare a Special Forecast specifically for his or her flight. This takes time and so at least 2 hours' notice is required (4 hours' if the route distance exceeds 500 nm).

Special Forecasts are issued via facsimile, AFTN or, less frequently, via telex, facsimile or telephone. Special Forecasts can also include Aerodrome Forecasts for the departure, destination and up to three alternates.

NOTE As Special Forecasts only cover that portion of the route outside the area of coverage of UK Area Forecasts, an appropriate UK Area Forecast must also be obtained. For further information consult AIP GEN 3-5.

Terminal Aerodrome Forecasts (TAFs)

Aerodrome Forecasts, known as TAFs, are text messages which follow the international (ICAO) format for aerodromes where observations are taken.

TAFs describe the forecast prevailing conditions at an aerodrome and usually cover periods of 9 to 24 hours.

The 9-hour TAFs are updated and re-issued every 3 hours; TAFs valid for 12–24 hours are updated and re-issued every 6 hours. Amendments are issued as and when necessary.

They may be preceded on a print-out by the term TAF, or, when on a list of one or more aerodromes, by FC or FT (forecast), followed by UK to represent the country: for instance 'FCUK'.

The TAF decode is included at the end of this chapter and can be found in AIP GEN 3-5. The four-figure ICAO location identifiers for UK aerodromes are listed in AIP GEN 2-4 and *Pooley's Flight Guide*.

NOTE All TAFs and METARs include the date and time of origin,

e.g. TAF EGDM **041330Z 0415/0424 12015G25KT 9999 SCT020=**

At the time of writing this change was not reflected in some of the PPL exam papers.

Aerodrome Forecast Examples

EXAMPLE 1

TAF EGPD 040600Z 0407/0416 13012KT 4000 BR OVC004=

This decodes to read:

Location: Aberdeen (Dyce)

Time of report: 0600UTC on 4th of the month

Period of validity: 0700 on 4th of the month to 1600 UTC on 4th of the month

Surface wind: 130°T/12 knots

Visibility: 4,000 metres

Weather: mist

Cloud: sky overcast with cloud, base 400 ft above aerodrome elevation

Significant variations: nil

NOTE The '=' sign after 004 indicates the end of the forecast message.

EXAMPLE 2

EGSS 170900Z 1710/1719 18015KT 9999 SCT022 TEMPO 1710/1717 20017G27KT 5000 SHRA BKN012=

This decodes to read:

Location: London (Stansted)

Time of report: 0900UTC on 17th of the month

Period of validity: 1000 on 17th of the month to 1900 UTC on 17th of the month

Surface wind: 180°T/15 knots

Visibility: in excess of 10 km

Weather: moderate rain shower

Cloud: 3–4 oktas (scattered) layer, base 2,200 ft aal (above aerodrome level)

Significant variations: temporary periods (TEMPO), i.e. less than 60 minutes in a given hour and less than 50% of the forecast period, from 1000 until 1700 UTC:

Surface Wind: 200°T/17 gusting 27 knots.

Visibility: Reduced to 5,000 metres with moderate rain shower.

Cloud: 5–7 oktas of cloud (broken), base 1,200 ft aal.

EXAMPLE 3

EGNV 230900Z 2310/2319 21015G25KT 8000 -RA SCT010 BKN045
OVC100 BECMG 2310/2314 24022KT 3000 RA OVC005 PROB30
TEMPO 2316/2319 9999 NSW BKN025=

This decodes to read:

Location: Teesside

Time of report: 0900 UTC on 23rd of the month

Period of validity: 1000 on 23rd of the month to 1900 UTC on 23rd of the month

Surface wind: 210°T/15 knots, with gusts to 25 knots

Visibility: 8,000 metres

Weather: slight rain

Cloud: 3–4 oktas (scattered), base 1,000 ft aal, 5–7 oktas (broken), bases 2,500 ft and, 8 oktas (overcast) 10,000 ft aal.

Significant variations: A significant change to the general conditions is indicated by BECMG over a four hour period from 10Z to 14Z:

Surface wind: 240°T/ 22 knots

Visibility: 3,000 metres

Weather: moderate rain

Cloud: 8 oktas (overcast) base at 500 ft aal.

After this change there is a 30% probability that conditions will temporarily change between 16Z and 19Z to:

Surface wind: No Change

Visibility: 10km or greater

Weather: No Significant Weather

Cloud: 6-7 oktas (broken) base at 2500 ft aal.

Meteorological Reports

METARs

METARs are routine aerodrome reports representing weather observations taken at half to one hourly intervals. A code identical to that used for TAFs is used though the report is preceded by METAR and only carries a date and time of the observation as a six figure group (date-hour-minutes). TAFs have two groups, a six-figure group representing the date and time of the forecast, followed by an eight-figure group giving the validity period, i.e. the date and hour of commencement of the period, and the date and hour at which it ends, separated by a forward slash). The METAR will report the two temperatures are given: e.g. 09/07, where 09 is the actual air temperature (at 1.2 metres above ground level) and 07 is the dewpoint temperature – the difference between them acting as a guide to the possibility of mist/fog that will occur should the temperature and the dewpoint become the same. Also, the METAR will contain the QNH e.g. Q1010 represents a QNH of 1010 hPa.

EXAMPLE 4

EGPE 110750Z 08009KT 3500 -RA SCT003 SCT005 BKN007 09/08 Q1006=

This METAR (actual aerodrome meteorological observation) decodes as:

Location: Inverness (Dalcross)

Time of report: 0750 UTC on 11th

Surface wind: 080°T at 9 knots

Visibility: 3,500 metres

Weather: slight rain

Cloud: 3–4 oktas, base 300 ft and 500 ft; 5–7 oktas, base 700 ft aal

Air temperature: +9°C

Dewpoint temperature: +8°C

QNH: 1006 hectopascals

Trends (or Landing Forecasts)

Trend forecasts are sometimes added to the end of METARs to forecast the weather changes expected to occur in the **two hours** immediately after the time of the observation. If no significant change is expected, the observation will be followed by the trend statement: NOSIG.

A Trend Forecast Attached to a METAR

EXAMPLE 5

METAR EGBO 180940Z 25015G28KT 3000 +RA BKN035 05/M02 Q1002 NOSIG=

This decodes as:

Actual weather for Halfpenny Green at 0940 UTC, on the 18th.

Wind: 250°T/15 knots gusting to 28 knots

Visibility: 3,000 metres in heavy rain

Cloud: 5–7 oktas (broken), base 3,500 ft aal

Temperature: 5°C; dewpoint: minus 2°C

QNH: 1002 hectopascals

No significant change forecast for the two hours to 1140 UTC.

Other more involved Trend Forecasts will often be preceded by BECMG (becoming) or TEMPO (temporary periods less than 60 minutes), with the time that the change is expected preceded by FM (from), TL (until) or AT (at). These terms are explained in more detail shortly.

VHF In-Flight Weather Reports

Weather information may be obtained at any time by radio from the Flight Information Service (FIS) or Air Traffic Control (ATC), who will also initiate a broadcast of any hazardous or significant weather that may be relevant to aircraft in the area (e.g. severe turbulence, thunderstorm activity, icing conditions, fog, etc.).

As mentioned previously, weather reports and trends for selected aerodromes are broadcast continuously on discrete VHF frequencies. This service is called **VOLMET**. The VOLMET broadcast for each aerodrome is updated each hour and half-hour and includes:

- the actual weather report;
- landing forecast;
- SIGMET (significant weather, if any); and
- the forecast trend for the two hours following the time of the report.

Information is also obtainable from the **Automatic Terminal Information Service (ATIS)** – a tape-recorded message of the current aerodrome information and is broadcast on appropriate VOR or discrete VHF frequencies to off-load the ATC VHF communications frequencies.

Some aerodromes have both an arrivals and departure ATIS. One variation on the ATIS is that the wind direction is given in degrees magnetic to allow the pilot to relate it to the runway direction (which is in °M) more easily. This also applies to winds passed to the pilot by the tower.

Cloud Bases

- The cloud base in a TAF (Aerodrome Forecast) or a Trend Forecast (both of which refer to a particular aerodrome), is given **above aerodrome level (aal)**; whereas
- Area Forecasts give the cloud base **above mean sea level (amsl)**, i.e. as altitudes.

TAFs and Trend Forecasts, then, provide the pilot with an immediate appreciation of the cloud ceiling at a particular aerodrome; 'aal' is, in fact, the height above the highest point in the landing area.

Over large areas of countryside, however, with mountains, valleys, plateaux and coastlines, a constant reference for cloud height is needed; of course the only satisfactory one is mean sea level (msl). To determine the expected level of the cloud base above the ground from the information in an Area or Regional Forecast you need to know the ground elevation. This can be determined from a suitable aeronautical chart.

Flight Crew Interpretation of Area Forecasts

Understanding what meteorological forecasts mean for a flight is dependent on how flight crew interpret the data relative to their qualifications, experience, airframe, route and type of operation. The F215 Area Weather Forecast *(fig. 26-12)* shows a frontal system across the United Kingdom separated into distinct weather zones:

Area A: Polar Maritime Air Mass
Area B: Frontal Zone *(including occlusion, cold front and warm front)*
Area C: Tropical Maritime *(Warm Sector)*
Area D: High Pressure

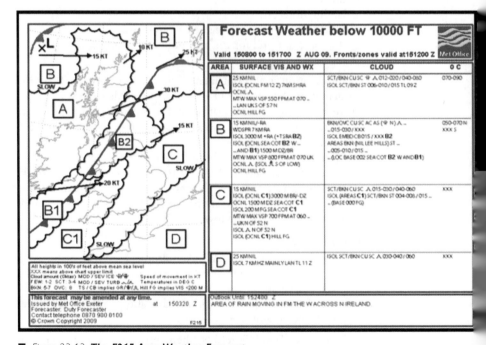

■ *Figure 23-13* **The F215 Area Weather Forecast**

The need for appropriate interpretation can be demonstrated through a hypothetical example – treating the whole of the forecast area as flat with a minimum safe altitude of 1500ft AMSL. A VFR operation would view such a weather situation as presenting considerable meteorological threats *(highlighted in red)*, borderline conditions *(orange)* and hazards *(pink)* that will affect the airframe. Aside from zone D, a VFR operation would be at best challenging and at worst unsafe.

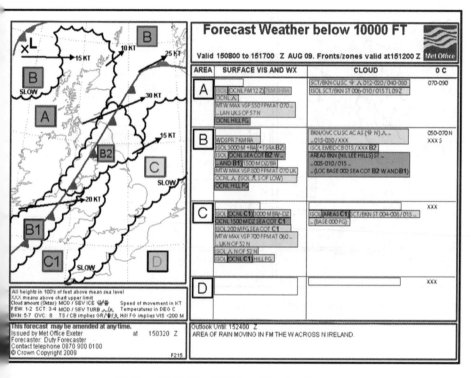

■ *Figure 23-14* **The F215 Area Weather Forecast**

Conversely, an IFR operation with a suitable airframe (with de-icing/anti-ice) may interpret the conditions completely differently – as generally permissive but with considerable aviation hazards that may affect the airframe.

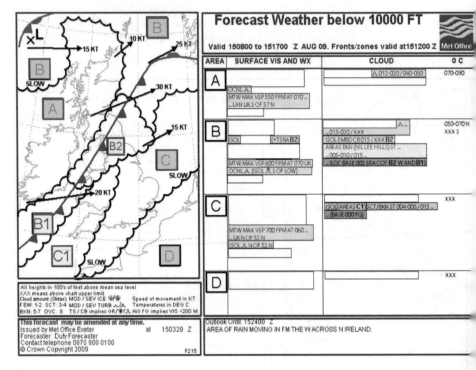

■ *Figure 23-15* **The F215 Area Weather Forecast**

Meteorological Observations: Satellite and Radar

Satellite observations and weather radar have revolutionised meteorology and are now available to flight crew from most National Meteorological Services or satellite operators themselves (**https://eumetview.eumetsat.int/mapviewer/**). Visible satellite images can help identify most weather features but are especially useful in helping a pilot to detect actual fog and stratus (as featureless grey areas) during the day-time. Infra-red satellite images can provide 24 hour coverage of weather systems and pick up deep convection (bright clumps) and frontal systems (bright bands) but a pilot will find it difficult to use this type of image to detect low cloud or fog. Radar helps establish the intensity of rainfall from which the type of weather system (front/showers) can be inferred. Lightning detection is also available and can help flight crew determine where the most active thunderstorms are before flight.

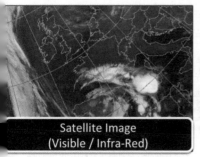
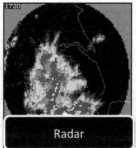
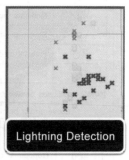

■ *Figure 23-16* **Satellite, Radar and Lightning Detection**

It is important for a pilot to interpret data from top-down; using the synoptic situation, satellite and radar to place METARs in context and monitor the progression of forecasts.

Symbols and Abbreviations

Symbols on UK Low-Level Weather Charts

Graphic Area Forecasts and Special Forecasts will contain symbols and abbreviations from the following standard sets.

1	Symbols for significant Weather, Tropopause and Freezing Level, etc.		
↟	Thunderstorm	″ ″ / ″ ″	Rain
⚲	Tropical cyclone	✳	Snow
⤜	Severe squall line	⊹	Widespread blowing snow
△	Hail	▽	Shower
⌒	Moderate turbulence	⟋	Severe sand or dust haze
⋀	Severe turbulence	⟋	Widespread sandstorm or duststorm
◯	Marked mountain waves	∞	Widespread haze
⋎	Light aircraft icing	=	Widespread mist
⋎	Moderate aircraft icing	≡	Widespread fog
⋎	Severe aircraft icing	≢	Freezing fog
◌	Freezing precipitation	⌐	Widespread smoke
•	Drizzle	⌂	Volcanic eruption

Note: Altitudes between which phenomena and any associated cloud are expected are indicated by flight levels, top over base or top followed by base. 'XXX' means the phenomenon is expected to continue above and/or below the vertical coverage of the chart. Phenomena of relatively lesser significance, for example light aircraft icing or drizzle, are not usually shown on charts even when the phenomenon is expected. The thunderstorm symbol implies hail, moderate or severe icing and/or turbulence.

400 Tropopause spot altitude (eg FL400)

〜〜〜 Boundary of area of significant weather

H 440 High point or maximum in tropopause topography (eg FL440)

– – – – Boundary of area of clear air turbulence. The CAT area may be marked by a numeral inside a square and a legend describing the numbered CAT area may be entered in the margin

340 L Low point or minimum in tropopause topography (eg FL340)

10 State of sea (wave height in metres)

0°:100 Freezing level

(18) Sea surface temperature (°C)

■ *Figure 23-17* **Symbols for significant weather on MET charts**

Altitudes between which phenomena are expected are indicated by flight levels, top over base. 'XXX' means the phenomenon is expected to continue above and/or below the vertical coverage of the chart.

Phenomena of relatively lesser significance – for example, light aircraft icing or drizzle – are not usually shown on charts even when the phenomena are expected. The thunderstorm symbol, for example, implies hail, moderate or severe icing and/or turbulence.

2	**Fronts and Convergence Zones**		
 ▲▲	Cold front at the surface	 ———	Axis of trough
 ●●	Warm front at the surface	 ∧∧∧∧∧	Axis of ridge
▲▲▲▲	Occluded front at the surface	 ≻≻≻≻	Convergence line
▲▲	Quasi-stationary front at the surface	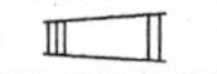 ⫿⫿⫿⫿	Inter-tropical convergence zone

Note: An arrow with associated figures indicates the direction and the speed of the movement of the front (knots). Dots inserted at intervals along the line of a front indicate it is a developing feature (frontogenesis), while bars indicate it is a weakening feature (frontolysis).

■ *Figure 23-18* **Symbols for fronts and convergence zones on met charts**

NOTE An arrow with associated figures indicates the direction and speed of movement of the front in knots.

Weather Abbreviations

Cloud types are listed according to the standard set of abbreviations:

CLOUD TYPE ABBREVIATIONS	
CI	Cirrus
CC	Cirrocumulus
CS	Cirrostratus
AC	Altocumulus
AS	Altostratus
NS	Nimbostratus
SC	Stratocumulus
ST	Stratus
CU	Cumulus
*CB**	Cumulonimbus *CB implies hail, moderate or severe icing and/or turbulence*
LYR	Layer or layered (instead of cloud type)

Altitudes are indicated in flight levels, top over base. For example 30/220 is base 3,000 ft, tops at 22,000 ft.

The amount of **cloud coverage** in Area Forecasts (and in TAFs and METARs in countries such as Australia) is expressed in *eighths* of the sky covered, or *oktas*. 4 oktas means that half of the sky is covered by the cloud mentioned, whereas 8 oktas means complete cloud coverage.

In Aerodrome Forecasts and Reports, the amount of cloud coverage is indicated by the following abbreviations:

CLOUD AMOUNT ABBREVIATIONS (EXCEPT CB)	
SKC	Sky clear (0 oktas)
FEW	Few (1–2 oktas)
SCT	Scattered (3–4 oktas)
BKN	Broken (5–7 oktas)
OVC	Overcast (8 oktas)

Visual navigation with reference to the ground or water is difficult above more than 4 oktas of cloud (half the sky covered). If more than 4 oktas (or two lots of 1–4 oktas) appear on the Area Forecast, you should compare the forecast cloud base with the elevation of the en route terrain and consider carefully whether or not safe navigation to your destination is possible beneath the clouds.

   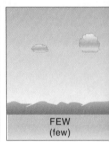

| OVC (overcast) | BKN (broken) | SCT (scattered) | FEW (few) |

■ *Figure 23-19* **Cloud amount abbreviations**

Think about how much of the ground you would actually see if you were navigating en route above 4 oktas of cloud predicted in an Area Forecast.

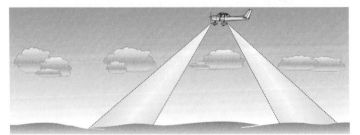

■ *Figure 23-20* **4CU035 severely restricts the pilot's view of the ground**

Thunderstorms

Thunderstorms (TS), which are best avoided by aircraft, are associated with cumulonimbus (CB) clouds. The amount of CB cloud in an area is indicated by the following abbreviations: *(Note these do not apply exclusively to CB - see main table below).*

CB AMOUNT ABBREVIATIONS	
ISOL	*Isolated – for individual CB clouds*
OCNL	*Occasional – for well-separated CB clouds*
FRQ	*Frequent – for CB clouds with little or no separation*
EMBD	*Embedded – CB clouds contained in layers of other clouds*

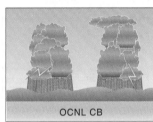
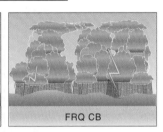

ISOL CB   OCNL CB   FRQ CB

■ *Figure 23-21 **Cumulonimbus amount variations***

CAUTION TS and CB each imply hail, moderate or severe icing and/or turbulence.

Descriptive Abbreviations

In addition to the abbreviations already covered, the following main weather abbreviations may be found in text forecasts and reports, including AIRMET regional forecasts obtained from the METFAX Service or in an aerodrome briefing office. (AIP GEN 3-5 has an extensive abbreviations list, including those which apply to meteorological forecasts and reports.)

COMMON MET ABBREVIATIONS							
+	*Heavy*	**AS**	*Altostratus*	**BL**	*Blowing*		
–	*Light*	**ASR**	*Altimeter setting region*	**BLO**	*Below clouds*		
AC	*Altocumulus*	**AUG**	*August*	**BLW**	*Below*		
AD	*Aerodrome*	**AUTO**	*Automated METAR*	**BR**	*Mist*		
AGL	*Above ground level*	**BASE**	*Cloud base*	**BTN**	*Between*		
AMD	*Amend or amended*	**BCFG**	*Fog patches*	**C**	*Degrees Celsius*		
AMSL	*Above mean sea level*	**BECMG**	*Becoming*	**CAT**	*Clear Air Turbulence*		
APR	*April*	**BKN**	*Broken (5 to 7 oktas)*	**CAVOK**	*Ceiling and visibility OK*		

COMMON MET ABBREVIATIONS

CB	Cumulonimbus	**FC**	Funnel cloud	**INCR**	Increase
CC	Cirrocumulus	**FCST**	Forecast	**INTSF**	Intensifying
CI	Cirrus	**FEB**	February	**IR**	Ice on runway
CIT	Near or over large towns	**FEW**	Few (1 or 2 oktas)	**IRVR**	Instrumented RVR
CLD	Cloud	**FG**	Fog	**ISOL**	Isolated
COR	Correction	**FL**	Flight level	**JAN**	January
COT	At the coast	**FLUC**	Fluctuating	**JTST**	Jet stream
CS	Cirrostratus	**FM...**	From (followed by time weather change is to begin)	**JUL**	July
CU	Cumulus	**FPM**	Feet per minute	**JUN**	Jun
CUF	Cumuliform	**FRQ**	Frequent	**KM**	Kilometres
D	Downward (tendency in RVR in Civil observations)	**FT**	Feet	**KMH**	Kilometres per hour
DEC	December	**FU**	Smoke	**KT**	Knots
DECR	Decrease	**FZ**	Freezing (followed by DZ, FG or RA)	**L**	Low pressure centre
DEG	Degrees	**G**	Gust	**LAN**	Inland (or over land)
				LCA	Replaces LOC in Form 215)
DP	Dew point temperature	**GEN**	Generally	**LGT**	Light
DR	Low drifting (followed by DU, SA or SN)	**GND**	Ground	**LOC**	Locally
DS	Duststorm	**GR**	Hail (5 mm or more in diameter)	**LSQ**	Line squall
DTRT	Deteriorate	**GS**	Small hail or snow pellets	**LV**	Light & variable (relating to wind)
DU	Dust (in suspension)	**H**	High pressure centre	**LYR**	Layer(s), layered
DUC	Dense upper cloud	**HPA**	Hectopascals (= Millibar)	**M**	Less than 0 °C (temperature)
DZ	Drizzle	**HVY**	Heavy	**M**	Less than the lowest reportable value (RVR)
E	East or easterly	**HZ**	Haze	**M**	Metres
ENE	East-north-east or east-north-easterly	**IC**	Ice crystals (diamond dust)	**MAR**	March
ESE	East-south-east or east-south-easterly	**ICE**	Icing	**MAX**	Maximum
EMBD	Embedded	**IMPR**	improve(-ing)	**MB**	Millibars
ETA	Estimated time of arrival	**INS**	Inches (on F2309)	**METAR**	Aviation routine weather report
ETD	Estimated time of departure	**IMT**	Immediate	**MI**	Shallow (followed by FG)

COMMON MET ABBREVIATIONS

MNM	Minimum	NSC	No significant cloud	RWY	Runway
MOD	Moderate	NSW	No significant weather	RMK	Remarks
MON	Above or covering mountains	NW	North-west or north-westerly	S	South or southerly
MPS	Metres per second	OBSC	Obscured	SA	Sand (in suspension)
MS	Minus	OCNL	Occasional, occasionally	SC	Stratocumulus
MSL	Mean sea level	OCT	October	SCT	Scattered (3 or 4 oktas)
MT	Mountain	OVC	Overcast (8 oktas)	SE	South-east or south-easterly
MTW	Mountain waves	P	Greater than the highest reportable value (RVR)	SEA	At sea
N	North or northerly	PE	Ice pellets	SEP	September
NAT	North Atlantic	PO	Dust devils	SEV	Severe
NC	No change	PRFG	Fog banks	SFC	Surface
NCD	No Cloud Detected (on AUTO METARs only)	PROB	Probability	SG	Snow grains
NDV	No Directional Variation (on AUTO METARs only)	PROV	Provisional	SH...	Shower (followed by RA, SN, PL, GR, GS or combinations thereof)
NE	North-east or north-easterly	PS	Plus	SIG	Significant
NIL	None	PSYS	Pressure System (s)	SKC	Sky clear
NM	Nautical miles	QFE	Atmospheric pressure at specified datum	SN	Snow (flakes)
NNE	North-north-east or north-north-easterly	QNE	Aerodrome height expressed in pressure altitude	SPECI	Aviation special weather report
NNW	North-north-west or north-north-westerly	QNH	Altimeter sub-scale setting to obtain elevation when on the ground	SQ	Squall
NOSIG	No significant change expected	RA	Rain	SS	Sandstorm
NOTAM	Notice containing important aeronautical information to all personnel concerned with flight operations	RAG	Ragged	SSE	South-south-east or south-south-easterly
NOV	November	RE	Recent	SSW	South-south-west or south-south-westerly
NS	Nimbostratus	RVR	Runway visual range	ST	Stratus

COMMON MET ABBREVIATIONS

STNR	Stationary	**UA**	Air report	**WAFC**	World Area Forecast Centre
SW	South-west or south-westerly	**UP**	Unidentified Precipitation (on AUTO METARs only)	**WDSPR**	Widespread
T	Temperature	**UTC**	Co-ordinated Universal Time	**WKN**	Weaken(ing)
TAF	Terminal aerodrome forecast	**VA**	Volcanic ash	**WNW**	West-north-west or west-north-westerly
TCU	Towering cumulus	**VAL**	In valleys	**WRNG**	Warning
TEMPO	Temporary, temporarily	**VC...**	In vicinity of aerodrome (followed by FG, FC, SH, PO, BLDU, BLSA, BLSN)	**WS**	Wind shear
TL	Until	**VCY**	Vicinity	**WSPD**	Wind speed
TOP	Cloud top	**VER**	Vertical	**WSW**	West-south-west or west-south-westerly
TROP	Tropopause	**VIS**	Visibility	**WX**	Weather
TS	Thunderstorm (may also be followed by RA, SN, PL, GR, GS or combinations thereof)	**VRB**	Variable	**Z**	Co-ordinated Universal Time
TURB	Turbulence	**VSP**	Vertical speed		
U	Upward (tendency in RVR)	**W**	West or westerly		

CAVOK

The term CAVOK is used frequently and means that the following conditions occur simultaneously:

- visibility 10 km or more;
- no cloud below 5,000 ft above aerodrome level (aal) or below the highest minimum sector altitude, whichever is the higher, and no cumulonimbus;
- no significant weather phenomena at or in the vicinity of the aerodrome.

CAUTION Do not fall into the trap thinking that CAVOK means Sky Clear (SKC) as there could be complete clod coverage above 5,000ft.

Also, a complication with the term CAVOK, which can affect non-IMC and non-instrument-rated pilots, is that the criteria regarding changes in cloud amount and base for amending the TAF apply only when there are significant changes below 1,500 ft aal. This could mean that a forecast containing CAVOK may not be amended until the cloud base falls below 1,500 ft.

Perhaps the safest interpretation of CAVOK, even though it specifically refers to no cloud below 5,000 ft aal, is to assume that it really means that the cloud base should not fall below 1,500 ft for the period of the forecast.

Changing Weather in Forecasts

Temporary Change (TEMPO)

While the cumulonimbus cloud associated with a thunderstorm may exist for hours, its passage through the immediate vicinity of an aerodrome may take only a brief period – less than 60 minutes, or an even shorter time. During these *temporary* periods the weather in the vicinity of the aerodrome might be quite different when compared with the background of the prevailing weather.

In such a situation, the Aerodrome and Landing Forecasts would state the general conditions existing at the aerodrome (i.e. the **prevailing conditions**), and **any temporary changes** to the conditions would be indicated by the term TEMPO.

TEMPO. Temporary variation lasting less than 60 minutes or, if recurring, lasting in total less than half the TREND (or TAF, see AIP GEN 3-5) period; that is, changes take place sufficiently infrequently for the prevailing conditions to remain those forecast for the period.

EXAMPLE 6

TAF EGBS 171900Z 1720/1808 12010KT 9999 SCT010 BKN020
TEMPO 2023 5000 + SHRAGR BKN010CB=

We interpret this to mean:

TEMPO can relate to improvements as well as deteriorations in wind, visibility, weather or cloud.

- the Aerodrome Forecast (TAF) is for Shobdon issued at 1900 hr zulu (UTC) on the 17th of the month
- for the period 2000 on the 17th of the month to 0800 UTC on the 18th of the month

prevailing conditions:

- wind velocity 120°T/10 knots
- visibility in excess of 10 km (indicated by 9999)
- no significant weather
- cloud: 3–4 oktas at base 1,000 ft aal;
  5–7 oktas at base 2,000 ft aal

with periods of less than 60 minutes (TEMPO):

- between 2000 and 2300 UTC on the 17th of the month, with
- visibility reduced to 5,000 metres, heavy rain showers with large hail.
- 5–7 oktas of cumulonimbus at base 1,000 ft aal[*].

---

[*]. Temporary deteriorations in the Shobdon weather during the three hours from 2000 to 2300 UTC; conditions as specified.

Lasting Changes

Whereas TEMPO is used to indicate a temporary variation from the prevailing weather, when lasting changes in the prevailing weather are forecast, the term **BECMG** (becoming) is used preceding an expected permanent change in the weather conditions.

In an Aerodrome Forecast (TAF), BECMG will be followed by a four-figure time group; in a Trend Forecast that is appended to an aerodrome report (METAR), BECMG may be followed by a four-figure time group in hours and minutes preceded by one of the abbreviations: **FM** (from), **TL** (until) or **AT** (at).

Once the BECMG changes are completed, there is new prevailing weather. Once TEMPO events are finished, however, the original prevailing weather re-asserts itself.

EXAMPLE 7

TAF EGDL 190600Z 1907/1916 08008KT 9999 BKN008 BECMG
1910/1912 9999 BKN020 BECMG 1315 CAVOK

We interpret this Aerodrome Forecast (TAF) for Lyneham aerodrome, valid from 0700 to 1600 UTC on the 19th of the month, to mean:

initial prevailing weather:

− wind from 080°T at 8 knots
− visibility in excess of 10 km
− 5–7 oktas at 800 ft aal, plus:

becoming new prevailing conditions over a two-hour period commencing around 1000 UTC and completed by around 1200 UTC:

− visibility in excess of 10 kilometres; cloud: 5–7 oktas at 2,000 ft aal

(this should be the weather at 1200 hours lasting until the next forecast change), plus:

becoming, between 1300 and 1500 UTC, CAVOK.

EXAMPLE 8

FCUK EGBN 310600Z 310700Z/311600Z 33018G35KT 3600 +RA
BKN008 BKN020 OVC070 MOD TURB BLW 6000 FT BECMG
3113/3114 16015KT 9999 NSW BKN020

9-hour Aerodrome Forecast (TAF) for Nottingham, valid 0700 to 1600 UTC on the 31st

Prevailing weather:

− wind mean speed of 18kt with gusts to 35 knots from the north-west (330°T);
− visibility 3,600 metres in heavy rain
− cloud: 5–7 oktas base 800 ft and 2,000 ft aal, and 8 oktas at 7,000 ft aal

- moderate turbulence below 6,000 ft

becoming, between 1300 and 1400 UTC

- a southerly wind of 15 knots (from 160°T)
- visibility in excess of 10 kilometres with no significant weather
- cloud: 5–7 oktas with base 2,000 ft aal.

In other words, the forecaster is expecting quite a significant improvement in the weather.

EXAMPLE 9

SAUK EGSS 24023KT 210V300 8000 RERA SCT006 BKN012 10/09 Q0988 BECMG AT 1300 CAVOK

This is an aerodrome observation (METAR) for Stansted aerodrome:

- wind varying between 220°T 25 knots varying between 210°T and 300°T
- visibility 8,000 metres
- recent rain
- cloud: 3–4 oktas at 600 ft aal; 5–7 oktas at 1,200 ft aal
- temperature: 10°C and dewpoint 09°C (close to mist or fog conditions)
- QNH: 988 millibars (quite low).

Trend: becoming, at 1300 UTC, CAVOK conditions.

Other descriptive terms that appear on Trend statements are: **NOSIG:** no significant change, **NSC:** no significant cloud, and **NSW:** no significant weather.

Probability

If the forecaster is uncertain that weather conditions will occur but assesses the probability of them occurring as 40% or less, the message may be prefaced with a PROB (probability) percentage.

EXAMPLE 10

PROB40 TEMPO 2210/2212 VRB30G45KT 1000 +TS BKN005 BKN040CB

If the above was included in an Aerodrome Forecast (TAF), it means that the forecaster has placed **a 40% probability factor** of periods of less than 60 minutes' duration (TEMPO), between the hours of 1000 and 1200 UTC, with:

- Wind variable 30 knots gusting 45 knots
- 1,000 metres visibility, thunderstorm and heavy shower of rain
- 5–7 oktas at 500 ft aal
- 5–7 oktas cumulonimbus with a base of 4,000 ft aal.

What if Poor Weather is Forecast?

During VFR flight training most flights are conducted in reasonably good weather conditions, however, this may not always be the case. When widespread, significant poor weather conditions is anticipated or reported the decision not to fly is relatively straightforward. Very often complication arises when conditions are marginal or intermittently poor which make the decision to fly difficult - does the flight commence and if so under what conditions?

Like most things in flying, it is not the everyday situation that is testing, but rather the unusual situations that have a habit of occurring from time to time. Making sound operational decisions is what flying is all about and your ability to do so will be a function of training, skills and experience gained.

Dissemination of Weather Information

Weather information is issued by Meteorological Forecast Offices on a routine basis in three formats.

- **Internet services** that include the text-based and graphical data already mentioned. The mandated minimum service is provided free or after registration.
- **Text-based teleprinter AIRMET messages** transmitted to aerodrome briefing offices via the Aeronautical Fixed Telecommunications Network (AFTN), the Facsimile Broadcast Service ARTIFAX, and telex; AIRMET information is also available to individual users via the public telephone network and the dial-up METFAX Service.
- **Graphic weather charts and data** distributed via the Facsimile Broadcast Service to aerodrome briefing offices and via the METFAX Service to individual users.

The primary method of obtaining a pre-flight meteorological briefing in the United Kingdom is by **self-briefing**, using:

- facilities, information and documentation routinely available or displayed in aerodrome briefing areas;
- the Internet services provided by the UK Meteorological Office (www.metoffice.com/aviation) or from other service providers who are authorised to provide the same information via the Internet;
- the public telephone system to obtain AIRMET forecasts and reports; or Self-briefing does not require prior notification by the pilot. It is important to familiarise with Meteorological Services and associated, approved internet resources in any given country before conducting a flight operation.

Where necessary, the personal advice of a forecaster or the supply of additional weather information can be obtained from the designated forecast office for the departure aerodrome (listed in AIP GEN 3-5).

All of the Met Office services to pilots are summarised in the publication *Get Met,* which is available free of charge from the Met Office. This booklet is a joint Met Office and CAA publication and may be ordered or downloaded via the Met Office website (www.metoffice.com). *Get Met* complements the information found in AIP GEN 3-5 and is updated annually.

Perhaps the easiest way to understand the weather service is to use it - using internet services, by visiting an aerodrome briefing office to obtain the information in text form, an/or by using the public telephone network.

Try phoning the listed telephone numbers and writing down the AIRMET information. Telephone numbers for voice-based forecasts for the Northern, Southern and Scottish Regions in UK AIP GEN 3-5.

Internet Services

The internet is now a rich source of aviation meteorological information, however, it is vitally important for a pilot to understand whether any particular resource is from an authorised provider and current/updated. Some flight planning software will have weather automatically included and the source of this information should be checked before being used in flight planning or for the conduct of a flight. Whilst providing useful context, if the information is not from an authorised provider it should not be used to base fight operational decisions on. Examples of approved providers include; Met Office (UK) **www.metoffice.gov.uk/aviation** US National Weather Service (NOAA) **https://aviationweather.gov**

In the UK the following web-based products are available:
• Forms 214 and 215 (UK low level spot wind charts)
• Global TAFs and METARs
• UK AIRMETs
• Radar
• Ballooning forecasts
• Pressure charts
• Climate statistics for British Isles airfields
• Satellite images

Further services are available by subscription:
• 15 minute rainfall radar
• Lightning observations
• Animated cloud, precipitation and pressure forecasts
• Animated visibility forecasts
• Animated European synoptic analysis
• Visible satellite pictures

- Infrared satellite pictures
- Three-day planning forecasts for England, Wales and Scotland
- Jetstream.

Forecast Offices

Clarification and consultation on weather information is available direct from the various forecast offices. These are listed in AIP GEN 3-5 and on the AIRMET copy form, with telephone numbers to use.

While the recorded AIRMET messages may be listened to for as long as a pilot wishes, it is requested that phone calls to a Meteorological Office that will involve meteorological personnel be kept reasonably brief.

Now complete: **Practice Questions - Weather Forecasts & Reports**

---

1. Where would you find out about the official meteorological services available at a given aerodrome:

   (a) Aeronautical Information Publication (AIP) – Specific Aerodrome Index – Textual Data.
   (b) National Meteorological Service (NMS) website.
   (c) ATIS.
   (d) Google.

2. The time is currently 0600Z. The estimated time of departure for a planned route is 1300Z. What meteorological product should be used for best planning for weather enroute:

   (a) Area forecast covering the route valid 0800Z to 1700Z. Terminal Aerodrome Forecasts (TAFs) valid 0900Z to 1800Z for departure, destination and diversion airfields.
   (b) Meteorological reports (METARs) for all airfields enroute at 0620Z.
   (c) Satellite and Radar picture valid at 0530Z.
   (d) Significant Meteorology (SIGMET) report valid at 0530Z.

3. The time is 1500Z. The estimated time of arrival at an airfield is 1520Z. What meteorological product should be used for best decision making with regards to weather on arrival:

    (a) *Area forecast covering the route valid 0800Z to 1700Z.*

    (b) *Terminal Aerodrome Forecasts (TAFs) valid 1300Z to 2200Z for departure, destination and diversion airfields.*

    (c) *Meteorological reports (METARs) for the arrival and diversion airfield at 1450Z supplemented by observations of the weather from the flight deck.*

    (d) *Visible satellite picture valid at 1430Z.*

4. Which of the following are significant weather phenomena which may affect the safety of flight operations and that could be passed by the Flight Information Service to the pilot in the form of a SIGMET:

    (a) *Active thunderstorms. Severe turbulence. Severe airframe icing. Marked mountain waves.*

    (b) *Moderate turbulence. Drizzle. Low cloud. Fog.*

    (c) *Moderate turbulence. Moderate airframe icing. Low cloud. Moderate rain.*

    (d) *Moderate airframe icing. Drizzle. Low cloud. Moderate rain.*

5. AIRMET information:

    (a) *Is an area weather forecast that covers a localised region, is text based and available at aerodrome briefing offices connected to AFTN or Telex.*

    (b) *Is a regional forecast and available over radio (ATIS).*

    (c) *Is a set of weather observations over a localised region, is text based and available at aerodrome briefing offices connected to AFTN or Telex.*

    (d) *Is a set of weather observations over a localised region, is text based and available over VHF frequencies.*

6. The service in which meteorological reports and trends for a number of selected aerodromes are broadcast continuously on discrete VHF frequencies is called:

    (a) *METAR*

    (b) *TAF*

    (c) *VOLMET*

    (d) *SIGMET*

7. The published AIP for an airfield highlights that it has an
    ATIS, what does this mean:

    (a) *Airfield Telecommunications Information Service (ATIS) that
        includes the provision of current airfield weather observations
        over a dedicated fixed telephone line.*
    (b) *Automatic Terminal Information Service (ATIS) that includes
        the provision of current airfield weather observations over a
        dedicated VHF frequency.*
    (c) *Automatic Terminal Information Service (ATIS) that includes
        the provision of current weather conditions for a localised region
        over a dedicated VHF frequency.*
    (d) *Automatic Terminal Information Service (ATIS) that includes
        the provision of forecast area conditions up to 24,000ft above
        mean sea level.*

8. In TAFs and METARs, the cloud base is given as:

    (a) *The height above aerodrome.*
    (b) *The height above mean sea level.*
    (c) *The highest ground within 10nm.*
    (d) *Flight level.*

9. In a Meteorological Aerodrome Report (METAR) or
    Terminal Aerodrome Forecast (TAF) 'BKN035' means:

    (a) *4 to 6 oktas of cloud at 3500 feet above the aerodrome.*
    (b) *5 to 7 oktas of cloud at 3500 feet above sea level.*
    (c) *5 to 7 oktas of cloud at 3500 feet above the aerodrome.*
    (d) *3 to 4 oktas of cloud at flight level 35.*

10. In a Meteorological Aerodrome Report (METAR) or
    Terminal Aerodrome Forecast (TAF) '9999' means:

    (a) *Visibility in excess of 10 kilometres.*
    (b) *Visibility in excess of 5 nautical miles.*
    (c) *Visibility less than 999.9 metres.*
    (d) *Visibility in excess of 5 kilometres.*

11. An airfield has the following TAF; when is VFR flight unlikely to be possible? EGJB 141100Z 141212 23015KT CAVOK BECMG 0407 VRB05KT 0200 FG OVC000 BECMG 0710 25020KT 3000 BR BKN016=

    (a) *On the 15th, between 0400 and 1000 zulu, because of fog and haze.*
    (b) *On the 14th, between 0400 and 1000 zulu, because of fog and mist.*
    (c) *On the 14th, between 0400 and 1000 zulu, because of haze.*
    (d) *On the 15th, between 0400 and 1000 zulu, because of fog and mist.*

12. An airfield has the following TAF, what are the most hazardous conditions being forecast: EGPC 191100Z 19 1221 24015G25KT 9999 SCT035 TEMPO 1221 5000 SHRA BKN015 PROB30 TEMPO 1216 26022G32KT 3000 +TSRA BKN008CB=

    (a) *Strong winds with gusts up to 32 knots. Poor visibility of 3000 metres associated with heavy rain and thunderstorm. Low cloud, base 800ft above aerodrome, associated with cumulonimbus.*
    (b) *Strong winds with gusts up to 25 knots. visibility of 3000 metres associated with tropical revolving storm. Low cloud, base 800ft above aerodrome, associated with cumulonimbus.*
    (c) *Mountain waves. Observed visibility of less than 30 metres. 3000ft cloud base associated with additional rainfall.*
    (d) *Mountain waves. Wind temporarily backing by 150° true.*

13. A route is being planned which passes through a frontal zone. The area forecast for the zone has "OCNL EMBD CB 020-040 / XXX". What safety implications does this have:

    (a) *Occasional cumulonimbus cloud. Visibility of 2000 to 4000 metres.*
    (b) *Cumulus cloud embedded within frontal zones. Tops 2000 to 4000 feet above sea level. Visibility unlimited. Occasional mountain waves.*
    (c) *Occasional mountain waves embedded within cloud whose base is between 2000 and 1000 feet and tops are at the top of the troposphere.*
    (d) *Occasional cumulonimbus cloud which are embedded within frontal cloud and will not be visually identifiable from the flight deck. Cloud bases from 2000 to 4000 feet above sea level, tops above the limit of the forecast. Hazards associated with them including severe icing, turbulence and thunderstorm.*

14. A METAR finishes off 'Q1014 NOSIG='. What does the Q1014 mean?

(a) *There is a QNH of 1014 hectopascals at the airfield.*
(b) *There is a QFE of 1014 millibars at the airfield.*
(c) *Standard pressure setting is 1014 hectopascals.*
(d) *There is a visibility of 1014 metres.*

15. The current weather radar picture covering your planned route is shown below. What is the likely weather associated with this radar output:

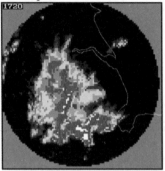

(a) *Nothing significant, it is anomalous propagation.*
(b) *Widespread heavy rain associated with cumulonimbus and possible thunderstorms.*
(c) *Slight rain and drizzle.*
(d) *Mountain waves.*

Part-FCL Abbreviations (see ICAO terminology on p199)

Definitions for Part-FCL terms begin on page 145. Definitions for ICAO terms used in the Part-FCL begin on page 201.

A	Aeroplane
A/C	Aircraft
AMC	Acceptable Means of Compliance;
AeMC	Aeromedical Centre
AME	Authorised Medical Examiner
AMS	Aeromedical Section
ATC	Air Traffic Control
ATO	Approved Training Organisation
ATP	Air Transport Pilot
ATPL	Air Transport Pilot Licence
CFI	Chief Flying Instructor
CGI	Chief Ground Instructor
CPL	Commercial Pilot Licence
CQB	Central Question Bank
CRE	Class Rating Examiner
CRI	Class Rating Instructor
EASA	European Aviation Safety Agency
FCL	Flight Crew Licensing
FE	Flight Examiner
FI	Flight Instructor
FIE	Flight Instructor Examiner
FNPT	Flight and Navigation Procedures Trainer
FSTD	Flight Simulation Training Device
H	Helicopter
HT	Head of Training
ICAO	International Civil Aviation Organisation
IEM	Interpretative and Explanatory Material
IFR	Instrument Flight Rules
IMC	Instrument Meteorological Conditions
IR	Instrument Rating
IRE	Instrument Rating Examiner
IRI	Instrument Rating Instructor
JAA	Joint Aviation Authorities
JAR	Joint Aviation Requirements

LAPL	Light Aircraft Pilot Licence
LOFT	Line Orientated Flight Training
LPC	Licensing Proficiency Check
LST	Licensing Skill Test
L&TS	Licensing and Training Standards
MCC	Multi Crew Cooperation
ME	Multi-engine
MEP	Multi-engine Piston
MET	Multi-engine Turboprop
MPA	Multi-pilot Aeroplane
MPH	Multi-pilot Helicopter
NM	Nautical Miles
OML	Operational Multicrew Limitation
OSL	Operational Safety Pilot Limitation
OTD	Other Training Devices
PF	Pilot Flying
PIC	Pilot-in-Command
PICUS	Pilot-in-Command Under Supervision
PNF	Pilot Not Flying
PPL	Private Pilot Licence
R/T	Radiotelephony
SE	Single-engine
SEP	Single-engine Piston (Aeroplanes)
SET	Single-engine Turboprop
SFE	Synthetic Flight Examiner
SFI	Synthetic Flight Instructor
SPA	Single-pilot Aeroplane
SPH	Single-pilot Helicopter
STD	Synthetic Training Devices
TMG	Touring Motor Glider
TR	Type Rating
TRE	Type Rating Examiner
TRI	Type Rating Instructor
TRTO	Type Rating Training Organisation
VFR	Visual Flight Rules
VMC	Visual Meteorological Conditions

Index